Problem Solving with FORTRAN 77

Brian D. Hahn

Edward Arnold

© Brian D. Hahn 1987

First published in Great Britain 1987 by
Edward Arnold (Publishers) Ltd, 41 Bedford Square, London WC1B 3DQ

Edward Arnold, 3 East Read Street, Baltimore, Maryland 21202, USA

Edward Arnold (Australia) Pty Ltd, 80 Waverley Road, Caulfield East, Victoria 3145, Australia

British Library Cataloguing in Publication Data
Hahn, Brian D.
    Problem solving with Fortran 77.
    1. FORTRAN (Computer program language)
    I. Title
    005.13′3   QA76.73.F25

ISBN: 0 7131 3592 1

Text set in 10/11 Times Linotron 202 by Parker Typesetting Service, Leicester
Printed and bound by Whitstable Litho Ltd, Kent

Preface

So many books on FORTRAN have been written that the appearance of yet another one seems to require some justification. There are three particular areas where this book can claim to make a distinctive contribution.

Firstly, the approach taken is a problem-solving one, developed over many years of teaching programming to first-year university students with no computing experience. The computer is presented as a tool (probably the most exciting one of the 20th century) for solving interesting, real world problems, and examples from many areas, particularly science and engineering, are discussed. The technicalities of each new FORTRAN construction are therefore generally presented only after motivation by the posing of a suitable problem. Since the objective of this book is to enable you to solve problems using a computer, the first 12 chapters are in a sense a preparation for the final three. In these later chapters you will be introduced to some modern computer applications such as simulation, modelling and numerical methods. There are also a large number of exercises, involving a variety of applications. Most of these have solutions provided. Those that do not have solutions may be suitable for use as class projects in a teaching situation.

Secondly, structured programs are developed throughout. The beginner is shielded from the devastating effect of the GOTO statement until well into the text. When it is introduced, the use of GOTO is encouraged in one well-defined situation only: this feature appears to be unique in all the vast literature on FORTRAN.

Thirdly, emphasis is laid throughout the book on what has come to be called programming style, and guidelines for writing clear, readable programs are presented.

This book has developed out of notes originally written as a supplement to lectures for students taking courses in applied mathematics at the University of Cape Town, with no prior experience of computing. It can therefore be used as a 'teach yourself' guide by anyone who wants to learn FORTRAN 77 (officially known as FORTRAN ANSI X3−9 1978), the current international standard, which is the version used here.

Although this is primarily a text for beginners, the more experienced programmer should be able to find plenty of interest, particularly in the applications. He may even learn something! The appendices contain summaries of all the FORTRAN 77 intrinsic functions and statements (including those which are not recommended for stylistic reasons), with examples of their general usage.

No specialized mathematical background is needed to follow most of the examples. There are occasional forays into first-year university mathematics, but these are self-contained and may be glossed over without loss of continuity (you may even find them instructive!).

Thanks are due to John Newmarch of the University of Cape Town Information Technology Services for his critical reading of the original manuscript on which this book is based, and for his invaluable suggestions regarding programming style. Thanks are also due to the generations of students who have patiently endured my efforts to improve my methods of teaching computing. I also wish to thank my colleague, Ruth Smart, who collaborated with me on an earlier version of this book, for her helpful advice and painstaking reading of the manuscript. Finally, I should like to acknowledge a deep debt of gratitude to my wife, Cleone, for her continual support and encouragement during the preparation of this book.

It is hoped this book will give some insight into the ways that computers may be used to solve real problems, and that after working through it you will be better able to find out more about this fascinating subject for yourself.

Brian D. Hahn
1986

Contents

1

Getting Going

As little as fifteen years ago computers were still regarded with a great deal of suspicion. However, at this late stage in the 20th century it is surely not necessary to justify the need to learn computing. The last few years have seen a flood of microcomputers into offices, factories, schools, hospitals, supermarkets, homes, farms, game parks, and even universities! Apart from the interest factor, anyone who is 'computer literate' is better equipped for a wide range of careers than someone who is not.

1.1   Computers

You are probably familiar with using an electronic calculator to find numerical answers to arithmetic problems. The simplest sort can only do arithmetic and display an answer. The next step up is one with a single memory—where an intermediate result may be stored— and with function keys, such as sin, cos, log, etc. Even better calculators may have more memory locations, so that different intermediate results may be stored during a long and involved calculation.

However, if you have to perform the same sequence of operations on a calculator many times for different sets of data, it can become extremely tedious. So even more sophisticated calculators allow you to store, in some suitable coded form, the sequence of operations (or instructions) needed to calculate the solution of the problem. This sequence of instructions is called a program. To carry out the entire set of calculations, you need only load the program into the calculator, press the 'run' key, provide the necessary data, and sit back while the calculator churns out the answer. A calculator like this is called programmable. A computer, whether it is a 'micro' like the IBM PC, or a 'mainframe' like the IBM 370, is really only an advanced programmable calculator, capable of executing and storing sets of instructions, called programs, in order to solve specific problems.

1.2   FORTRAN Programs

The particular set of rules or conventions for coding the instructions to the computer may be called a programming language, or a job control language, depending on the nature of its task. There are many such languages, e.g. FORTRAN, BASIC, Pascal. FORTRAN, which stands for FORmula TRANslation, was the first 'high level' programming language to be written. The idea of FORTRAN was proposed in late 1953 by John Backus, in New York. The first compiler was ready in April 1957. Although by no means perfect, it is still considered by many programmers to be the best language for serious scientific programs.

Your ultimate aim will be to write your own program coding for whatever problem you want to solve, and you will be eager to get on with this task. However, the greatest hurdle facing you at the moment, if you are a computer novice, is getting your particular computer system to do some work for you. The first two examples are therefore very easy, and are given without explanation (which will follow in due course). You are advised to run these examples on a computer as soon as possible, and not to give up until you have successfully done so!

1.2.1   Computing an Average

The final mark for a certain first-year university course is computed as the average of the student's class record and the two papers written at the end of the year (all three marks are out of 100). The basic logical structure of this problem is:

1   Get marks into computer.
2   Compute final mark as average of three marks.
3   Print final mark.
4   Stop.

The following is a very simple FORTRAN program to solve this problem:

```
* *** MY FIRST PROGRAM!
* *** IT COMPUTES THE FINAL MARK FOR A COURSE AS
* *** AN AVERAGE OF THREE EQUALLY WEIGHTED MARKS.

      READ*, RECORD, PAPER1, PAPER2
      FINAL = (RECORD + PAPER1 + PAPER2) / 3
      PRINT*, 'FINAL MARK IS ', FINAL
      STOP
      END
```

Each of these nine lines (one is blank to make the program look neater) must be entered as a separate line at a computer terminal. The first three lines start with an asterisk in column one, but the rest should start in column seven or beyond.

The computer you are using (Sperry, IBM PC, Apple, etc.) will also require particular 'job control' statements, to a greater or lesser extent, to instruct it to run a FORTRAN program, and you will need to find our about these.

Finally, the program requires some data (the student's marks), e.g.

```
63.6   46   49
```

and these should be supplied on one line when the program executes (the computer you are using may require the data to be presented in some particular way). When the program successfully executes, it produces the following line of output on the screen or printer:

```
FINAL MARK IS   52.866666
```

1.2.2   Adding Two Numbers

The next program is even easier: compute and print the sum of two given numbers. It goes as follows:

```
* *** THE SUM OF TWO NUMBERS

      READ*, A, B
      C = A + B
      PRINT*, ' THE SUM OF', A, 'AND', B, 'IS:', C
      STOP
      END
```

Try it out on some sample data, e.g.

```
23.2    19.5
```

The output for this line of data is as follows:

```
THE SUM OF   23.200000    AND   19.500000    IS:   42.700000
```

The exact spacing and number of decimal places depends on the particular computer you are using. Ways of standardizing the output are discussed in Chapter 9.

1.3   Summary

* A computer program is a set of coded instructions for solving a particular problem.

* The instruction **READ** * is for getting data into the computer.

* The instruction **PRINT** * is for printing (displaying) results.

1.4   Exercises

1.1   Write a program to compute and print the sum, difference, product (the multiplication symbol is the asterisk) and quotient of two numbers A and B (supplied by you). Computers react differently to having to divide by zero. You can use this example to find out how the one you are using handles that problem.

1.2   The energy stored on a condenser is $CV^2/2$, where C is the capacitance and V is the potential difference. Write a program to compute the energy for sample values of C and V.

2

Inside Digital Computers

It is not necessary to know anything about the internal workings of computers in order to program them, but familiarity with some of the basic ideas may help (you can skip this chapter if you are not interested).

2.1 Organization

The basic conceptual design of a computer is as follows (the solid lines represent flow of control, the broken lines flow of information, and the times shown are typical access times):

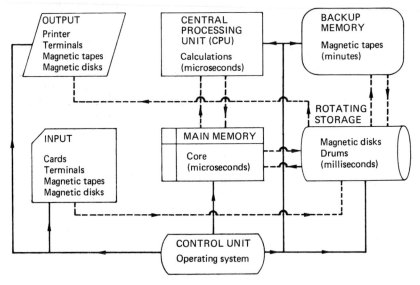

2.2 Representation of Information

The basic unit of information in the computer is the 'bit'—a thing that has only two possible states, usually described as 'on' and 'off'. Electronically this is very easy to represent, since a current can be either on or off, or a magnetic field in a ferrite ring can be orientated either clockwise or anti-clockwise. The binary digits 0 and 1 can therefore be used to represent the two states mathematically (hence the term 'digital' computer). The word 'bit' is a contraction of 'BInary digiT'.

Numbers in the computer memory must therefore be represented in binary code, where each bit in a sequence stands for a successively higher power of 2. The decimal numbers 0 to 15, for example, are coded in binary as follows:

Decimal	Binary	Decimal	Binary
0	0000	8	1000
1	0001	9	1001
2	0010	10	1010
3	0011	11	1101
4	0100	12	1100
5	0101	13	1101
6	0110	14	1110
7	0111	15	1111

Now computers would not be so universally popular if their users had to supply all their numerical information in binary code. For example, very few people could tell you instantly, if you asked them, that the binary code for 1985 is 11111000001. So obviously the computer must have built into it somewhere the ability to translate decimal numbers into binary, and vice versa.

2.3 Memory Organization

In the computer's memory, bits are grouped together into 'words'. On a Sperry mainframe, for example, a word is a string of 36 bits. Other machines may have different word-lengths. IBM mainframes, for example, have 32 bits to a word. A 'byte' is the amount of storage required for one character, and is generally eight bits long. Computer memory size is measured in words or bytes depending on the particular machine. Mainframes are usually word machines, so 20K of memory means 20 000 words. Microcomputers, however, are usually byte machines, so 56K on an Apple, for example, means approximately 56 000 bytes (since 1K means 1024).

Note that a word can hold a significant amount of information. Since each of its 32 bits (in the case of the IBM) can be on or off there are 2^{32} possibilities for each word. So, for example, an integer may be stored in binary notation in one word of memory:

1 bit is used to represent + or − ;
31 bits are left for the number, which could run from
  binary 00.....0 (i.e. decimal 0)
  to binary 11.....1 (i.e. decimal $2^{31}-1$).

Since $10^9 < 2^{31}-1 < 10^{10}$ this means that any integer with less than nine decimal digits fits into the storage space of one word, but there will be trouble (of an unexpected kind) with integers of more than nine digits. (This is called an 'overflow'.)

2.4 Coding Instructions

A program is a set of instructions designed for the solution of a specific problem on the computer. The essence of most computer programs is as follows:

1 Getting some numbers into the computer.
2 Processing the numbers (calculations, tests, etc.).
3 Getting the answers out of the computer.

The ways in which the instructions may be coded for the computer fall into three categories:

1)   machine code (or 'low level')
2)   assembly language
3)   compiler language (or 'high level', e.g. FORTRAN or Pascal).

Of these, the high level languages are the most sophisticated and convenient to use. However, to appreciate the subtleties of computer programming, it is instructive to look briefly at the first two categories.

2.4.1   Machine Code

This is the crudest level of programming. Each computer system has its own peculiar machine code. At this level, the basic instructions are very simple, like transferring a single word from memory to the central processing unit (CPU). Most instructions have two parts: an operation code (e.g. to add, print, read, etc.), and the address of the storage location(s) of the number(s) on which the operation is to be performed. So if the operation code for 'print' on a hypothetical computer is 20, the machine coded instruction

    20 01634

would mean 'Print the number in location 01634 of the memory'.
   Bearing in mind that arithmetic is done in registers in the CPU, the machine code for our hypothetical computer to read two numbers into memory and print out their sum could look as follows:

Location of Instruction	Operation Code	Address	Meaning
001	10	01634	Read (10) a number into location 01634
002	10	01635	Read (10) a number into location 01635
003	30	01634	Load (30) the contents of location 01634 into the register
004	31	01635	Add (31) the contents of location 01635 to the contents of the register
005	40	01634	Store (40) the contents of the register in location 01634
006	20	01634	Print (20) the contents of location 01634

Note that the original contents of location 01634 (the first of the two numbers to be added will be destroyed by instruction 005, and replaced by the sum. This is fine if you don't wan to use the first number again. Otherwise you could simply use a different location for th sum.
   You can easily see how a simple program could involve hundreds of dreary machine cod instructions. On top of everything else, in reality, binary code would have to be used for th opcode and address!

2.4.2   Assemblers

An assembly language overcomes the two major difficulties of machine code by allowin one to use symbolic opcodes and symbolic addresses. The above example written i assembly language could look like this:

Location of Instruction	Operation Code	Address	Meaning
001	R	X	READ a number into location X
002	R	Y	READ a number into location Y
003	L	X	LOAD the contents of X into the register
004	A	Y	ADD the contents of Y to the contents of the register
005	ST	X	STORE the contents of the register in X
006	P	X	PRINT the contents of X

Since the computer can still only understand machine code, this symbolic assembly code has to be translated into machine code by a special program sitting in the computer, called an **assembler**. There is a one-to-one translation from assembly code to machine code. The assembler therefore looks after the problem of precisely which of the many thousands of storage locations are being used (and makes sure that you don't use someone else's locations!). The user need only remember that they were called X, Y, etc., and need know nothing about the internal workings of the assembler.

2.4.3 Compilers

The instructions in assembly language are still very elementary. In high level languages a single instruction may often be used in place of a whole set of machine code instructions. This more sophisticated instruction is then translated into the appropriate machine code by a compiler. For example, the above program in FORTRAN would be simply:

```
READ*, X, Y
X = X + Y
PRINT*, X
```

This is only half the number of machine code instructions, and the ratio is usually even better. Note that the crucial statement

```
X = X + Y
```

is not an algebraic equation $(x = x + y)$. It is an instruction to the computer to do something:

'Take the number in X, add to it the number in Y, and put the answer in X.

If you wanted to keep the original contents of X, you would have to say something like:

```
Z = X + Y
```

To avoid confusing this type of instruction with an algebraic equation, the equal sign should be spoken 'becomes', i.e.

'X becomes X plus Y'.

So a compiler is a special program, which accepts as input the high level language (or 'source program') and produces as output the machine code (or 'object program'). A particular computer can therefore understand any language for which a compiler has been provided. These concepts are illustrated diagrammatically below.

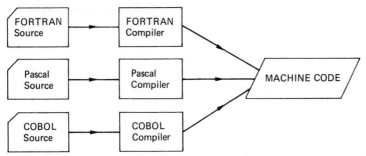

Compiling a program should not be confused with executing (i.e. running) it, since compiling and executing are two entirely separate and independent operations. So when your program does not work, it is very important to know whether the error (or 'bug') occurred during compile time or run time. This should be clear from the error message generated on the screen or printout.

2.5   Summary

* The basic unit of information in a computer is the bit.

* A byte (one character) is eight bits.

* A word is usually 32 bits.

* Machine code is the lowest level of coding instructions, and is the code the computer 'understands'.

* An assembler translates symbolic assembly language into machine code.

* A compiler translates high level languages (like FORTRAN) into machine code.

* A computer executes the machine code to run a program.

3

Elementary FORTRAN

We now begin to look in detail at how to write computer programs to solve particular problems. There are two essential requirements for successfully mastering this art:

1) THE EXACT RULES FOR CODING INSTRUCTIONS MUST BE USED.
2) A LOGICAL PLAN FOR SOLVING THE PROBLEM MUST BE DEVELOPED.

This chapter is devoted mainly to the first requirement: learning some coding rules. (A summary of all FORTRAN statements described in this book appears in Appendix A.) Once these are mastered, we can go on to more interesting problems.

3.1 Example: Compound Interest

We will start with a very simple example. Suppose you have $1000 saved in the bank, which compounds interest at the rate of 9% per annum. What will your balance be after one year? Of course, you must be able to do the calculation in principle yourself before you can begin to write the program. The logical breakdown of the problem, or 'structure plan', is as follows:

    1   Get data (initial balance and interest rate) into computer.
    2   Calculate interest (9% of $1000, i.e. $90).
    3   Add interest to balance ($90+$1000, i.e. $1090).
    4   Print out new balance.

N.B. You should *always* prepare a program in some such way, before coding and running it. The FORTRAN program to carry out this task is as follows.

```
*** COMPOUND INTEREST CALCULATION

    BALNCE = 1000
    RATE   = 0.09
    RINT   = RATE * BALNCE
    BALNCE = BALNCE + RINT
    PRINT*, 'NEW BALANCE IS', BALNCE
    STOP
    END
```

The statements are executed as follows:

    1   Put the number 1000 into storage location BALNCE.
    2   Put the number 0.09 into storage location RATE.
    3   Multiply the contents of RATE by the contents of BALNCE and store the answer in RINT.

4   Add the contents of BALNCE to the contents of RINT and store the answer in BALNCE.

5   Print the contents of BALNCE.

6   Stop.

After execution, the memory will look like this:

BALNCE: 1090.0
RATE   : 0.09
RINT   : 90.0

Note that the original contents of BALNCE (1000.0) is lost.

Exercise

1   Run the program as it stands.

2   Leave out the line

```
BALNCE = BALNCE + RINT
```

and rerun. Can you explain what happens?

A number of questions immediately arise, for example:

* What names are permissible for storage locations?
* In what ways can numbers be represented?
* What happens if a statement won't fit into one line?
* Why is there a **STOP** as well as an **END**?
* How can we organise the output more neatly?

These questions (and others) will be answered in the following sections.

3.2   Program Layout

This section covers the general physical layout of a FORTRAN program.

3.2.1   Program Lines

One line (at least) is needed for each statement (instruction). A line of FORTRAN has fou~~ distinct regions, as follows:

columns 1 to 5   : statement label (see Chapter 6);
column 6   : leave blank unless previous statement has to run over into this line;
column 7 to 72   : the statement itself;
columns 73 to 80   : ignored by the computer (a comment may be written here).

Blanks in the statement are ignored by the computer, except in character strings, a~~ described in Chapter 11.

3.2.2   Data Lines

Data (when used in conjunction with a **READ** statement as described in Section 3.9) ma~~ start anywhere on a line, and may be separated by blanks or commas.

3.2.3   Continuation Lines

Any non-blank character in column 6 of a FORTRAN statement causes the rest of the lir~~

to be logically joined onto the previous statement. So, for example, the statement

```
BALNCE = BALNCE + RINT
```

in the above program could be spread over two lines as

```
BALNCE = BALN
$CE + RINT
```

where the dollar symbol appears in column 6.

At most 19 continuation lines for one statement are allowed, but the entire statement may not contain more than 1320 significant characters (blanks are not significant characters).

3.2.4   The END Statement

This statement tells the compiler that there are no more FORTRAN statements in the program, and must therefore be the last line in the program.

3.2.5   The STOP Statement

This is logically quite different from **END**. **STOP** is only implemented during execution time, and tells the computer where the program must stop logically (i.e. where the user wants it to stop.

You may wonder why **STOP** is necessary as well as **END**. The reason is partly historical. In the old days of computing people were not very concerned about 'programming style', and wrote programs that stopped almost anywhere. Nowadays this is frowned upon, and **STOP** should always come immediately before **END**.

3.3.6   Comment Lines

If a 'C' or '*' appears in column 1 it is ignored by the compiler and treated as a comment line. The comment appears in the program listing. A line which is completely blank is also treated as a comment. Comments and blank lines should be used frequently in longer programs between logical sections. This makes the program more readable. Comment lines may appear anywhere within a program, even after an **END** statement.

3.3   Numeric Constants

This is the technical term that covers any number used as data, like the 1000 and 0.09 in the example in Section 3.1. A numeric constant may be written in various forms, and falls into various categories, depending on precisely how it is represented internally in the machine's memory. The two main types of constants that concern us here are called **integers** and **reals**.

3.3.1   Integer Constants

An integer must not contain a decimal point or comma. It may be preceded by a plus or minus sign. The maximum size of an integer varies according to the type of computer. On a Sperry mainframe, for example, the absolute value of an integer may not exceed $2^{35}-1$ ($= 34\,359\,738\,367$). The reason for this is discussed above in Section 2.3.

Valid integers	Invalid integers (why?)
1000	999.
0	19,84
+753	-1.0
-999999	0.
2501	.0

3.3.2   Real Constants

A real constant may be written in two ways: fixed point, and floating point.

In fixed point, the real constant is expressed as a string of digits, with a decimal point somewhere in the string. For example:

```
0.09
37.
37.0
-.6829135
```

In floating point, the number is expressed as a constant (fixed point real, or integer) followed by an integer exponent indicating the power of 10 by which the constant is to be multiplied. For example,

2.0E2	(means 200.0)
2E2	(means 200.0)
4.12E+2	(means 412.0)
-7.321E-4	(means -0.0007321)

Real constants are stored in binary floating point form in the computer, no matter how they are actually written. If a real has a fractional part it may therefore be stored approximately. Even if there is no fractional part the real is stored differently from an integer of the same value. So, for example, 43 is an integer, while 43.0 is a real. They will be represented differently in memory.

Again, the permissible range of a real constant differs with computer. On a Sperry mainframe, the absolute value of a real constant must lie in the range 1E38 to 1E−38 (approximately).

3.4   Variables

The symbolic name of a storage location that holds a single value is called a **variable** to signify the fact that the value may be changed during the execution of a program. A variable consists of one to six of the following characters:

> alphabetic letters (A to Z);
> numerics (0 to 9).

The first character of a variable must be alphabetic.

Valid variables	Invalid variables (why?)
X	X+Y
R2D2	HP41-C
SWAPO	10C
C3PO	$5
MAGGIE	NAMIBIA
TIME	OBI-WAN

Variables starting with the letters I, J, K, L, M, and N are assumed to be **integers**, i.e. their contents will be interpreted by the computer as integer constants. Variables starting with any other letter are assumed to be **real**.

Type may be mixed in a statement, but fractional parts of numbers will be truncated (chopped off) if they are assigned to integer variables. Because of this loss of precision, which may have disastrous results, like a division by zero, it is best to avoid mixed mode arithmetic. For example,

```
MARK    = 58.18     (becomes 58)
X       = -10       (becomes -10.0)
KGB     = 0.9999    (becomes 0)
INTRST  = 0.09      (becomes 0)
```

This implicit type rule may be over-ruled by an explicit type statement at the head of the program, *before* the first executable statement, for example

```
INTEGER X
REAL KENOBI
```

The effect is that X will be of integer type, while KENOBI will be of real type for the duration of the program.

To promote good programming habits, it is suggested that every variable used in a program be specified with the appropriate type (even if this is unnecessary) in alphabetical order, one per line, as in the next example. Every variable used should also be described briefly in a comment statement. This is not done consistently throughout this book, in order to save space.

3.5   Example: Vertical Motion under Gravity

Using simple dynamical laws, one can show that if a stone is projected vertically upward with an initial speed u, its vertical displacement s after a time t has elapsed is given by the formula

$$s = ut - 0.5gt^2.$$

where $g = 9.8$ metres/sec^2, the acceleration due to gravity. Air resistance has been ignored (the effect of air resistence is discussed in Chapter 15). We would like to compute s, given u and t. Notice that we are not concerned here with how to derive the formula, but how to compute its value. The logical preparation of the problem is very simple:

1   Get values of g, u, and t into the computer.
2   Compute the value of s according to the formula.
3   Print the value of s.
4   Stop.

The program is:

```
*** VERTICAL MOTION UNDER GRAVITY

*** DESCRIPTION OF VARIABLES
*** G :   ACCELERATION DUE TO GRAVITY
*** S :   DISPLACEMENT IN METRES
*** T :   TIME IN SECONDS
*** U :   INITIAL SPEED IN M/S

*** TYPE SPECIFICATION OF VARIABLES
    REAL   G
    REAL   S
```

```
REAL   T
REAL   U

PRINT*, ' TIME               DISPLACEMENT'
G = 9.8
U = 60
T = 6
S = U * T - G / 2 * T ** 2
PRINT*, ' '
PRINT*, T, S

STOP
END
```

This example is discussed further in the Exercises at the end of the chapter.

3.6   Arithmetic Expressions

A FORTRAN arithmetic expression is a combination of constants and variables using arithmetic operators, and specifies a rule for computing a value. There are five arithmetic operators.

3.6.1   Arithmetic Operators

Operator	Meaning	Example
+	Addition	A + 6.9
	or unary plus	+ F
–	Subtraction	X – Y
	or unary minus	– C
*	Multiplication	2. * A
/	Division	B / DELTA
**	Exponentiation	2 ** 4 (= 2 * 2 * 2 * 2)

It is recommended that blanks always appear on either side of an operator, to make programs more readable. This is done throughout this book.

3.6.2   Integer Division

This causes so many errors that it deserves a section of its own. When an integer variable or expression is divided by another integer variable or expression, the quotient is also of integer type, and is therefore truncated. The decimal part, if any, of the quotient is lost. For example,

10 / 3	is computed as 3;
19 / 4	is computed as 4
4 / 5	is computed as 0 (this often causes an unwanted division by zero!).

3.6.3   Real and Integer Mixed Type Rule

If the variables (or expressions) on either side of an operator are of a different type, the integer variable or expression is converted to real type, and the operation is performed in real arithmetic. If both operands are of type integer, the operation is performed in integer arithmetic. For example,

```
10 / 3.        is computed as 3.33333 (real);
19. / 4        is computed as 4.75 (real);
4. / 5.        is computed as 0.8 (real);
2 ** (- 2)     is computed as 0 (why?).
```

3.6.4 Precedence of Operators

Since an expression may contain many operators, it is necessary to know in what order the computer executes operations. The order of precedence is as follows:

Order	Operation
1st	Parentheses (brackets)
2nd	Exponentiation
3rd	Multiplication and division
4th	Addition, subtraction, and their unary operations

When operators with the same precedence occur together, an ambiguity could arise. For example, does $A/B*C$ mean $(A/B)*C$ or $A/(B*C)$? To resolve this, the FORTRAN compiler always performs operations with the same precedence from left to right. So $A/B*C$ is in fact evaluated as $(A/B)*C$. Note also the difference between

```
3 * 10 / 3     which is computed as 10, and
10 / 3 * 3     which is computed as 9.
```

There is **ONE EXCEPTION** to the precedence rules, for an expression of the form

```
A ** B ** C
```

where the **RIGHT-HAND** operation $B**C$ is evaluated **FIRST**.

3.7 Arithmetic Assignment Statements

The purpose of the arithmetic assignment statement is to compute the numeric value of an expression and assign it to a variable. Its general form is

```
Variable = Expression
```

Example:

```
X = A + B
```

The equal sign should be read 'becomes', so the above example should be read as 'X becomes A plus B', or more literally, 'The contents of X becomes the contents of A plus the contents of B'.

The variable and expression may be of different type, but if the variable is an integer the value of the expression will be truncated on assignment. For example:

```
N = 10. / 3    (value of N is 3)
X = 10 / 3     (value of X is 3.0)
Y = 10 / 3.    (value of Y is 3.33333)
I = 10 / 3.    (value of I is 3).
```

The danger of performing integer divisions inadvertently cannot be stressed too much. For example, you might want to average three marks which happen to be integers M1, M2 and M3. The most natural statement to write is

```
F = (M1 + M2 + M3) / 3
```

but this will truncate the decimal part of the average. It is best always to write constants as reals in this case:

```
F = (M1 + M2 + M3) / 3.0
```

3.7.1   Examples

The formulae

$$F = GME/r^2,$$
$$c = \sqrt{a^2+b^2}/2a,$$
$$A = P(1+r/100)^n$$

may be translated into the following FORTRAN statements:

```
F = G * M * E / R ** 2
C = (A ** 2 + B ** 2) ** 0.5 / (2 * A)
A = P * (1 + R / 100) ** N
```

3.8   Example: Conversion of Temperatures

Here we want to write a program which will convert a temperature on the Fahrenheit scale (where water freezes and boils at 32° and 212° respectively) to the Centigrade (Celsius) scale. The logical analysis, or structure plan, is as follows:

1   Get Fahrenheit temperature into computer (call it TEMPF).
2   Work out its Centigrade equivalent (call it TEMPC).
   2.1   Subtract 32 from TEMPF and multiply by 5./9.
3   Print the value of TEMPC.
4   Stop.

Suppose the Fahrenheit temperature is 98.4° (normal human body temperature). The conversion program is then

```
* *** CONVERTS FAHRENHEIT TO CENTIGRADE
* *** TEMPC : CENTIGRADE TEMPERATURE
* *** TEMPF : FAHRENHEIT TEMPERATURE

      REAL TEMPC
      REAL TEMPF

      TEMPF = 98.4
      TEMPC = (TEMPF - 32) * 5. / 9.
      PRINT*, TEMPC

      STOP
      END
```

3.9   Simple Input/Output

In this section we look at the READ and PRINT statements more closely.

3.9.1   Input

So far, variables have been given values by using arithmetic assignment statements, e.g.

```
      TEMPF = 98.4
```

in the example of the previous section. A large program may have hundreds of such statements, all in different parts of the program. If we wanted to run the program for different values of the data, it would be a great nuisance to have to find every such line in the program and change it. Therefore there is an alternative way of input, in which the data (input) required for the program appears separately on data lines, which are entered from the keyboard while the program is executing. In this way, it is much easier to change the data. We use the **READ** statement to do this. The temperature conversion program can then be rewritten as:

```
*  ***  CONVERSION FAHRENHEIT TO CENTIGRADE

      REAL    TEMPC
      REAL    TEMPF

      READ*, TEMPF
      TEMPC = (TEMPF - 32) * 5. / 9.
      PRINT*, TEMPC

      STOP
      END
```

The line of data to be supplied is then

```
98.4
```

To convert a different temperature, we now only have to supply a different data line.
    The general form of this type of **READ** statement is

```
      READ*, list of variables separated by commas
```

with values for all the variables in the list in one (or more) data lines, and separated by commas or at least one blank. For example:

```
      READ*, A, B, I, X
      ....
      ....
```

Data:

```
5.2, -10., 73, 1.2E-4
```

The effect of the **READ** plus the line of data is the same as if the following statements were used in the FORTRAN program:

```
      A = 5.2
      B = -10.0
      I = 73
      X = 1.2E-4
```

Note

1) Data may start in any column.
2) Each time a new **READ** statement is encountered in the program, the computer will go to a new data line.

Example

```
      READ*, X, Y, Z
```

This statement will be satisfied with one data line with three values on it:

```
3.0   4.0   5.0
```

But

```
        READ*,  X
        READ*,  Y
        READ*,  Z
```

will require three data lines, each with one value on it:

```
3.0
4.0
5.0
```

When a new **READ** is encountered, unread data on the current line is discarded, and the computer looks on the next data line for the new data.

3)   Data for one **READ** statement may run over onto a second data line if the first cannot contain all the values for the list of variables in the **READ** statement. The only modification that is required is that there is no comma after the last value on the first data line. (The computer assumes a comma if it reads to the end of the first line and still requires further values for the remaining variables in the **READ** statement.) This point and the previous one are illustrated by the following program segment:

```
        READ*,  A
        READ*,  B,  C
        READ*,  D
        ....
        ....
```

Data:

```
1,  2,  3
4
7,  8
9,  10
```

This has the same effect as the assignments

```
        A = 1
        B = 4
        C = 7
        D = 9
```

4)   If there are not enough data to satisfy a **READ**, the program may 'crash' (abort). Some compilers give an error message (diagnostic) to indicate in which line the error occurred. For example, the program segment.

```
        READ*,  A
        READ*,  B,  C
        ....
```

with the two data lines

```
1   2
3
```

will cause an error in line two of the program. A and B will be assigned the values 1.0 and

3.0 respectively, and there will be no data left for C. Some compilers, however, assume zero for the unspecified variables, which is a much more subtle error.

3.9.2   Output

We now look at the statements required to print out the results generated by a program. (Throughout this book 'print' means either 'display on a terminal screen', or 'print on paper', depending on what sort of computer system you are using.) The simplest statement that will achieve this has the following form:

```
PRINT*, list of variables separated by commas
```

For example, the variables A, B, I and X read at the beginning of the previous section may all be printed with one statement:

```
PRINT*, A, B, I, X
```

The values of these variables will be printed on one line in the same order as they occur in the **PRINT** statement, and will be separated and placed in the correct type (real fixed point, real floating point, or integer). The actual print line generated by this example (run with the ASCII FORTRAN compiler) is:

```
5.2000000       -10.000000              73   .12000000-003
```

Note

1)   Each time a **PRINT** statement is executed in the program a new line of print is started.
2)   The output line will have a fixed number of print fields, depending on the width of the screen or paper you are using. For example, if you are using paper that is 132 columns wide (standard fanfold computer paper), the output will have only eight print fields even if there are nine or more variables in the **PRINT** statement. The ninth value will be printed in the next line of the printout in the first print field, underneath the value of the first variable. The tenth value is then printed under the second, etc. (NB: this restriction only applies to **PRINT***. Chapter 9, on Advanced Input/Output, shows you how to get round it.)
3)   Messages (character strings) can also be printed. The message to be printed must be enclosed between single quotation marks as follows:

```
A = 1.3
B = 0.000000625
PRINT*, ' VALUE OF A =', A, 'VALUE OF B =', B
```

The output is:

```
VALUE OF A =    1.3000000       VALUE OF B =    .62500000-006
```

Note that everything between the quotation marks is printed exactly as it appears in the **PRINT** statement, including blanks. Note also that commas must separate messages from variables in the **PRINT** statements.
4)   If a **PRINT** statement is too long to fit into columns 7–72 inclusive, it can be continued on the next line in the usual way by placing a non-blank character in column 6 of the second line. This procedure can be repeated to extend the line even further if required.

Example

column number: 678 . . .   . . . $\begin{pmatrix} 7 \\ 2 \end{pmatrix}$

```
        PRINT*,'NOW IS THE TIME ....... FOR ALL GO
       $OD MEN TO COME TO THE AID OF THE PARTY'
```

This will all be printed on one line with no break between 'GO' and 'OD'.

5)   Arithmetic may be done explicitly in a **PRINT** statement, e.g.

```
PRINT*, A * B / C
```

will print the value of (**A*B/C**).

3.10   Character Variables

In this chapter we have seen that numbers may be stored in integer or real variables. There is a third type of variable, called a **CHARACTER** variable, which can store a literal character, or string of characters. Character variables are declared as follows:

```
CHARACTER*4 DOG
```

This means that DOG can hold up to four characters, which may be assigned as follows:

```
DOG = 'KELA'
```

The following example prints an address:

```
CHARACTER*20 STREET
INTEGER NUMBER

NUMBER = 3
STREET = 'CONIFER WAY'
PRINT*, NUMBER, ' ', STREET
```

The output is:

```
3 CONIFER WAY
```

Character variables are discussed fully in Chapter 11.

3.11   Summary

* Successful problem solving with a computer requires knowledge of the coding rules and a sound logical plan.

* Comment lines explain what is going on in a program.

* Numbers may be represented as reals or integers.

* A variable which stores a number may be real or integer.

* A variable name consists of up to six alphanumeric characters, starting with a letter.

* There are five arithmetic operators, which operate according to strict rules of precedence.

* Decimal parts are truncated when integers are divided.

* An assignment statement computes the value of an expression and assigns it to a variable.

* Characters may be stored in character variables.

3.12   Exercises

In all these exercises, the usual real/integer naming convention for memory variables applies.

3.1 Decide which of the following constants are not written in standard FORTRAN and state why not:

(a) 9,87 (b) .0 (c) 25.82 (d) -356231
(e) 3.57*E2 (f) 3.57E2 (g) 3.57E+2 (h) 3,57E-2

3.2 State, giving reasons, which of the following are not standard FORTRAN variable names, and state whether each valid one is of real or integer type:

(a) A2 (b) A.2 (c) 2A (d) 'A'ONE
(e) AONE (f) MIN2 (g) ALPHONE (h) INT+1

3.3 Translate the following formulae into FORTRAN expressions.

(a) $p + \dfrac{w}{u}$

(b) $p + \dfrac{w}{u+v}$

(c) $p + \dfrac{w}{u+v} \over p + \dfrac{w}{u-v}$

(d) x^2

(e) $x^{2.5}$

(f) $x^{\frac{1}{2}}$

(g) x^{y+z}

(h) $(x^y)^z$

(i) $x^{(y^z)}$

(j) $x - \dfrac{x}{3!} + \dfrac{x^5}{5!}$

(k) $\dfrac{-b+(b^2-4ac)^{\frac{1}{2}}}{2a}$

3.4 Translate the following into FORTRAN statements:

(a) Add one to the value of I and store the answer in I.
(b) Cube I, add J to this, and store the answer in I.
(c) Divide the sum of A and B by the product of C and D, and store the answer in X.

3.5 This question refers to the vertical motion example of section 3.5.

(a) Run the program as it stands. Can you work out whether the stone is moving up or down?
(b) Rerun for different values of t. In particular, use the program to find out where the stone is after 20 seconds, and interpret your results physically.
(c) Rearrange the formula in order to compute when the stone returns to the ground.
(d) Rearrange the formula to compute when the stone is at any particular height, i.e. compute t, given u and s. Interpret your results physically.

3.6 Evaluate the following arithmetic expressions (answers are given in brackets). Use the following values for A, B, C, I and J:

A = 2.   I = 2   C = 5.
B = 3.   J = 3

(a) A * B + C   (11.0)
(b) A * (B + C)   (16.0)
(c) B / C * A   (1.2)
(d) B / (C * A)   (0.3)
(e) A / I / J   (0.3333333)
(f) I / J / A   (0.0)
(g) A * B ** I / A ** J * 2   (4.5)
(h) C + (B / A) ** 3 / B * 2.   (7.25)
(i) A ** B ** I   (512.0)
(j) - B ** A * C   (-45.0)

```
(k)   J / (I / J)                         (division by zero)
(l)   10 * I / 4                          (5)
(m)   10 / 4 * I                          (4)
(n)   J / I * C                           (5.0)
(o)   I ** J / 3                          (2)
(p)   (9 * J / (2 * I)) * I / 5           (2)
```

3.7 The largest integer that can be stored on a mainframe computer is usually $2^{31}-1$, or $2^{35}-1$ (the reason for this is explained in Section 2.3). Suppose it is $2^{35}-1$. Write a FORTRAN statement which will compute this number, bearing in mind that the computer will not be able to compute 2^{35}.

3.8 Write a program to convert a temperature on the Centigrade scale to one on the Fahrenheit scale.

3.9 What will be the values of the variables in the following **READ**s, given the five data lines below?

```
READ*, A
READ*, B, C, N
READ*, X, J
READ*, Z
....
....
```

Data:

```
3.2, 6.5
-1, 4.2
8.99, 5
7.3, 2, 6.9, -4.98
17.5, 9.03
```

(*Answers:* $A = 3.2$; $B = -1.0$; $C = 4.2$; $N = 8$;
  $X = 7.3$; $J = 2$; $Z = 17.5$)

3.10 What are the contents of the variables A, B, C, D and E after the following program segment has been executed?

```
READ*, A, B, C
READ*, D
READ*, E
....
```

Data:

```
5, 6
7, 8
2, 3
10, 11
```

3.11 Write some lines of FORTRAN which will exchange the contents of two memory variables A and B, using only one additional memory variable T.

3.12 Write some lines of FORTRAN which will exchange the contents of two memory variables A and B, without using any additional memory variables.

3.13   What are the values of A and X after the following program has been executed (after you have studied Chapter 6 you will be able to rewrite this program with far fewer lines)?

```
A = 0
I = 1
X = 0
A = A + I
X = X + I / A
A = A + I
X = X + I / A
A = A + I
X = X + I / A
A = A + I
X = X + I / A
```

3.14   The steady-state electric current I flowing in a circuit that contains a resistance, capacitance and inductance in series, is given by

$$I = \frac{E}{\sqrt{R^2 + \left[2\pi FL - \dfrac{1}{2\pi FC}\right]^2}}$$

where E, R, L, C, and F are the input voltage, resistance, inductance, capacitance and frequency respectively. Translate this formula into a FORTRAN expression.

4

Program Preparation

Our examples so far have been very simple logically, since we have been concentrating on the technical aspects of writing FORTRAN statements correctly. However, real problems are far more complex, and to program successfully we need to understand the problem thoroughly, and to break it down into its most fundamental logical stages. In other words, we have to develop a systematic procedure, or 'algorithm', for solving the problem. There are a number of ways which assist in this process of algorithm development. In this chapter we outline two such methods: flowcharts, and structure plans (Ellis, 1982).

4.1 Flowcharts

The flowchart approach is rather old-fashioned, and tends to be frowned upon in 'with it' computing circles. However, for historical interest (and in case you actually prefer this visual method), some examples are given below.

The essential logical features of the problem to compute a student's final mark (see Section 1.2) can be represented by a flowchart as follows (the symbols are explained below):

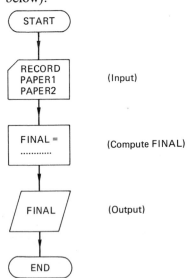

The main symbols used in flowcharts, and their meanings are:

Flow of logic

Start/Stop

Input (or assignment) of information

Processing (e.g. calculation of formulae)

Header for DO-loop (see Chapter 6)
Decision

End of DO-loop (see Chapter 6)

Decision (two- or three-way branch)

Printed output

4.2   Quadratic Equation: Flowchart

Every schoolchild must have solved hundreds of quadratic equations of the form

$$ax^2+bx+c=0$$

The algorithm for finding the solution x, given a, b, and c, is flowcharted as follows:

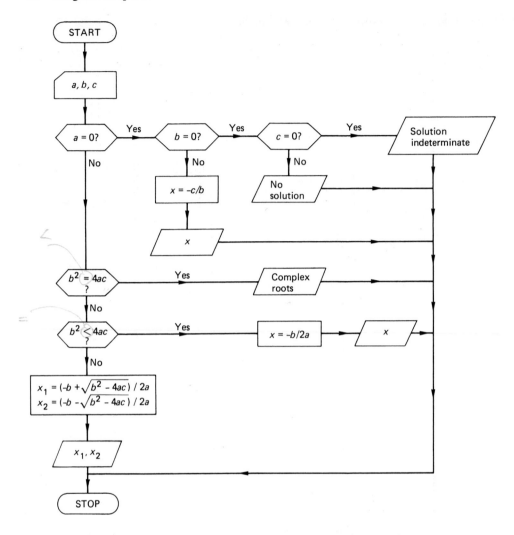

4.3 Structure Plans

This is an alternative method of program preparation, which has advantages when th
equivalent flowchart gets rather big. The plan may be written at a number of levels, c
increasing complexity, as the logical structure of the program is developed.

For example, a first level plan for the student mark problem of Section 1.2 might be
simple statement of the problem.

    1 Read marks.
    2 Calculate and print final mark.

The first step is pretty straightforward, but the second needs elaborating, so the secon
level plan could be something like:

    1 Read marks
    2 Calculate and print final mark.
        2.1 Calculate final mark as average of three marks.
        2.2 Print final mark.

There are no hard and fast rules about flowcharts or structure plans, and you should use whichever method you prefer. The essential point is to cultivate the mental discipline of getting the logic of a program clear before bothering about the detailed coding and rushing to the computer. The 'top down' approach of flowcharts or structure plans means that the overall structure of a program is clearly thought out before you have to worry about the details of syntax (coding), and this reduces the number of logical errors enormously.

4.4 Quadratic Equation: Structure Plan

The equivalent structure plan for the quadratic problem flowcharted in Section 4.2 is given below.

1   Start.
2   Read data (a, b, c).
3   If $a = 0$ then
    3.1   If $b = 0$ then
        3.1.1   If $c = 0$ then
            3.1.1.1   Print 'Solution indeterminate'
            Otherwise
            3.1.1.2   Print 'There is no solution'
        Otherwise
        3.1.2 $x = -c/b$
        3.1.3   Print x (equation is linear)
    Otherwise
    3.2   If $b^2 < 4ac$ then
        3.2.1   Print 'Complex roots'
        Otherwise
        3.2.2   If $b^2 = 4ac$ then
            3.2.2.1 $x = -b/2a$
            3.2.2.2   Print x (solutions equal)
            Otherwise
            3.2.2.3 $x_1 = (-b + \sqrt{b^2 - 4ac})/2a$
            3.2.2.4 $x_2 = (-b - \sqrt{b^2 - 4ac})/2a$
            3.2.2.5   Print x_1, x_2.
4   Stop.

Details of how to code the If-then decisions are discussed in Chapter 7.
  There are many more examples of structure plans throughout the book.

4.5 Structured Programming

Some examples later in the book (particularly in the last three chapters) will get rather involved. More advanced programs like these should be structured by means of 'subprograms', which are dealt with in detail in Chapter 12. A subprogram is a self-contained program unit which can communicate with the outside world in specific ways, and which may be invoked or 'called' by the main program. The main program will then look very much like a first level structure plan of the problem. For example, the quadratic equation problem may be structure planned as follows:

1   Input the data.
2   Find the solution.

3 Output the solution.
4 Stop.

Using subprograms this may be translated directly into a FORTRAN main program:

```
CALL INPUT
CALL SOLVE
CALL OUTPUT
STOP
END
```

The logic for the subprograms INPUT and OUTPUT will only involve some **READ** and **PRINT** statements, and the structure plan of the previous section gives the logic for the subprogram SOLVE. The details of how to code this problem are left as an exercise in Chapter 12, where subprograms are discussed in detail.

4.6   Summary

* An algorithm is a systematic logical procedure for solving a problem.

* An algorithm must be developed for a problem before it can be coded.

* A flowchart is a diagrammatic representation of an algorithm.

* A structure plan is a representation of an algorithm in words.

4.7   Exercises

4.1 Work through the following structure plan, which defines a geometric construction:

1 Draw two perpendicular $x-$ and $y-$axes.
2 Draw the points A $(10; 0)$ and B $(0; 1)$.
3 While A does not coincide with the origin repeat
    3.1 Draw the straight line joining A and B
    3.2 Move A one unit to the left along the x-axis
    3.3 Move B one unit up on the y-axis
4 Stop.

4.2 Consider the following structure plan, where M and N are FORTRAN integer variables:

1 Set $M = 44$ and $N = 28$.
2 While M not equal to N repeat
    2.1 While $M > N$ repeat
        2.1.1 Replace M by $M-N$
    2.2 While $N > M$ repeat
        2.2.1 Replace N by $N-M$
3 Print M.

(a) Sketch the contents of M and N during execution, and give the output.
(b) Repeat (a) for $M = 14$ and $N = 24$.
(c) What general arithmetic procedure does the structure plan achieve (try more values of M and N if necessary)?

See also Exercises 7.2, 7.3, 7.4, 7.5 and 7.6.

5

Special Functions

If you have mastered the contents of this book thus far you should be able to write a program which reads data into the computer, performs arithmetic operations on the data, and prints the results of the computation in a comprehensible form. However, more interesting problems are likely to involve special mathematical functions like sines, tangents, logarithms, exponentials, etc. Just as most calculators have keys for these functions, FORTRAN allows you to compute many functions directly. These functions are called supplied or intrinsic functions.

5.1 Example: Projectile Motion

Write a program to compute the position (x- and y-coordinates) and velocity (magnitude and direction) of a projectile, given t, the time since launch; u, the launch velocity; a, the initial angle of launch (in degrees); and g, the acceleration due to gravity.

The horizontal displacement is given by the formula

$$x = u\cos(a)t$$

and the vertical displacement by

$$y = u\sin(a)t - gt^2/2.$$

The velocity has magnitude V such that

$$V^2 = [u\cos(a)]^2 + [u\sin(a) - gt]^2,$$

and makes an angle θ with the ground such that

$$\tan(\theta) = [u\sin(a) - gt]/[u\cos(a)].$$

The program is:

```
* *** COMPUTES PROJECTILE POSITION AND VELOCITY
      READ*, A, G, T, U
      A     = A * 3.14159 / 180.
      X     = U * COS(A) * T
      Y     = U * SIN(A) * T - G * T * T / 2.
      VX    = U * COS(A)
      VY    = U * SIN(A) - G * T
      V     = SQRT( VX * VX + VY * VY )
      THETA = ATAN( VY / VX )
      PRINT*, 'Y=', Y, 'X=', X
```

```
      PRINT*, 'V=', V, 'THETA=', THETA

      STOP
      END
```

Note

1)   The argument of a function may be any valid FORTRAN expression, including another function. So in the example above, V could have been computed directly, as

```
      V = SQRT( (U * COS(A)) ** 2 + (U * SIN(A) - G * T) ** 2 )
```

(The argument for **SQRT** is always positive here (why?) so no problems can arise.)
2)   Angles for the trigonometric functions must be expressed in radians. To convert degrees to radians, multiply the angle in degrees by 3.14159/180. If you can't remember the value of π you can cunningly exploit the mathematical fact that the arc tangent of 1.0 is $\pi/4$, and use the **ATAN** intrinsic function.

5.2   Some Useful Intrinsic Functions

A complete list of the intrinsic functions of FORTRAN 77 is given in Appendix B. Most functions have 'generic' as well as 'specific' names. If the generic name is used, the value returned by the function is of the same type as its argument. E.g. **ABS**(-5) returns the integer value 5, whereas **ABS**(-5.2) returns the real value 5.2. The following is a list of the generic names of the more frequently used functions:

Function	Meaning
`ABS(X)`	absolute value
`ACOS(X)`	arc cosine (answer returned in radians)
`ASIN(X)`	arc sine (answer returned in radians)
`ATAN(X)`	arc tangent (answer returned in radians)
`COS(X)`	cosine
`COT(X)`	cotangent
`EXP(X)`	exponential
`FLOAT(I)`	converts integer to real
`INT(X)`	converts real X to integer by truncating
`LOG(X)`	natural logarithm
`LOG10(X)`	logarithm to the base 10
`MAX(X1,X2,..)`	maximum of the given list of arguments
`MIN(X1,X2,..)`	minimum of the given list of arguments
`MOD(K,L)`	remainder when K is divided by L
`NINT(X)`	nearest integer to X
`SIN(X)`	sine
`SQRT(X)`	square root (X must be non-negative)
`TAN(X)`	tangent

N.B. Where trigonometric functions require angles as arguments, these are assumed to be in radian measure.

5.3 Examples

Function	Value returned
INT(3.9)	3
INT(4.1)	4
INT(-2.9)	-2
INT(-3.1)	-3
NINT(3.9)	4
NINT(-2.9)	-3
MOD(13, 5)	3
MOD(4, 4)	0
MOD(0, 4)	0
FLOAT(2) / 4	0.5
FLOAT(2 / 4)	0.0

MOD is useful in testing divisibility of integers, or in 'clock arithmetic'. E.g. if MINS is the total time elapsed in minutes,

```
M = MOD( MINS, 60 )
```

gives the number of minutes past the hour (remainder when minutes are divided by 60). The same result can be achieved without using the MOD function:

```
M = MINS - MINS / 60 * 60
```

Convince your self that this is correct with some numeric examples.

FLOAT may be used to avoid unwanted integer divisions. For example, the following lines will each give the real quotient of the integer variables K and L:

```
Q = FLOAT(K) / L
Q = K / FLOAT(L)
Q = FLOAT(K) / FLOAT(L)
```

5.4 Summary

* Intrinsic functions may be used to compute a variety of mathematical and trigonometric functions directly.

5.5 Exercises

5.1 A fruit co-operative wants a program which reads the number of apples (BOX) that can be packed into one box and the number of apples to be packed (APPLES) and prints out the number of boxes needed (FULL) and the number of apples left over (LEFT).
(a) Write a structure plan for the problem.
(b) Write the FORTRAN program.

5.2 Write some FORTRAN statements which will:
(a) find the length C of the hypotenuse of a right-angled triangle in terms of the lengths A and B of the other two sides;
(b) find the length C of a side of a triangle given the lengths A and B of the other two sides and the size in degrees of the included angle THETA, using the cosine rule.

5.3   Translate the following formulae into FORTRAN expressions:

(a) $\log_e(x+x^2+a^2)$ (b) $\log_{10}y$

(c) $(e^{3t}+t^2\sin 4t)\cos^2 3t$ (d) $4\tan^{-1}(1)$

(e) $\sec^2 x+\cot y$ (f) $\sec^{-1}(|x/a|)$

5.4   A sphere of mass m_1 impinges obliquely on a stationary sphere of mass m_2, the direction of the blow making an angle a with the line of motion of the impinging sphere. If the coefficient of restitution is e it can be shown that the impinging sphere is deflected through an angle b such that

$$\tan b = \frac{m_2(1+e)\tan a}{(m_1-em_2)+(m_1+m_2)\tan^2 a}$$

Write a program to read values of m_1, m_2, e and a (in degrees) and to compute and print out the angle b in degrees.

6

Repetition: The DO Statement

It often happens that we want to repeat a group of statements a number of times, either to process a large amount of data in an identical way, or to repeat an operation with different values for the variables each time. FORTRAN has a construction called the **DO** statement which handles repetition very easily, and which enables us to write much more powerful programs.

6.1 Final Mark Calculation

In Section 1.2 we wrote a program to compute a single student's final mark as the average of her class record, and two examination papers. In reality, this calculation will need to be done for a class of, say, 200 students, each of whom has three marks. The program is easily amended:

```
*  ***  COMPUTES FINAL MARKS FOR 200 STUDENTS

        INTEGER STUDNT
        REAL    FINAL
        REAL    PAPER1
        REAL    PAPER2
        REAL    RECORD

        DO 90 STUDNT = 1, 200
           READ*, RECORD,  PAPER1,  PAPER2
           FINAL = (RECORD + PAPER1 + PAPER2) / 3
           PRINT*, 'NUMBER', STUDNT, 'HAS MARK', FINAL
90      CONTINUE

        STOP
        END
```

Data:

$$
\left.\begin{array}{l}
63.6\ 46\ 49 \\
72.9\ 85\ 98 \\
\ldots \\
98.4\ 74\ 78
\end{array}\right\} \text{ exactly 200 data lines}
$$

Note

1) The **CONTINUE** statement is a 'dummy' statement which serves only as a marker in a

program. It is recommended that you always end a DO-loop with **CONTINUE**, as this allows you to add extra statements to the body of the loop at a later stage.

2)　The number 90 on the **CONTINUE** statement is a statement label and must appear anywhere in the first five columns. Its precise value is arbitrary, but it must match the number quoted in the preceeding DO statement.

3)　The statements between the DO 90 .... and the one labelled 90 are executed repeatedly, with the DO- variable STUDNT starting at one, and increasing by one each time, until the set of statements has been executed with STUDNT not exceeding 200. The statements following statement 90 are then executed in the usual sequential fashion. Note that these statements have been indented by two columns to make it easier for the user to spot the loop.

4)　The DO-variable may not appear on the left-hand side of an assignment statement inside the DO-loop, since this will interfere with the loop's counter. However, it may be used in any valid FORTRAN expression. For example, the following program segment uses K to print out the first 20 powers of two:

```
      DO 70 K = 1,  20
         J = 2 ** K
         PRINT*,  J
70    CONTINUE
```

5)　The parameters of the DO statement may themselves be variables, set by preceding statements in the program. The final mark program is repeated in outline below, but this time it can cope with a variable number N of students. The first data line must therefore indicate the exact number of students in the class (179 in this example):

```
      READ*,  N

      DO 90 STUDNT = 1,  N
         . . . .

90    CONTINUE

      STOP
      END
```

Data:

```
179
63.6 46 49    ⎫
. . . .       ⎬  exactly 179 data lines with marks
27.1 98 72    ⎭
```

6.2　Definition of the DO Statement

Form:　　DO　s　i = e1, e2, e3

where:

s　is the statement label of the terminal statement of the DO-loop. It is recommended that **CONTINUE** always be used as the terminal statement, and that the label be multiple of 10;

i　is an integer or real variable, called the DO-variable;

$\left.\begin{array}{l} e1 \\ e2 \\ e3 \end{array}\right\}$ are each an integer or real expression (parameters of the DO);

and e3 may be omitted, in which case it is set to one by default.
   The DO-loop is executed as follows:

1)   If e1, e2, and e3 are integers, the statements in the range of the DO-loop (i.e. the statements following the DO statement up to and including the terminal statement of the DO-loop) are executed repeatedly, first with $i=e1$, and subsequently with i increased by e3 each time (if e3 is negative, i will obviously decrease each time) until the statements in the range have been executed for the largest value of i not exceeding e2 (if e3>0), or for the smallest value of i not less than e2 (if e3<0).

2)   **N.B.** The DO-loop will **NOT** be executed at all if

   (a) e1>e2 and e3>0 (or e3 omitted);
   (b) e1<e2 and e3<0.

3)   The number of executions of a DO-loop is determined before the first execution begins, and is called the 'iteration count'. It is computed as follows:

$$INT((e2-e1+e3)/e3)).$$

If the value of this expression is negative, the iteration count is set to zero. An iteration count of zero means that the DO-loop will not be executed at all. For example, the DO statement

```
DO 10 I = 1, 9, 2
```

has an iteration count of

$$INT((9-1+2)/2) = 5,$$

whereas the statement

```
DO 10 I = 1, -4, -2
```

has an iteration count of

$$INT((-4-1-2)/-2) = 3.$$

4)   When the DO-loop has been completed the DO-variable retains its last defined value.

6.3   Newton's Method to Find a Square Root

The square root X of any positive number A may be found using only the arithmetic operations of add, subtract, multiply and divide, with Newton's method (see Section 15.1), as follows:

```
      READ*, A
      X = 1

      DO 10 L = 1, 10
         X = (X + A / X) / 2.
         PRINT*, X
   0   CONTINUE
      STOP
      END
```

The values of X printed will be seen to 'converge' to a limit, which will be the square root of A. Most computers and calculators use a similar method internally to compute **SQRT** and other intrinsic functions.

There is no universal convention on how to flowchart a **DO**-loop, but one way is to use an elongated diamond to give the conditions under which the body of the loop is executed, with a small circle to indicate the end of the loop, as follows:

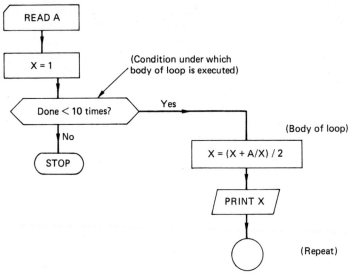

Alternatively, the structure plan would be something like this:

1   Read A.
2   Initialize X to 1.
3   Repeat 10 times
     3.1. X = (X+A/X)/2.
     3.2. Print X
4   Stop.

6.4   Vertical Motion under Gravity

The example of Section 3.5, where a stone is projected vertically, may be amended with a **DO** statement to print the stone's displacement at regular intervals, say, of half a second:

```
C *** COMPUTES VERTICAL DISPLACEMENT UNDER GRAVITY

        PRINT*, ' TIME              DISPLACEMENT'
        PRINT*, ' '
        G = 9.8
        U = 60

        DO 90 T = 0,   11,   0.5
           S = U * T - G / 2. * T ** 2
           PRINT*, T, S
90      CONTINUE

        STOP
        END
```

If you run this example, you will see that·the stone goes up and comes down during this period. Use trial and error to find out more precisely when the stone reaches the ground again.

6.5   Damped Oscillations

The current flowing in a circuit consisting of a resistance, inductance and initially charged capacitor connected in series is given by

$$i = A \exp(-Rt/2L) \sin(2\pi f_1 t)$$

where

$$A = 2\pi f_0^2 Q/f_1$$
$$f_0 = 1/2\pi \sqrt{1/LC}$$
$$f_1 = 1/2\pi \sqrt{1/LC - R^2/4L^2}$$

and the symbols have the meanings

    i: current (amperes) at time t;
    A: maximum current;
    t: time (seconds) elapsed since circuit connected;
    R: resistance (ohms);
    L: inductance (henrys);
    f_0: frequency (cycles/sec) of undamped ($R = 0$) circuit;
    f_1: frequency of damped circuit;
    C: capacitance (farads);
    Q: initial charge (coulombs) on capacitor.

We want to compute the current over a period of CYCLES complete cycles, where PERCY evaluations per cycle are made. The current must therefore be computed CYCLES*PERCY times altogether. The time DT between successive evaluations will be given by

```
DT = 1 / (PERCY * F1)
```

since the period of the oscillations is $1/f_1$ seconds. The program is as follows:

```
*** DAMPED OSCILLATIONS

    INTEGER CYCLES
    INTEGER PERCY
    REAL I
    REAL L

    Q = 1E-5
    R = 1
    C = 1E-5
    L = 0.002
    CYCLES = 2
    PERCY = 10
    PI = 3.1415927
    FO = SQRT( 1 / (L * C) ) / (2 * PI)
    F1 = SQRT( 1 / (L * C) - R ** 2 / (4 * L ** 2) ) / (2 * PI)
    A = 2 * PI * FO ** 2 * Q / F1
    T = 0
    DT = 1.0 / (PERCY * F1)
```

```
        PRINT*, ' TIME (SECS)      CURRENT (AMPS) '
        PRINT*, ' '

        DO 10 K = 1, CYCLES * PERCY + 1
          I = A * EXP( - R * T / (2 * L) ) * SIN( 2 * PI * F1 * T )
          PRINT*, T, I
          T = T + DT
10      CONTINUE

        STOP
        END
```

Output:

```
TIME (SECS)       CURRENT (AMPS)

.00000000         .00000000
.88913249-004     .40674445-001
.17782650-003     .64365870-001
.26673975-003     .62950910-001
.35565299-003     .38050534-001
.44456624-003     .20124786-008
.53347948-003   -.36395982-001
.62239273-003   -.57595356-001
.71130597-003   -.56329237-001
.80021921-003   -.34048086-001
.88913245-003   -.13731864-007
.97804569-003     .32567551-001
.10669589-002     .51537016-001
.11558722-002     .50404088-001
.12447854-002     .30466655-001
.13336986-002     .35049775-007
.14226119-002   -.29141821-001
.15115251-002   -.46115937-001
.16004383-002   -.45102194-001
.16893516-002   -.27261950-001
.17782648-002   -.54434711-007
```

The output clearly exhibits oscillations which are smaller each cycle. A program to display these results graphically is discussed in Chapter 11.

6.6   More Examples

1)   Print the even numbers from 10 to zero in descending order (i.e. loop backwards):

```
        DO 20 I = 10, 0, -2
          PRINT*, I
20      CONTINUE
```

2)   What is the output from the next segment?

```
        DO 40 I = 2, 13, 3
          PRINT*, I
40      CONTINUE
```

(the integers 2, 5, 8, 11, all on separate lines).

3)   And from this one?

```
      DO 30 I = 3, -2, -2
         PRINT*, I
30       CONTINUE
```

(the integers 3, 1, −1, on separate lines again).

4)   What is the output of the following segment?

```
      DO 70 M = 1, 6, -2
         PRINT*, M**3
70       CONTINUE
```

(No output: loop is not executed at all, under note 3 of Section 6.2.)

6.7   Nested DOs

DO statements are allowed within the range of a DO-loop, as long as the range of the inner DO-loop lies completely within the range of the outer one.
   This is valid nesting:

```
      DO 90 I = 2, 6
         DO 80 J = 1, 8
         ....

            A = A + 1
80          CONTINUE
90       CONTINUE
```

(The statement $A = A + 1$ will be executed 40 times altogether.)
   The following, however, is invalid:

```
      DO 20 I = 3, 9
      ....

         DO 40 K = 6, 89
         ....

20       CONTINUE
         ....

40          CONTINUE
```

6.8   Computing the Limit of a Sequence

DO-loops are ideal for computing successive members of a sequence. This example also highlights a problem that sometimes occurs when computing a limit. Consider the sequence

$$x_n = a^n/n!, \quad n = 1, 2, 3, ...$$

where a is any constant and $n! = n(n-1)(n-2)...1$. The question is: what is the limit of this sequence as n gets indefinitely large. Let us take the case of $a = 10$. If we try to compute x_n directly we will soon be in trouble, because $n!$ gets large very rapidly as n increases, and a machine overflow occurs very quickly (see Exercise 6.3 below). However, the situation is neatly transformed if we spot that x_n may be formed from x_{n-1} as follows:

$x_n = a\, x_{n-1}/n.$

There are no overflow problems now. The following program computes x_n for $a = 10$, and increasing values of n, and prints it for $n = 10, 20, \ldots, 80$:

```
A = 10
X = 1
DO 10 N = 1, 80
    X = A * X / N
    IF( MOD( N, 10 ) .EQ. 0 )PRINT*, N, X
10  CONTINUE
STOP
END
```

The output is as follows:

```
10   2755.7318
20   41.103171
30   .37699869-002
40   .12256171-007
50   .32879483-014
60   .12017800-021
70   .83482366-030
80   .00000000
```

From the results it appears that the limit of x_n as n gets indefinitely large is zero, and this may be proved mathematically. For more examples of calculus with computers, see Bitter (1983).

6.9   Bending of a Beam

A uniform beam is freely hinged at its $x = 0$ and $x = L$, so that its ends are at the same level. It carries a uniformly distributed load of W per unit length, and there is a tension T along the x-axis. The deflection y of the beam a distance x from one end is given by

$$y = \frac{WEI}{T^2}\left[\frac{\cosh a(L/2 - x)}{\cosh aL/2} - 1\right]\frac{Wx(L-x)}{2T},$$

where $a^2 = T/EI$, E being the Young's modulus of the beam, and I the moment of inertia of a cross-section of the beam. Suppose the beam is 10m long, the tension 1000N, the load 100N/m, and EI is 1E4. The following program computes the deflection of the beam from the horizontal every metre along the beam up to its midpoint.

```
* *** DEFLECTION OF A LOAD-BEARING BEAM

    REAL L
    L = 10
    W = 100
    EI = 1E4
    T = 1000
    A = SQRT( T / EI )

    DO 10 X = 0, L/2
        Y = W * EI / T ** 2 * (COSH( A * (L / 2 - X) ) /
    $   COSH( A * L / 2 ) - 1) + W * X * (L - X ) / (2 * T)
        PRINT*, X, Y
```

```
10       CONTINUE

         STOP
         END
```

Output:

```
.00000000        .00000000
1.0000000        .20500777
2.0000000        .38614762
3.0000000        .52639231
4.0000000        .61467454
5.0000000        .64477096
```

6.10   A Servomechanism Frequency Response

In electrical engineering the response (output) of a linear system is characterized by its transfer function. The system may be thought of as a 'black box'. An input signal with a given angular frequency (ω radians/sec) is applied at one end of the box. The output from the other end is then given by the input multiplied by the absolute value of the transfer function, with its phase shifted by the phase angle of the transfer function.

Suppose a certain servomechanism is characterized by the transfer function (McCracken, 1965)

$$T(j\omega) = \frac{K(1+0.4j\omega)(1+0.2j\omega)}{j\omega(1+2.5j\omega)(1+1.43j\omega)(1+0.02j\omega)^2}$$

where j is the symbol used in electrical engineering for the unit imaginary number $\sqrt{-1}$, and K is an amplification factor. $T(j\omega)$ is a complex number, which may be represented as

$$T(j\omega) = a + jb$$

where a and b are its real and imaginary parts. Its absolute value is then given by

$$\sqrt{a^2+b^2},$$

while its phase angle ϕ is given by arctan(b/a). If the **ATAN2** intrinsic function is used, the angle returned will be in the range $-\pi$ to π, so that the correct quadrant is given (which is not the case for **ATAN**). The program below shows how the servomechanism responds to different input frequencies, which is necessary information in the design of stable feedback control devices.

This example also serves to introduce a fourth type of FORTRAN variable: **COMPLEX**. A variable of this type is specified in a **COMPLEX** type statement. Complex variables may be constructed with the **CMPLX** intrinsic function as illustrated below. They may also be assigned real and imaginary parts, as shown in Section 15.1. The **REAL** and **AIMAG** intrinsic functions are used to find the real and imaginary parts of a complex variable.

The program starts with an input frequency of 0.02 radians/sec. This is multiplied by a factor of 1.25 each time for a given number of steps. The amplification factor K is 900. The phase shift of the output is in degrees. Note that pure imaginary numbers (like $j\omega$) must be set up as complex numbers, whereas pure reals may be represented directly by real variables.

```
* *** SERVOMECHANISM FREQUENCY RESPONSE

      COMPLEX JOM
      COMPLEX T
      REAL K
      INTEGER STEPS

      K = 900
      OMEGA = 0.02
      FACT = 1.25
      STEPS = 40
      PI = 3.1415927

      PRINT*, '   Omega            Real T            Im T',
    $ '              Abs T        Phase'
      PRINT*, ' '

      DO 10 I = 0, STEPS
         JOM = CMPLX( 0.0, 1.0 ) * OMEGA
         T = K * (1 + 0.4 *JOM) * (1 + 0.2 * JOM) /
    $    (JOM * (1 + 2.5 * JOM) * (1 + 1.43 * JOM) *
    $    (1 + 0.02 * JOM) ** 2)
         TABS = CABS( T )
         A = REAL( T )
         B = AIMAG( T )
         PHASE = ATAN2( B, A ) * 180 / PI
         PRINT*, OMEGA, A, B, TABS, PHASE
         OMEGA = OMEGA * FACT
10    CONTINUE

      STOP
      END
```

Output:

Omega	Real T	Im T	Abs T	Phase
.200000-001	-3023.6005	-44825.416	44927.275	-93.8589
.250000-001	-3018.3352	-35782.113	35909.190	-94.8216
.312500-001	-3010.1394	-28528.307	28686.674	-96.0232
.390625-001	-2997.4096	-22701.678	22898.704	-97.5215
.488281-001	-2977.7029	-18011.603	18256.083	-99.3873
.610351-001	-2947.3516	-14224.929	14527.060	-101.705
.762939-001	-2900.9742	-11154.863	11525.911	-104.577
.953674-001	-2830.9619	-8652.5811	9103.9280	-108.117
.119209	-2727.1864	-6601.3163	7142.4732	-112.446
.149011	-2577.4951	-4912.6788	5547.7828	-117.684
.186264	-2369.9301	-3524.5779	4247.2600	-123.916
.232830	-2097.6029	-2399.0702	3186.7657	-131.164
.291038	-1765.7844	-1517.1366	2328.0244	-139.331
.363797	-1397.4899	-867.69839	1644.9555	-148.163
.454747	-1031.1956	-432.70277	1118.3005	-157.236
.568434	-707.92748	-176.77200	729.66408	-165.979
.710542	-454.85653	-49.784822	457.57293	-173.753
.888178	-277.35732	-.27009078	277.35745	-179.944
1.11022	-163.64659	11.616026	164.05834	175.939

1.38777	-95.370681	9.7045366	95.863156	174.1898
1.73472	-55.857738	5.0283196	56.083606	174.8560
2.16840	-33.255993	1.3112486	33.281834	177.7420
2.71050	-20.239685	-.85931121	20.257919	-177.5688
3.38813	-12.614604	-1.8497126	12.749497	-171.6580
4.23516	-8.0559841	-2.1285926	8.3324538	-165.1992
5.29395	-5.2775946	-2.0380729	5.6574504	-158.8847
6.61744	-3.5556179	-1.7838665	3.9780143	-153.3569
8.27180	-2.4720084	-1.4762755	2.8792733	-149.1544
10.3397	-1.7784018	-1.1689707	2.1281931	-146.6824
12.9246	-1.3232010	-.88534609	1.5920737	-146.2137
16.1558	-1.0116914	-.63440721	1.1941491	-147.9091
20.1948	-.78400722	-.41981073	.88933030	-151.8323
25.2435	-.60330513	-.24447912	.65095862	-157.9405
31.5544	-.44978340	-.11173282	.46345370	-166.0492
39.4430	-.31697404	-.23323969-001	.31783101	-175.7915
49.3037	-.20702156	.23999513-001	.20840802	173.3873
61.6297	-.12397783	.39887500-001	.13023639	162.1654
77.0371	-.68086871-001	.37407063-001	.77685973-001	151.2155
96.2964	-.34607508-001	.27950691-001	.44485062-001	141.0739
120.370	-.16514201-001	.18296359-001	.24647020-001	132.0692
150.463	-.75115049-002	.11000131-001	.13320119-001	124.3274

Note how the input signal is amplified at first, but is then attentuated. The phase shift starts at about $-90°$ and moves gradually to about $-180°$, after which it swings backwards and forwards across the real axis as the input frequency gets larger.

6.11 Summary

* The DO statement is used to repeat a set of statements.

* The iteration count specifies how many times a DO-loop is not executed at all.

* If the iteration count is zero, the DO-loop is to be repeated.

* CONTINUE is a dummy statement which should be used to end a DO-loop.

* A statement label is a number in the range 1–99999 and may appear only in columns one to five.

* The terminal statement of a DO-loop must be labelled. It is recommended that the label be a multiple of 10.

* A DO-variable retains its last defined value on leaving the DO-loop.

* A DO-loop should be used to program a repeat structure when the number of repeats is known to the computer (i.e. in principle to the programmer) **before** the repeat structure is encountered (this is **not** always the case, as we shall see in Chapter 7). Another way of stating this is that a DO-loop should be used to repeat whenever the **condition** for repeating is **unchanged** in the body of the loop. This situation is characterized by the general structure plan:

    1 Repeat N times
        1.1 Statement(s) to be repeated

where N is known or computed **before** step 1 is encountered, and is **not** changed by the statement(s) in step 1.1.

6.12   Exercises

6.1   Write a program to compute the sum of the integers 1 to 100.

6.2   Write a program to compute the sum of the series

$$1+1/2+1/3+...+1/100.$$

6.3   Write a program to print a table of N and $N!$ (spoken as 'N factorial', and defined as $1 \times 2 \times 3 \times ... \times N$) for some values of N. See how far you can go.

6.4   There are many formulae for computing π (the ratio of a circle's circumference to its diameter). The simplest is

$$\pi/4 = 1-1/3+1/5-1/7+1/9-... \qquad (1)$$

which comes from the series

$$\arctan(x) = x-x^3/3+x^5/5-x^7/7+x^9/9-... \qquad (*)$$

by letting $x = 1$.

(a)   Write a program to compute π using series (1). Use as many terms in the series as your computer system will reasonably allow (start modestly, with 100 terms, say, and rerun your program with more and more each time). You should find that the series 'converges' very slowly, i.e. it takes a lot of terms to get fairly close to π.
   Rearranging the series speeds up the convergence:

$$\pi/8 = 1/(1 \times 3)+1/(5 \times 7)+1/(9 \times 11)+... \qquad (2)$$

(b)   Write a program to compute π using series (2) instead. You should find that you need fewer terms to reach the same level of accuracy that you got in (a).
   One of the fastest series used to compute π is

$$\pi/4 = 6 \arctan(1/8)+2 \arctan(1/57)+\arctan(1/239). \qquad (3)$$

(c)   Use formula (3) to compute π. Don't use the intrinsic function **ATAN** to compute the arctangents, since that would be cheating. Rather use the series (*) above.

6.5   The following method of computing π is due to Archimedes. A derivation and discussion of it is given by Breuer and Zwas (1984), who present the following algorithm:

   1   Set $A = 1$ and $N = 6$.
   2   Repeat a fixed number (e.g. 10) of times
      2.1   Replace N by 2*N
      2.2   Replace A by **SQRT**$(2-$**SQRT**$(4-A^{**}2))$
      2.3   Set $L = N^{*}A/2$
      2.4   Set $U = L/$**SQRT**$(1-A^{**}2/4)$
      2.5   Set $P = (U+L)/2$ (estimate of π)
      2.6   Set $E = (U-L)/2$ (estimate of error)
      2.7   Print N, P and E
   3   Stop.

Write a program to implement the algorithm.

6.6   Write a program to compute a table of the function

$$f(x) = x \sin(\pi(1+20x)/2)$$

over the interval $[-1; 1]$ using increments in x of (a) 0.2 (b) 0.1 and (c) 0.0625. Use your tables to plot a graph of $f(x)$ for the three cases, and observe that the tables for (a) and (b) give totally the wrong picture of $f(x)$.

6.7   The transcendental number e ($=2.718281828....$) can be shown to be the limit of

$$1/(1-x)^{1/x}$$

as x tends to zero (from above). Write a program which shows how this expression converges to e as x gets closer and closer to zero.

6.8   Rewrite the program of Exercise 3.13 using a DO statement.

6.9   A 'square wave' of period T may be defined by the function

$$f(t) = 1 \ (0 < t < T),$$
$$= -1 \ (-T < t < 0).$$

The Fourier series for $f(t)$ is given by

$$\frac{4}{\pi} \sum_{k=0}^{\infty} \frac{1}{2k+1} \sin \frac{(2k+1)\pi t}{T}.$$

It is of interest to know how many terms are needed for a good approximation to this infinite sum. Taking $T=1$ write a program to compute n terms of the Fourier series for t from 0 to 1 in steps of 0.1. Run the program for different values of n, e.g. 1, 3, 6, etc.

7

Branching: The IF Statements

Apart from the computer's ability to add numbers tremendously quickly, its other major attribute is to be able to make decisions, based on evaluation of objects called logical expressions, which may have only one of the two values TRUE or FALSE. It is this facility which gives the computer its great problem-solving power. There are two major decision making constructions in FORTRAN: the logical **IF** and the block **IF** structure, both of which allow conditional branching in a program. In addition, there is the **GOTO** statement, which allows unconditional branching

7.1 An Easy Example of Logical IF

Suppose we have a set of 150 students' test marks (out of 100). The students are numbered from 1 to 150. We want to print out how many of them obtained first class passes (75% and above). The following program will do this:

```
* *** PRINTS NUMBER OF FIRSTS IN CLASS

      INTEGER FIRSTS
      INTEGER STUDNT
      REAL    MARK

      FIRSTS = 0

      DO 100 STUDNT = 1, 150
        READ*, MARK
        IF( MARK .GE. 75.0 )FIRSTS = FIRSTS + 1
100   CONTINUE

      PRINT*, FIRSTS, ' FIRST CLASS PASSES'
      STOP
      END
```

Data:

48
· · · · } exactly 150 data lines
92

The program works exactly as it sounds in English. For each student, a mark is read. If the 'logical expression'

```
      MARK .GE. 75.0
```

(where .GE. means 'is greater than or equal to') is true, then the statement FIRSTS = ...
is executed. If it is not true, the statement FIRSTS = ... is ignored. In both cases the
computer then proceeds to the statement after the IF, which is CONTINUE. In this way,
all the marks are processed.

Exercise
Adjust the program to print out how many students passed the test (i.e. obtained marks of
50% or more).
   The IF statement used in this program is called a logical IF statement. Having seen an
example of how to use it, we need to define some terms more fully.

7.2   Logical Constants

The basis of decision making rests on the two logical constants .TRUE. and .FALSE. (All
logical constants and operators are written between full-stops.) A logical variable (see
Section 7.15) may be assigned one of these values.

7.3   Logical Expressions

A logical expression is a thing that may be evaluated as a logical constant, i.e. it has a truth
value. Logical expressions are usually constructed from common or garden arithmetic
expressions, connected by logical relational operators, of which there are six:

Relational Operator	Example	Meaning
EQ.	I .EQ. J	$I = J$
NE.	K .NE. M	$K \neq M$
GE.	X+4 .GE. 5*Y	$X+4 \geq 5Y$
LE.	A .LE. 1E-5	$A \leq 1E-5$
GT.	B .GT. SIN(X)	$B > SIN(X)$
LT.	W+X .LT. A-B	$W+X < A-B$

Note that .NE., .GE. and .LE. mean 'not equal to', 'greater than or equal to' and 'less than
or equal to' respectively. Note also that if blanks appear on either side of the relational
operators (but not the arithmetic operators) in a logical expression, then the logical
structure is much clearer to the user.

7.4   The Logical IF Statement

The general syntax is:

```
IF ( le ) s
```

where le is a logical expression and s is any executable statement except DO or IF.

Operation
Statement s is executed only if the expression le is true. The next statement to be executed
is the one following the IF. The statement s must appear on the same line as the IF.

7.5   An Easy Example of IF-THEN-ELSE

The logical **IF** statement introduced above is of rather limited use, since only one statement can be executed if the logical expression is true, and it doesn't allow for the execution of a different statement if it is false. Returning to the problem of Section 7.1, suppose that we wanted to run through the 150 marks, and then print which students passed or failed, with appropriate comments. The structure plan for this problem is:

    1   Repeat 150 times
        1.1   Read mark
        1.2   If mark ⩾ 50 then
              1.2.1 Print: student passed
              otherwise
              1.2.2 Print: student failed
    2   Stop.

The structure is quite clear in English, and the program reads just like it:

```
* *** DECIDES WHO PASSES AND WHO FAILS!

      INTEGER STUDNT
      REAL    MARK

      DO 70 STUDNT = 1, 150
        READ*, MARK
        IF( MARK .GE. 50.0 )THEN
          PRINT*, STUDNT, ' PASSED!'
        ELSE
          PRINT*, STUDNT, ' FAILED'
        END IF
70    CONTINUE

      STOP
      END
```

Note that nothing follows the words **THEN, ELSE** and **END IF**. They are used to separate the actions required when the logical expression is true or false. The precise rules of syntax are defined in Section 7.8, after some more examples.

7.6   Final Mark Again

The final mark problem that we first looked at in Section 1.2 needs some improvement. At the moment, the student's final mark is computed as the average of the class record and the two final examination papers. However, a fairer deal for the student emerges if we decide to count the class record only if it helps the student. If the class record does not help, the final mark is simply the average of the two final papers. As before, all the marks are given as percentages, three to a line. The first data line will contain only one number, being the total number of students in the class, and as a final flourish, we will also compute the average final mark for the class. The structure plan is as follows:

    1   Initialize running total.
    2   Read in number of students.
    3   Repeat for each student
        3.1   Read class record and two exam marks
        3.2   Compute average of two exams

3.3 If class record > exam average then
    3.3.1 Final mark = average of record and both exams
    Otherwise
    3.3.2 Final mark = average of two exams
3.4 Add final mark to running total
3.5 Print student's number and final mark
4 Compute class average.
5 Print class average.
6 Stop.

The program follows fairly easily once the structure plan has been sorted out:

```
*****  COMPUTES FINAL MARK FOR A COURSE ***************************
*      CLASS RECORD ONLY COUNTS IF IT EXCEEDS AVERAGE OF          *
*      TWO EXAMS                                                  *
*                                                                 *
*****  DESCRIPTION OF VARIABLES ***********************************
*                                                                 *
*      NUM      :  NUMBER OF STUDENTS/ STUDNT :  STUDENT COUNTER   *
*      CLSAVG  :  AVG FINAL MARK      / EXMAVG :  AVG OF 2 EXAMS   *
*      EX1      :  1ST EXAM MARK       / EX2    :  2ND EXAM MARK    *
*      FINAL   :  FINAL MARK          / RECORD :  CLASS RECORD     *
*      TOTAL   :  TOTAL FINAL MARK    /                            *
******************************************************************

       INTEGER   NUM
       INTEGER   STUDNT
       REAL      CLSAVG
       REAL      EXMAVG
       REAL      EX1
       REAL      EX2
       REAL      FINAL
       REAL      RECORD
       REAL      TOTAL

       TOTAL = 0
       READ*, NUM

       DO 60 STUDNT = 1, NUM
         READ*, RECORD, EX1, EX2
         EXMAVG = (EX1 + EX2) / 2.
         IF( RECORD .GT. EXMAVG )THEN
           FINAL = (RECORD + EX1 + EX2) / 3.
         ELSE
           FINAL = EXMAVG
         END IF
         TOTAL = TOTAL + FINAL
         PRINT*, STUDNT, 'OBTAINED', FINAL, '%'
60     CONTINUE
       CLSAVG = TOTAL / NUM
       PRINT*, 'CLASS AVERAGE:', CLSAVG
       STOP
       END
```

Data:

```
182
67.3 78 63  ⎤
46.7 56 45  ⎟        exactly 182 data lines
....        ⎟
            ⎟
78.4 74 74  ⎦
```

Note that this program is laid out according to the requirements for good programming style. There is a description of what the program does, all the variables are described in comment lines and specified real or integer in alphabetical order, and statements inside the **DO** and **IF** are indented. Blank lines are also used to make the final effect more pleasing. Guidelines for what is considered good programming style are set out in the Epilogue.

7.7   An Easy Example of ELSE IF

Suppose we want to print out the larger of two given numbers, or if they are equal, a message to that effect. The structured plan shows how you could structure the logic in plain English.

> 1   Read x, y
> 2   If $x > y$ then
>   2.1 Print: x is larger
>   but if $x < y$ then
>   2.2 Print: y is larger
>   otherwise
>   2.3 Print: they are equal
> 3   Stop.

The program has the same structure:

```
* *** PRINTS LARGER OF TWO NUMBERS

      READ*, X, Y

      IF( X .GT. Y )THEN
         PRINT*, X, 'IS LARGER'
      ELSE IF( X .LT. Y )THEN
         PRINT*, Y, 'IS LARGER'
      ELSE
         PRINT*, 'THE NUMBERS ARE EQUAL'
      END IF

      STOP
      END
```

The structure from the initial **IF** to **END IF** is called a block **IF** structure and the initial **IF-THEN** is called a block **IF** statement. The block **IF** structure *must* always end with an **END IF** statement. The formal definition is given in the next section.

7.8   The Block IF Structure

This is a useful structure as it allows execution of whole blocks of statements under variou conditions.

7.8.1 Definition of the Block IF

The general form is:

```
IF( L1 )THEN
   S1
ELSE IF( L2 )THEN
   S2
ELSE IF( L3 )THEN
   S3
   ....
   ....
ELSE
   Sn
END IF
```

where L1, L2, etc., are logical expressions, not more than one of which should be true, and S1, S2, etc., are blocks of FORTRAN statements (i.e. one or more), which may themselves include DOs or block IF structures.

The action is straightforward. If L1 is true, the block S1 is executed, and then the statement following the END IF statement. If L1 is false, L2 is examined, and if it is true, the block S2 is executed, and then the statement following the END IF, and so on. If none of the logical expressions is true, the block Sn following ELSE is executed, and then the statement following the END IF. In all, at most *one* of the blocks S1 to Sn is executed.

There may be any number of ELSE IF statements, or none at all. There may be one ELSE statement, or none at all. The structure must conclude with an END IF statement.

7.8.2 Nesting of block IFs

A block IF may contain further block IFs, provided that each inner block is terminated by a separate END IF. The first END IF encountered closes the most deeply nested block IF, and so on, until the last END IF closes the outermost block IF.

7.8.3 Example of Nesting

The following (artificial) example illustrates nesting of block IFs. L1 and L2 are two logical expressions, and I and J are to be set according to the truth values of L1 and L2. If L1 is true, I and J are set to 1 and 2 respectively. If L1 is false and L2 is true, I and J are set to 2 and 3. If L1 and L2 are both false, I and J are set to 3 and 4. First the flowchart:

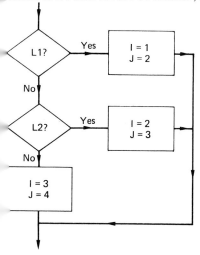

Next the coding:

```
IF( L1 )THEN
    I = 1
    J = 2
ELSE
    IF( L2 )THEN
       I = 2
       J = 3
    ELSE
       I = 3
       J = 4
    END IF
END IF
```

Note how each level of **IF** is indented a further two columns to make the program more readable.

This example may also be done without nesting the IFs, by using an **ELSE IF** statement as follows (either version is acceptable):

```
IF( L1 ) THEN
    I = 1
    J = 2
ELSE IF( L2 )THEN
    I = 2
    J = 3
ELSE
    I = 3
    J = 4
END IF
```

Exercise
In the program section below, $L1$ and $L2$ are logical expressions and $s1$, $s2$, . . . $s5$ represent blocks of statements. Under what conditions will they be executed?

```
IF( L1 )THEN
   s1
ELSE
   s2
   IF( L2 )THEN
      s3
   END IF
   s4
END IF
s5
```

Answer
If $L1$ is true, $s1$ is executed. If $L1$ is false, $s2$ and $s4$ are executed. If $L1$ is false and $L2$ is true, $s3$ is executed. $s5$ is executed unconditionally.

7.8.4 DOs and IFs

A block **IF** structure may contain a **DO**-loop and vice versa. The basic rule is that the IFs or DOs must be completely contained within each other, with no overlapping. Furthermore, the terminal statement of a **DO**-loop may not be an **IF**, **ELSE IF**, **ELSE**, or **END IF** statement.

The following is valid:

```
IF(   )THEN
   ....

ELSE
   DO 90 I = 1, 234
      ....

90       CONTINUE
   ....

END IF
```

However, the following is invalid:

```
IF(   )THEN
   DO 90 I = 1, 234
      ....

ELSE
   ....

90       CONTINUE
END IF
```

The next program segment is also incorrect:

```
DO 90 I = 2, 345
   IF(   )THEN
      ....

90       CONTINUE
   END IF
```

7.9   Bending Moment in a Beam

A light uniform beam $0 < x < L$ is clamped with its ends at the same level, and carries a concentrated load W at $x=a$. The bending moment M at any point x along the beam is given by two different formulae, depending on the value of x relative to a, viz.

$$M=W(L-a)^2[aL-x(L+2a)]/L^3 \qquad (0{\leqslant}x{\leqslant}a),$$
$$M=Wa^2[aL-2L^2+x(3L-2a)]/L^3 \qquad (a{\leqslant}x{\leqslant}L).$$

The following program computes the bending moment every metre along a 10m beam, with a load of 100N at a point 8m from the end $x=0$.

```
* *** BENDING MOMENT

      REAL L
      REAL M

      L = 10
      W = 100
      A = 8

      DO 10 X = 0, L
```

```
      IF( X .LE. A )THEN
         M = W * (L - A) ** 2 / L ** 3 * (A * L - X * (L + 2 *
    $    A))
      ELSE
         M = W * A ** 2 / L ** 3 * (A * L - 2 * L ** 2 +
    $    X * (3 * L - 2 * A))
      END IF

      PRINT*, X, M
10    CONTINUE

      STOP
      END
```

Output:
```
.00000000         32.000000
1.0000000         21.600000
2.0000000         11.200000
3.0000000          .80000000
4.0000000         -9.5999999
5.0000000        -20.000000
6.0000000        -30.400000
7.0000000        -40.800000
8.0000000        -51.200000
9.0000000         38.400000
10.000000         128.00000
```

7.10   Classification of Test Results

Here is an example of how **ELSE IF** statements may be used to classify marks into mutuall
exclusive categories. Each student in a class of 217 students has a test mark (out of 100). W
want to print out each mark and its class (first, upper second, lower second, etc.):

```
* *** CLASSIFIES MARKS

      DO 20 KSTU = 1, 217

         READ*, TST
         IF( TST .GE. 75 )THEN
            PRINT*, TST, ' I'
         ELSE IF( TST .GE. 70 .AND. TST .LT. 75 )THEN
            PRINT*, TST, ' II+'
         ELSE IF( TST .GE. 60 .AND. TST .LT. 70 )THEN
            PRINT*, TST, ' II-'
         ELSE IF( TST .GE. 50 .AND. TST .LT. 60 )THEN
            PRINT*, TST, ' III'
         ELSE
            PRINT*, TST, ' FAIL - SORRY ABOUT THAT'
         END IF.

20    CONTINUE

      STOP
      END
```

7.11   Conditional Loops: Charging a Capacitor

When a resistor (R), capacitor (C) and battery (V) are connected in series, a charge (Q) builds up on the capacitor according to the formula

$$Q(t)=CV(1-e^{-t/Rc})$$

if there is no charge on the capacitor at time t=0. The problem is to monitor the charge on the capacitor every 0.1 seconds in order to detect when it reaches a level of 8 units, given that $V=9$, $R=4$ and $C=1$. The time and charge must be printed out every 0.1 seconds until the charge first exceeds 8 units. The structure plan and program are as follows:

```
1  Initialize.
2  While Q < 8 repeat
     2.1  Update T
     2.2  Compute Q
     2.3  Print T and Q
3  Stop.
```

```
*****  CHARGE ON A CAPACITOR  ***********************************
*        PRINTS OUT CHARGE UNTIL IT EXCEEDS 8 UNITS            *
*                                                              *
*****  DESCRIPTION OF VARIABLES  ********************************
*                                                              *
*        C  : CAPACITANCE                                      *
*        Q  : CHARGE ON CAPACITOR                              *
*        R  : RESISTANCE                                       *
*        T  : TIME                                             *
*        V  : VOLTAGE                                          *
****************************************************************

        REAL C
        REAL Q
        REAL R
        REAL T
        REAL V

        C = 1
        Q = 0
        R = 4
        T = 0
        V = 9

10      IF( Q. LT. 8 )THEN
            T = T + 0.1
            Q = C * V * (1 - EXP( - T / (R * C) ))
            PRINT*, T, Q
            GOTO 10
        END IF

        STOP
        END
```

Output:

```
.10000000+000    2.9671195
.20000000        4.9560394
.30000000        6.2892521
.39999999        7.1829313
.49999999        7.7819824
.59999999        8.1835383
```

Note

1) This type of conditional loop has the same effect as a **DO-WHILE** structure in other languages.
2) The **GOTO** statement transfers control to the statement label referred to in the **GOTO**. Many programmers consider that it should **only** be used in such a **DO-WHILE** structure, and that it is bad programming style to use the **GOTO** under **any** other circumstances.
3) Experienced FORTRAN users might find this construction irritating and be tempted rather to use a **DO**-loop with an **IF/GOTO** to exit when the condition to stop repeating is met. Many programmers, however, prefer the above construction because the code is clearer to read: the condition for another repeat is immediately apparent at the head of the loop in statement 10.

7.12   Logical Operators

These operate on logical expressions, as shown below. The table illustrates the effect of the operators (.**NOT.**, .**AND.**, .**OR.**, .**EQV.**, .**NEQV.**), depending on the truth values (T or F) of the logical expressions e1 and e2.

e1	e2	.NOT.e1	e1.AND.e2	e1.OR.e2	e1.EQV.e2	e1.NEQV.e2
T	T	F	T	T	T	F
T	F	F	F	T	F	T
F	T	T	F	T	F	T
F	F	T	F	F	T	F

If more than one logical operator appears in a statement, the following precedence is observed:

> parentheses (brackets)
> .**NOT.**
> .**AND.**
> .**OR.**
> .**EQV.**, .**NEQV.** (from left to right if in the same expression)

For example, if **L1**, **L2** and **L3** are logical expressions, then

```
        L1 .AND. .NOT. L2 .OR. L3
```

is equivalent to

```
    ( L1 .AND. ( .NOT. L2 ) ) .OR. L3
```

7.13   Taylor Series for Sin (x)

You may have wondered how the computer calculates functions such as sine and cosine. Really ancient computers actually used to look up tables entered in memory, but young up and coming ones are more cunning. Mathematically, it can be shown that sin (x) is the sum of an infinite series (called a Taylor series), as follows:

$$\sin (x) = x - x^3/3! + x^5/5! - x^7/7! + \ldots$$

where $n!$ is defined as $n(n-1)(n-2) \ldots 2 \times 1$

We cannot compute an infinite series (why not?), but we can at least arrange to stop after the terms in the series are all less than some prescribed value, say 0.000001. It can be shown that we can always get a term less than some arbitrarily small number by going far enough in the series. As an exercise you should try to draw the flowchart or structure plan before studying the program. The main idea here is to construct each term in the series from the previous one (see Section 6.8). In constructing the denominator each time, use has been made of the fact that if k is any integer, then $2k$ is even and $2k+1$ is odd. The program is as follows:

```
*****  COMPUTES SIN(X) WITH TAYLOR SERIES  ************************
*                                                                *
*      ERR    : MAX ERROR REQUIRED  / K       : TERM COUNTER     *
*      SINE   : SUM OF SERIES       / TERM    : GENERAL TERM     *
*      X      : ANGLE IN RADIANS    /                            *
******************************************************************

*  ***  INITIALISATION

       READ*, X
       TERM = X
       SINE = TERM
       ERR = 1E-6
       K = 1

10     IF( ABS( TERM ) .GT. ERR )THEN
          TERM = - TERM * X * X / (2 * K * (2 * K + 1))
          SINE = SINE + TERM
          K = K + 1
          GOTO 10
       END IF

       PRINT*, 'AFTER', K, ' TERMS SIN(X) =', SINE
       PRINT*, 'COMPUTER''S INTRINSIC FUNCTION GIVES', SIN(X)

       STOP
       END
```

Note how an apostrophe within a character string is handled in the second **PRINT** statement, by duplicating it.

7.14   A Dreadful Example of Spaghetti

Throughout this book the **GOTO** statement is used **only** in the conditional **DO-WHILE** structure as shown in the last two programs, and **nowhere else**. It is recommended that you do the same. Unfortunately, when new programmers discover **GOTO**, it can go to their heads to the great detriment of their programming style. The following program is a dreadful example of how **not** to us GOTO (to solve the first problem of Section 7.8.3) and is what better programmers call 'spaghetti', because the equivalent flowchart looks like a tangle of spaghetti (blanks and indentations have also been omitted to add to the effect):

```
        IF(.NOT.L1)GOTO 10
        I=1
        J=2
        GOTO 30
10      IF(.NOT.L2)GOTO 20
        I=2
        J=3
        GOTO 30
20      I=3
        J=4
30      CONTINUE
```

7.15   Logical Variables

Variables of logical type may be specified with a statement of the form

```
        LOGICAL X
```

at the head of the program. They can then appear in logical assignment statements with logical constants or expressions.

Example

```
        LOGICAL L1
        LOGICAL L2
        LOGICAL L3
        LOGICAL L4

        L1 = .TRUE.
        L2 = .FALSE.
        ....

        L3 = A .GT. 4.67
        L4 = B*B-4*A*C .LT. 0.0
```

The next section has an interesting example of the use of logical variables.

7.16   Simulation of a Switching Circuit

In the two program segments that follow, the logical variables S1 and S2 represent the state of two switches (TRUE=ON; FALSE=OFF) and L represents the state of a light. The programs simulate the circuits alongside them, where the switches are arranged either in series or in parallel.

Switches in series:

```
LOGICAL L
LOGICAL S1
LOGICAL S2
READ*, S1, S2
L = S1 .AND. S2
IF( L )THEN
     PRINT*, 'ON'
ELSE
     PRINT*, 'OFF'
END IF
```

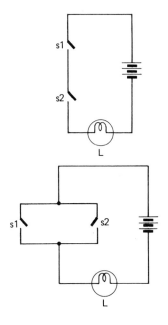

Switches in parallel:
Replace fifth line by

```
L = S1 .OR. S2
```

Note

1) The logic rests on the fact that with the switches in series, the light will be on only if both switches are on, represented by (**S1 .AND. S2**), whereas with the switches in parallel, the light will be on if at least one of the switches is on, represented by (**S1 .OR. S2**).
2) Logical values for S1 and S2 may be read in by typing **T**'s or **F**'s on data lines, separated by spaces or commas in the usual way.

7.17   Summary

* Logical constants, variables or expressions can have only one of two values: **.TRUE.** or **.FALSE.**.

* Logical expressions are formed from arithmetic expressions with logical relational operators (**.NE.**, **.GT.**, etc.).

* The logical **IF** statement allows for the conditional execution of a single statement (except **DO** or **IF**).

* The block **IF** statement allows for the conditional execution of a block of statements.

* A block **IF** statement must have only one **THEN** and **END IF**. It may have no more than one **ELSE**. It may have any number of **ELSE IF**s.

* A **DO**-loop may not end on an **IF**, **ELSE IF**, **ELSE** OR **END IF**.

* The logical operators (**.NOT.**, **.AND.**, etc) may be used to form more complex logical expressions from other logical expressions.

* The **IF/GOTO** combination (as used in Sections 7.11 and 7.13) should be used to program a repeat structure when the exact number of repeats is **not** known in advance. Another way of saying this is that the **IF/GOTO** combination should be used to repeat

whenever the **condition** for repeating is **changed** in the body of the loop. This situation is characterized by the general structure plan:

> 1   While CONDITION is TRUE repeat
> 1.1   Statement(s) to be repeated
> 1.2   Reset CONDITION (if necessary).

The best way to program this is:

```
n       IF( condition )THEN
          ....
          body of loop
          ....
          reset condition (if necessary)
          GOTO n
        END IF
```

7.18   Exercises

7.1   Translate into FORTRAN statements:

(a)   Set G equal to the larger of the two values E and F.
(b)   If D is greater than zero, set X to minus B.
(c)   If K is even, set X to minus X.

7.2   Write a structure plan and program for the following problem: read in ten integers, one per data line, and print out how many of them are positive, negative, or zero.

7.3   Develop an algorithm and then write a structure plan which will determine the value of the largest number in a list of 100 numbers.

7.4   Extend the structure plan of Exercise 7.3 to find the position in the list of the largest number (assume that there is only one maximum). Write the program.

7.5   Design an algorithm (draw the flowchart or structure plan) for a machine which must give the correct amount of change from a $10 note for any purchase costing less than $10. The plan must specify the number and type of all notes and coins in the change and should in all cases give as few notes and coins as possible. You can arrange, if you wish, for the machine to deal with a variable percentage sales tax, or with the problem of insufficient coins or notes available of any particular denomination.

7.6   Develop a structure plan for the solution of two simultaneous linear equations (i.e. two straight lines). Your algorithm must be able to handle all possible situations, viz. lines intersecting, parallel, or coincident. Write a program to implement your algorithm, and test it on some equations for which you know the answers, e.g.

$$x+y=3$$
$$2x-y=3,$$

the solution of which is $x=2$, $y=1$.
Hint: begin by deriving an algebraic formula for the solution of the system:

$$ax+by=c$$
$$dx+ey=f.$$

7.7   Use the Taylor series

$$\cos(x) = 1 - x^2/2! + x^4/4! - x^6/6! + \ldots$$

to write a program to compute cos(x) correct to four decimal places (x is in radians). The problem is similar to the one in Section 7.13. See how many terms are needed to get four-figure agreement with the intrinsic function **COS(X)**.

7.8 Write a program to implement the structure plan of Exercise 4.2.

7.9 A sum of $1000 is deposited in a bank. Interest is compounded each month at the rate of 1%. Write a program which prints out a monthly statement of the balance (after the interest has been added) only as long as it is less than $2000. *Hint*: use the **IF/GOTO** combination.

7.10 A man borrows $10000 to buy a used car. Interest on his loan is compounded at the rate of 2% per month while the outstanding balance is greater than $5000, and at 1% per month otherwise. He pays back $300 every month, except for the last month, when the repayment must be less than $300. He pays at the end of the month, after the interest on the balance has been compounded. The first repayment is made one month after the loan is paid out to him. Write a program which prints out a monthly statement of the balance (after the monthly payment has been made), what the final payment will be, and how long it will take to pay back the loan. *Hint*: use the **IF/GOTO** combination. *Answer*: $157.75 in the 54th month (don't forget the interest in the final month).

7.11 A projectile, the equations of motion of which are given in Section 5.1, is launched from the point O with an initial velocity of 60 m/s at an angle of 50° to the horizontal. Write a program which computes and prints out the time of flight and horizontal and vertical displacement from the point O every 0.5 seconds, as long as the projectile remains above a horizontal plane through O.

7.12 Rewrite the program in Section 7.11 so that the charge is printed only while it is strictly less than 8 units.

8

Errors

Programs seldom run correctly the first time, even for experienced programmers! In computer jargon, an error in a program is called a 'bug', and the process of detecting and correcting such errors is called 'debugging'. To assist us in this sometimes arduous task, the compiler prints various types of warning or error messages. These messages are called the diagnostics. There are three main types of error: compile time errors, run time errors, and errors of logic. There is also a more subtle error—rounding error—which creeps in sometimes because of finite machine precision. In this chapter we deal with the sort of errors that can arise with the programming we have done so far. Other possible sources of error will be pointed out in later chapters in the appropriate places.

8.1 Compilation Errors

These are errors of syntax and construction, like spelling mistakes, that are picked up by the compiler during compilation. They are the most frequent type of error. Compilation errors are generally fatal, in that the computer will not execute the program. The diagnostics generated if your programs crash will depend on your particular computer system. The following two examples, which were run under the ASCII FORTRAN compiler on a Sperry mainframe, show programs bristling with compilation errors. The diagnostics are explained where necessary after each example.

Example 1

```
      VERTICAL MOTION UNDER GRAVITY
      PRINT*,'TIME','DISPLACEMENT
      G = 9,8
      U = 20
      T = 5
      S = UT - (G/2*T??2
      PRITT*,' '
      PRINT*,T,S
      STOP
```

The output generated consists of error messages,

```
             1.             VERTICAL MOTION UNDER GRAVITY
*ERROR 112 at line 1 UNRECOGNIZABLE STATEMENT
             2.             PRINT*,'TIME','DISPLACEMENT
*ERROR 113 at line 2 STATEMENT CONTAINS UNCLOSED LITERAL CONSTAN
             3.             G = 9,8
*ERROR 112 at line 3 UNRECOGNIZABLE STATEMENT
             4.             U = 20
```

```
        5.              T = 5
        6.              S = UT - (G/2*T??2
*ERROR 110 at line 6 STATEMENT CONTAINS EXCESS LEFT PARENTHESES
        7.              PRITT*,' '
*ERROR 112 at line 7 UNRECOGNIZABLE STATEMENT
```

and warning messages,

```
        8.              PRINT*,T,S
        9.              STOP
*WARNING 114 at line 8 END STATEMENT IS MISSING
*WARNING 2606 VARIABLE 'STOP' IS REFERENCED BUT IS NEVER ASSIGNED
A VALUE

END FTN 5 ERRORS 2 WARNINGS 9 IBANK 14 DBANK
    ENTERING USER PROGRAM
 5.0000000         .00000000
END PROGRAM EXECUTION
```

Explanation

Line 1: Since the symbol 'C' or '*' is missing from column one, a valid FORTRAN statement is expected.

Line 2: A single quote is missing after DISPLACEMENT. The compiler automatically checks that single quotes are paired.

Line 3: A comma is used instead of a decimal point.

Line 6: Open bracket is not closed. The compiler checks that every left bracket is paired with a right one. Note that the ?? typed instead of ** is not flagged (signalled) as an error. Once the first error is detected (unpaired brackets), the compiler unfortunately stops looking for errors. The subsequent errors are only detected on the next run.

Line 7: **PRINT** is misspelt.

The remaining warnings are generated during run time.

Line 8: The **END** statement is missing.

Warning 2606 is interesting, since the program doesn't actually use a variable called STOP. However, on careful inspection it will be seen that the S of **STOP** appears in column six of line nine, thus joining the line from column seven onwards onto the end of line eight, which the compiler actually sees as

```
    PRINT*,T,STOP
```

It therefore bravely tries to print the variable STOP during run time, hence the second number (zero) printed out after ENTERING USER PROGRAM. This is a good example of how an error may be misdiagnosed (which can happen, since the compiler is not intelligent).

   In this example the program runs in spite of the compilation errors. This is not generally the case. Many compilers will only continue if there are 'warnings' as opposed to 'errors', and some compilers stop in both cases.

Example 2

```
TTL = 0
DO 69 I = 1,223
   READ*,R,P1,P2
   AVG = (P1 + P2)/2
   IF(R.GT.AVG)THEN FNL = (R+P1+P2)/3
   ELSE
      FNL = AVG
   ENDIF
TTL = TTL + FNL
STOP
END
```

The following output is generated:

```
FTN 10R1A   02/17/83-15:59
           1.              TTL = 0
           2.              DO 69 I = 1,223
   1       3.                READ*,R,P1,P2
   1       4.                AVG = (P1 + P2)/2
   1       5.                IF(R.GT.AVG)THEN FNL = (R+P1+P2)/3
*ERROR 105 at line 5 LONG NAME TRUNCATED TO 'THENFN'
IF(R.GT.AVG)<THENFN>L=(R+P1+P2)/3
   1       6.                ELSE
*ERROR 2224 at line 6 END IF, ELSE, OR ELSE IF STMT. IS NOT IN
BLOCK IF STRUCTURE
   1       7.                  FNL = AVG
   1       8.                ENDIF
*ERROR 2224 at line 8 END IF, ELSE, OR ELSE IF STMT. IS NOT IN
BLOCK IF STRUCTURE
   1       9.              TTL = TTL + FNL
   1      10.              STOP
   1      11.              END
*ERROR 2203 at line 11 DO LOOPS ARE INCORRECTLY NESTED

END FTN 4 ERRORS 31 IBANK 22 DBANK
```

Explanation

Line 5: This is an interesting one. The programmer intended to use an **IF-THEN-ELSE**, but forgot to leave the line blank after **THEN**. The compiler therefore assumed a logical **IF** was intended, and interpreted THEN FNL as a variable name, which it thoughtfully truncated to THENFN. This, however, caused a further error in the next line!

Line 6: The compiler has encountered an **ELSE** without a preceding **IF-THEN**, and gets upset about it.

Line 8: Same as line six—**ENDIF** without a preceding **IF-THEN**.

Line 11: The **DO**-loop, initiated in line two, has no terminal statement before the final **END**. The compiler waits hopefully until the last possible statement before signalling an error.

8.2   Execution Errors

These arise during execution time and can be 'fatal', i.e. the program may 'crash' at the point of error, and not end normally.

As an example, suppose we are given the time of flight TF of a projectile on a horizontal plane, launched at an angle AL radians. We are required to compute the launch velocity UL, the time T at which the projectile will be at a given height HT (less than its maximum height) above the ground, on its way up, and the angle AV to the horizontal at which it is moving at time T.

The following program is an attempt to solve the problem:

```
* *** TEST PROGRAM
        TF = 10
        G = 9.8
        HT = 10
        UL = G * TF / SIN( AL )
        T = (2 * UL + SQRT( 4 * UL ** 2 - 8 * G * HT )) / (2 * G)
        AV = ATAN(( UL * SIN( AL ) - G * T ) / (UL * COS( AL )))
        PRINT*, UL, T, AV
        STOP
        END
```

The following output is generated (if the compiler's 'debug' options are used):

```
ERROR     CONDITION    IN  SQRT       ROUTINE CAUSED BY
ARGUMENT UNNORMALIZED OR OUTSIDE ALLOWABLE RANGE
ARG1=       -783.99999
ARG1 OCTAL   565170000000
SQRT       REFERENCED AT ABSOLUTE ADDRESS   053501   BDI 300017
THIS ADDRESS   IS   AT LN.      6   OF   MAIN PROGRAM

ENTER DEBUG MODE
AL      /*
              .00000000
AV      /*
              .00000000
G       /*
              .98000000+001
HT      /*
              .10000000+002
T       /*
              .00000000
TF      /*
              .10000000+002
UL      /*
              .00000000
```

This time there are no compilation errors, but according to the error message there seems to be a problem with the argument of **SQRT** in line six being negative. If there were no further diagnostics, the error would be inexplicable.

Fortunately, however, the programmer has developed the good habit of using the available debug options when executing, whenever possible, and this causes a listing of all the variables in the program at the time of the crash. From this we see that UL is zero, which explains at once the negative argument for **SQRT** (does it?). But the reason for UL being zero is not quite so clear. Further examination of the output shows that the launch angle AL is also zero. This in fact is the only programming error: a value for AL was neither read nor assigned. This particular compiler sets undefined variables to zero (not generally the case!). This causes a division by zero in line five, since **SIN(AL)** is then zero, and unfortunately the compiler doesn't mind dividing by zero: it sets the quotient to zero, and continues!

Note that the crash occurs before the final **PRINT** statement, which is therefore not executed.

This is a good example of how one mistake early in a program (leaving out a **READ**) can ·generate an apparently unrelated error later on (attempting to find the square root of a negative number).

Many compilers do not have such a 'debug' option. In that case, the best way to track down errors is to insert **PRINT** statements at strategic points in the program to see what is happening to the variables as the program executes.

8.3 Errors in Logic

If you make a mistake in coding a method you have worked out, or if the method itself is wrong, there is no way the computer can spot your mistake, unless you make extra mistakes in the FORTRAN. It will do exactly as you ask it, and the answer will be wrong!

Example

Tabulate a power curve $y = 10^{kx}$ at intervals of 0.1 in x:

```
      READ*, K
      DO 70 I = 1, 100
         X = I / 10.
         Y = 10 ** (K * X)
         PRINT*, X, Y
70    CONTINUE
      STOP
      END
```

Some tables will be printed out correctly, but if you read in, for example, 0.5 for K, then all the Y values are printed as 1. Why?

You have read a fraction into an integer variable K, and so it has to be truncated to an integer. The calculations are all performed with $K = 0$.

Moral: always look critically at the results produced by your program. When possible, test several different cases for which you know the answers, and check that the program gets them right.

The worst thing about logical errors is that you may never realize that the answer is wrong! If you are suspicious, it sometimes helps to engineer an artificial error in a program (like square-rooting a negative number) and to use the debug options available on your compiler (if any) to get a complete 'dump' of the memory, i.e. the values of all the variables at the time of the crash.

8.4 Decreasing the Likelihood of Programming Errors

You are less likely to make errors (and you can locate them more easily if you do) if you write clear, logical, well structured programs. Already, you will have noticed how block IFs organize the logic in a systematic way, whereas indiscriminate use of **GOTO**s can (and often does) tie the program into a logical tangle (called spaghetti).

Then there are good habits that can make program structure more recognizable. It has been recommended, for example, that you reserve statement labels divisible by 10 for the ends of DO-loops. It can be extremely helpful in reading a program to know that there must be a DO-loop that finishes on a particular statement.

Another good habit is to specify **all** variables at the start of a program as **REAL**

INTEGER, etc., as well as describing in comment statements what they mean. The example in Section 8.3 gave rise to its difficult-to-spot error because the programmer expected K to be real. The statement

```
REAL K
```

at the beginning, before any executable statement, will correct the error. This has been stressed in earlier chapters.

More useful hints will be included in the appropriate places later, and guidelines for good programming style are laid out in the Epilogue.

8.5 Rounding Error

At times the computer gives numerical answers to a problem which appear inexplicably different from what we know to be the correct mathematical answers. This can be due to rounding error, which results from the finite precision available on the computer, e.g. 32 or 36 bits per word instead of an infinite number.

A good example of this is seen if you write a program to solve the quadratic equation

$$ax^2+bx+c=0$$

and use the values $a = 14.4$, $b = 12.0$ and $c = 2.5$. A quick mathematical check shows that the two roots are equal since the discriminant is zero. However, a program run on a Sperry mainframe gives the roots as -0.416619 and -0.416715, which are not equal. Further investigation shows that the computer calculates the discriminant as $0.1907E-5$, which is by no means zero. The basic reason for this problem is that real constants not exactly divisible by 2 cannot be represented exactly in binary form. (This problem will never arise with integers.) There are two steps that can be taken to minimize rounding error.

The first is to use **DOUBLE PRECISION** type where necessary. This reserves double the number of bits for a variable. For example, the statement

```
DOUBLE PRECISION A
```

with the other type specifications at the beginning of a program will allocate twice as many bits to A. This facility should be used carefully in large programs, since it takes up twice as much storage space. Using double precision for all the variables in the quadratic equation program gives a value of -0.416667, correct to six figures, for both roots, although they are still not equal, as is pointed out below. Double precision constants are written in floating point form in the same way as reals except that the E is replaced by D. E.g. the constant 1.0 is written as 1D0 in double precision.

The second step is to avoid using the .EQ. or .NE. relational operators in logical expressions involving arithmetic or real variables. It is better to rearrange the logical structure. So in the quadratic problem, you should not have

```
IF( B*B-4*A*C .EQ. 0.0 )THEN
    ....(equal roots)....
```

but rather

```
IF((ABS( B*B - 4*A*C ) .LT. 1E-5 )THEN
    ....(equal roots)....
```

This is necessary, since even using double precision with the values of a, b and c above gives a discriminant of $0.222E-15$, which is still not exactly zero!

This point is also well illustrated by the program segment

```
A = 16.
B = A / 3. * 3.
```

Later in the program, we would expect the logical expression (**A** .EQ. **B**) to be true, but it is not, since (A−B) is computed as 0.24E−6 with single precision, and as 0.28E−16 with double precision. A test for 'equality' should rather use the logical expression

```
ABS( A - B ) .LT. 1E-6
```

If this is true, then A and B are about as close as they can ever be on this computer.

8.6   Summary

* Compilation errors are mistakes in the syntax (code).

* Execution errors occur while the program is running.

* Logical errors are errors in the algorithm used to solve the problem.

* Rounding error occurs because the computer can store numbers only to a finite accuracy.

* Double precision variables can store twice as many decimal places, and reduce the effect of rounding error.

8.7   Exercises

8.1   Find the errors in the following statements and decide whether they occur at compilation or execution:

```
(a)   X = LOG( 3 / 4 )
(b)   DO 10 I = 1 TO 99
(c)   IF( I > 10 ) X = 2
(d)   X = ( -B + SQRT( B ** 2 - 4 * A * C ) / ( 2 * A)
(e)   IF( I .EQ. 0 )THEN J = 10
(f)   X = J / (4 / 5)
(g)   X = X
(h)   Y = SQRT( COS( 2 ) )
(i)   J = 5 * -I
(j)   10   IF( ... )THEN
           ....

           END IF
           GOTO 10
```

8.2   Find the compilation errors in the following program (check your answers by running it on your computer system):

```
READ N
DO 20 I = 1, N,
   READ* MARK
     IF( MARK .GR. 50 AND MARK .LT. 75 )THEN
        IF( MARK .GR. 60 )THEN
           PRINT "SECOND CLASS"
        ELSE
20      END IF
     STOP
     END.
```

8.3   The Newton quotient

$$[f(x+h)-f(x)]/h$$

may be used to compute the first derivative $f'(x)$ of a function $f(x)$, if h is 'small'. Write a program to compute the Newton quotient for the function $f(x)=x^2$ at the point $x=2$ (the exact answer is 4) for values of h starting at 1, and decreasing by a factor of 10 each time. The effect of rounding error becomes apparent when h gets 'too small'. (See the solution to Exercise 12.1 for the coding, and Section 15.3 for a discussion.)

8.4   The solution of the set of simultaneous equations quoted in Exercise 7.6 is given by

$$x = (ce-bf)/(ae-bd)$$
$$y = (af-cd)/(ae-bd).$$

If $(ae-bd)$ is small, rounding error may cause quite large inaccuracies in the solution. Consider the system (McCracken and Dorn, 1964):

$$0.2038x+0.1218y=0.2014$$
$$0.4071x+0.2436y=0.4038.$$

Show that with four-figure floating point arithmetic the solution obtained is $x=-1.714$, $y=4.286$. This level of accuracy may be simulated in the solution to Exercise 7.6 with some statements like

```
AE = NINT( A * E * 1E5 ) / 1E5
```

and appropriate changes in the coding. The exact solution, however, which can be obtained with normal single precision arithmetic, is $x=-2.000$, $y=5.000$. If the coefficients in the equations are themselves subject to experimental error, the 'solution' of this system using limited accuracy is totally meaningless. This problem can be detected by re-running the program using double precision, which provides a good check on the numerical accuracy of the solution.

8.5   This problem, suggested by R. V. Andree (cited by McCracken and Dorn, 1964), demonstrates another numerical problem called 'ill-conditioning', where a small change in the coefficients causes a large change in the solution. Show that the solution of the system

$$x+   5.0y=17.0$$
$$1.5x+7.501y=25.503$$

is $x=2$, $y=3$, using the program in Exercise 7.6 with full precision. Now change the constant term in the second equation to 25.501, a change of about one part in 12000, and observe that a totally different solution emerges. If the coefficients are subject to experimental errors, the solution is again meaningless. One way to anticipate this sort of error is to perform a 'sensitivity analysis' on the coefficients: change them all in turn by the same percentage, and observe what effect this has on the solution.

9

Advanced Input/Output

So far we have concentrated on writing programs that give the right answer, without paying much attention to exactly how the numbers are printed (e.g. number of decimal places, number of spaces between items, etc.). In this chapter we look at, among other things, how to produce printout that is neater and more pleasing to the eye. We also look at how to get input from, and send output to files.

9.1 Rabbit Breeding the Fibonacci Way

To make the exercise more interesting, we will write a program to model a rabbit population under the following assumptions:

1) We start with one new-born male/female pair.
2) A new-born pair produce (instantaneously!) a male/female pair after two months.
3) Male/female pairs of age two months and older produce a male/female pair every month.

If we represent the number of male/female pairs after N months by the variable FN, it can be shown quite easily that FN takes the following values:

Month N	Population FN
1	1
2	1
3	2
4	3
5	5
6	8
7	13
8	?

The sequence {FN} is called the Fibonacci Sequence. We want to write a program that computes the population for up to, say, 12 months. (Note that the model does not allow for deaths.) Since each FN is the sum of the previous two members of the sequence (call them FNM1 and FNM2) we need to have three variables in the program which are updated each month. An interesting feature of the Fibonacci sequence is that the ratio FN/FNM1 tends to a limit $(1+\sqrt{5})/2 = 1.6180.$ . . for large N, and we will also compute this ratio, to verify that it has a limit (in fact the limit is the same whatever the two starting values in the sequence are). The program and some sample output are given below. Then the program is repeated with the layout, or format, of the output arranged with a combination of **PRINT** and **FORMAT** statements, to show the improved effect of these statements (which are discussed in detail throughout the rest of the chapter). The **PRINT** * statement which has been used up to now enables you to avoid the dreaded **FORMAT** statement, but then of course you have no control over the layout of the output.

```
*****  RABBIT BREEDING WITH FIBONACCI  ******************************
*                                                                  *
*      FN    : TOTAL AFTER N MTHS     /  FNM1 : TOTAL AFTER N-1 MNTHS
*      FNM2 : TOTAL AFTER N-2 MNTHS /  J     : MONTH COUNTER       *
*******************************************************************
```

```
       INTEGER   J
       REAL      FN
       REAL      FNM1
       REAL      FNM2

       FNM2 = 1
       FNM1 = 1

       DO 110 J = 3, 12
          FN = FNM1 + FNM2
          PRINT*, J, FN, FN / FNM1
          FNM2 = FNM1
          FNM1 = FN
110    CONTINUE

       STOP
       END
```

Output:

```
       3   2.0000000        2.0000000
       4   3.0000000        1.5000000
       5   5.0000000        1.6666667
       6   8.0000000        1.6000000
       7   13.000000        1.6250000
       8   21.000000        1.6153846
       9   34.000000        1.6190476
      10   55.000000        1.6176471
      11   89.000000        1.6181818
      12   144.00000        1.6179775
```

Now we put **FORMAT** statements into the program, and run it again. The program and output appear below (note that in the line for month 3 the characters 'b' and 'x' have been inserted into the text to aid the eye: they will not be literally printed).

```
* ***  RABBIT BREEDING WITH ** FANCY ** FORMAT
* ***  FIRST THE VARIABLE DECLARATIONS *******

       INTEGER J
       REAL      FN
       REAL      FNM1
       REAL      FNM2

* ***  NOW THE FORMAT SPECIFICATIONS *********

5      FORMAT( '1MONTH', T12, 'POPULATION', T27, 'RATIO' /
      &' ', 5('-'), T12, 10('-'), T27, 5('-') / )
15     FORMAT( ' ', I3, T12, F7.1, T27, F6.4 )
25     FORMAT( '1' )
```

```
* *** NOW THE EXECUTABLE CODE ***************

        FNM2 = 1
        FNM1 = 1
        PRINT 5

        DO 110 J = 3, 12
          FN = FNM1 + FNM2
          PRINT 15, J, FN, FN / FNM1
          FNM2 = FNM1
          FNM1 = FN
110     CONTINUE

        PRINT 25
        STOP
        END
```

The output now starts on a new page (if you are using a printer), and looks as follows:

MONTH	POPULATION	RATIO
-----	-----------	-----
bb3xxxxxxxbbbb2.0xxxxxxxx2.0000		
4	3.0	1.5000
5	5.0	1.6667
6	8.0	1.6000
7	13.0	1.6250
8	21.0	1.6154
9	34.0	1.6190
10	55.0	1.6176
11	89.0	1.6182
12	144.0	1.6180

A full description of the **FORMAT** statement follows in Section 9.2, but a brief explanation of the main features used in the above example is given below. First, some general remarks.

1)   The basic idea is that instead of using **PRINT***, we use **PRINT** *n*, where *n* is the label (appearing in the first five columns) of a **FORMAT** statement which specifies how the variables in the **PRINT** statement (the output list) are to be printed. More precisely, a **FORMAT** statement describes what is called a 'record', or line of output. The things that appear in the **FORMAT** statement are called **FORMAT** specifications, or editing codes, and are separated by commas. E.g.,

n   FORMAT (specifications separated by commas)
      . . . .
      PRINT n, list of variables separated by commas

2)   The **FORMAT** statement is non-executable and may therefore appear anywhere in the program. It is a good habit to group all the **FORMAT** statements together in one place for easy reference. It is recommended that you place the **FORMAT** statements after the variable declarations at the head of the program, and before the first executable statement. It is also a good idea to reserve statement labels ending with 5 for the **FORMAT** statements, since that way they can never be confused with terminal statements of **DO**-loops.

3)   A **FORMAT** statement always opens a new output record, and may generally be thought of as a description of how that record will appear when printed or displayed on a screen.

4)   Different **PRINT** statements may refer to the same **FORMAT** statement, if this is convenient.

We now come to the particular example given above.

1)   **PRINT 5** is only executed once, and it sets up a heading for the output.

2)   '1MONTH' (in **FORMAT 5**): characters between single quotes are printed literally, as in the **PRINT*** statement. However, the leading '1' has curiously disappeared! This introduces one of the most confusing features of **FORMAT**. The very first character in a line to arrive at the printer is used to control the printer carriage. If the first print character is '1' the printer starts that line on a new page.

3)   T12: tabulates to column 12. But bearing in mind that the first column is gobbled up by the printer (or screen), the next character is actually printed in column 11. Similarly with T27.

4)   /: starts a new record.

5)   ' ': leaves the first position blank. However, since this blank is the first print character to arrive for the new record, it is used for carriage control. A blank in the first position signifies single spacing, so the output continues to the same record.

6)   5('–'): the single dash '–' is printed five times. The 5 is called a repetition factor. Similarly for 10('–'). Note that the use of T12 and T27 again ensures that the underlining comes directly below the headings.

7)   /: this final specification, which incidentally doesn't need a comma before or after it, opens a new output record. The effect is to leave one line blank under the dashes, since the next **FORMAT** statement automatically opens another new record.

8)   **PRINT 15** is executed repeatedly in the **DO**-loop, and each time the three values J, FN and FN/FNM1 are printed according to **FORMAT 15**, which we now examine.

9)   I3: the I stands for Integer and specifies how the first variable in the list (J) is to be printed, and assumes it to be an integer. The 3 means print J over three positions, right justified, with blanks filled in on the left, if necessary. (The blank in quotes before I3 is used for printer control.)

10)   T12: tabulates to column 11 as before.

11)   F7.1: prints a real variable (FN) in fixed point form over the next seven positions (with room for a possible sign and the decimal point), with one decimal figure (0 in this case). The number is right justified, so blanks are filled in from the left. The field of seven positions starts in column 11, because of the T12.

12)   F6.4: prints a real variable (FN/FNM1) over six columns, starting in column 26, with four decimal figures (rounded, as can be seen by comparing the outputs from both versions of the above program).

13)   '1': the final **FORMAT 25** gives a new page for the final messages from the compiler, so that the program output appears neatly on a page by itself.

9.2   **FORMAT Specifications**

The various **FORMAT** specifications are described in detail in this section, with some examples at the end. Field width (*w*) always stands for the total number of print positions in a record occupied by an item. There are 132 print positions on standard fanfold computer paper.

9.2.1   Editing Codes

An editing code specifies how to print numbers, literal characters, and blanks.

I*w*   Integer occupying *w* positions, right justified. If the field width *w* is not large enough to contain the entire integer, including a possible sign, the field is filled with asterisks. If *w* is too big, the field is blank-filled from the left. E.g. the editing code I5 prints the number 747 over five columns as bb747

where the **b** stands for a blank.

F*w.d*   Fixed point real, over a total of *w* positions for the whole number, including a possible sign and the decimal point. In other words, *w* must be large enough to include the integer part, the decimal part, the decimal point, and a possible sign. The fractional part of the number has *d* digits, and is rounded in the usual way. It follows that (*w–d–*2) positions are left for the integer part of the number. The field *w* is blank-filled from the left if it is too large, and asterisk-filled if it is too small. E.g. the editing code F6.2 prints the number –1.23567 over a total of six columns with two decimal places as

b-1.24

and the code F8.3 prints 12.3449 as

bb12.345

E*w.d*   Real floating point, over *w* positions. The number has two parts: a mantissa of length *d*, and an exponent prefaced by a plus or minus sign. The field *w* must be large enough to hold a possible sign for the mantissa, the decimal point, *d* digits for the mantissa, and four positions for the exponent (this includes the sign of the exponent). The field *w* is blank-filled from the left if it is too large, and asterisk-filled if it is too small. E.g. the editing code E12.3 prints the number -89356.7 as

bbb-.894+005

G*w.d*   General. Prints the number in fixed point form if it can, otherwise in floating point. This is useful if you have no idea of the magnitude of the number.

SP/S   Sign. If SP is used, all positive numbers are printed with plus signs. The field widths of the numbers must be large enough to handle the sign or the field will be filled with asterisks. S turns this option off, and then only minus signs will be printed, as usual (see Section 9.2.6 for an example).

*w*X   Skip. Leaves the next *w* print positions blank.

T*w*   Tabulate. Starts printing the next item in position (*w*−1) in the line. This is an absolute position, not a relative one as with the skip. E.g. the two **FORMAT**s

```
FORMAT( 10X, F6.1 )     and
FORMAT( T11, F6.1 )
```

will have the same effect. T*w* is useful for getting columns of output (tables) in the right place.

'. .'   Literals. Prints all the characters between the single quotes. To print a single quote mark (apostrophe), type the single quote twice. E.g. to print DON'T put 'DON''T' in the FORMAT statement.

A*w*   Alphanumeric. Prints a character string over *w* positions, left justified. See Chapter 11 (Character Variables) for examples.

The *w* is optional in the A format. If it is missing, the A format may be used to print a literal string specified in the corresponding **PRINT** statement. E.g.

```
5     FORMAT( ' ', I3, A )
      ID = 21
      PRINT 5, ID, 'ST'
      ID = 22
      PRINT 5, ID, 'ND'
```

prints out

```
21ST
22ND
```

9.2.2 Repetition of Editing Codes

Editing codes may be repeated singly or in groups. E.g. the following two **FORMAT**s have the same effect:

```
FORMAT( ' ', I3, I3, F12.2, I2, F12.2, I2, F12.2, I2 )
FORMAT( ' ', 2I3, 3(F12.2, I2) )
```

9.2.3 Carriage Control

The first character in an output record which is sent to a printer controls the carriage. There are four options:

' '   Single spacing.
'0'   Double spacing.
'1'   New page.
'+'   Suppress carriage movement (this effectively overprints on a printer, but is often not operative on a terminal).

This may cause some surprise effects. The most common is if you print a number starting with a 1 in position one (as in the example with **FORMAT 25** below). The 1 gives a page throw, and the number is printed at the top of a new page, but without the leading 1! This could cause havoc if you were printing a table of values all starting with 1. Each number would be on a new page. The remedy is always to start a **FORMAT** with ' ', T2 or 1X.

9.2.4 Multiple Line Format

A slash (/) after a **FORMAT** editing code terminates the current output record. A new record starts with the editing code following the slash. It follows that if n slashes are placed before the first editing code, n blank records will be output, whereas if n slashes are placed between two editing codes, $n-1$ blank records will be output at that stage. E.g. the statement

```
5       FORMAT( ' 3 CONIFER WAY' // ' PINELANDS' )
```

produces the output

```
3 CONIFER WAY

PINELANDS
```

9.2.5 End of Output Test

A colon after an editing code indicates that the output record must terminate at that point if there are no more items in the output list. This can be used to prevent an unwanted message from being printed. E.g. the statements

```
15      FORMAT( ' I=', I3 : , ' J=', I3 )
        PRINT 15, 10
```

result in the output

        I= 10

whereas if the colon is left out the output will be

        I= 10   J=

9.2.6   Examples

1)   The standard editing codes are illustrated here with a sample program and output.

```
15      FORMAT( T2, I6 )
25      FORMAT( I4 )
35      FORMAT( T2, I4 )
55      FORMAT( T2, F7.1 )
65      FORMAT( T2, F7.0 )
75      FORMAT( T2, F6.3 )
85      FORMAT( T2, F9.2 )
95      FORMAT( T2, E10.3 )
105     FORMAT( T2, E8.3 )
115     FORMAT( T2, E12.7 )
125     FORMAT( T2, SP, 3I3, S, I3 )

        K = 1234
        PRINT 15, K

        PRINT 25, K
        K = -1234
        PRINT 35, K
        X = .123456E3
        PRINT 55, X
        PRINT 65, X
        PRINT 75, X
        PRINT 85, -X
        Y = 0.00009876543
        PRINT 95, Y
        PRINT 105, -Y
        Y = 5432.234
        PRINT 115, Y
        I = 1
        PRINT 125, I, 2 * I, 3 * I, 4 * I
        STOP
        END
```

Output:

    1234

234   (this starts on a new page, as explained in Section 9.2.3)
****
    123.5
     123.
******
   -123.46
    .988-004
****
.5432234+004
 +1 +2 +3   4

2) The next example illustrates the point that various specifications may be used in **FORMAT** statements, which are apt to get rather long. Note also the use of A editing code. Suppose that the variables M, RNT and BAL have been assigned values of 8, 102.64 and 36846.96 respectively in the following program:

```
5       FORMAT( /// T30, A /T30, 20('=') ///' ', A, I3, A //
        $' ', A, F6.2, T30, A, F10.2 /// )
        ....

        PRINT 5, 'STATEMENT OF ACCOUNT', 'THIS IS THE', M,
        $'TH MONTH WITHOUT OVERDRAFT!', 'INTEREST:   R', RNT,
        $'CLOSING BALANCE:   R', BAL

        STOP
        END
```

Output:

```
                    STATEMENT OF ACCOUNT
                    ====================


THIS IS THE   8TH MONTH WITHOUT OVERDRAFT!

INTEREST:   R102.64            CLOSING BALANCE:   R   36846.96
```

3) The compiler usually prints a warning if the editing code is not appropriate to the type of the variable to be printed. E.g.

```
15      FORMAT( ' ', I3 )
        X = 123
        PRINT 15, X
```

with the ASCII FORTRAN compiler gives the output

```
FTN ERR ON UNIT-PRINT      FORMAT TYPE NOT SAME AS INTERNAL TYPE

I/O    REFERENCED AT LN.    3   OF   MAIN PROGRAM
***
```

Note that asterisks are printed instead of the number. The problem here is that X is real, and should be printed with an F or E editing code. The I editing code is for printing variables of integer type only.

9.2.7 Repeated FORMATs

If a **PRINT** statement has more variables listed than there are specifications in the corresponding **FORMAT** statement, the **FORMAT** is repeated on different lines each time until all the variables have been printed. E.g. if I, X, J and Y have been assigned values of 1, 101.00, 2, and 203.01, the statements

```
        PRINT 25, I, X, J, Y
25      FORMAT( T2, I3, F8.2 )
```

will give the following output:

```
  1   101.00
  2   203.01
```

However, if brackets are used within a **FORMAT**, the repeat (when there are too many variables) takes place only from the opening bracket which is the last to be closed inside the **FORMAT** statement. So, for example,

```
n       FORMAT( T2, I3, 2(F8.2, 3(I3)) )
```

repeats from 2(F8.2 . . . if there are more than nine variables in

```
    PRINT n
```

9.3 WRITE

This is a powerful statement which is more general than **PRINT**, and can also be used to direct output to data files stored on magnetic disks. The **WRITE** statement may be used to produce three types of output records: unformatted, formatted, and list-directed (free formatted). Unformatted records are not directly intelligible to most human beings, and are generally used in connection with files, which are discussed in Section 9.5.

9.3.1 Formatted WRITE

In this form a **FORMAT** statement must be supplied to describe the layout of the output record, and also an output unit number, to indicate the peripheral unit or device to which the output must be sent. The 'standard output unit' is the line printer, or terminal, which is usually connected to your computer system. This unit has a number which varies between installations. In this text it is taken to be 6, but it must be stressed that you need to find out the particular standard output unit for your computer system. The statements

```
15      FORMAT( ' ', 3F10.4 )        1 on multics
        WRITE( 6, 15 )X, Y, Z
```

will therefore send an output record to the line printer or terminal screen with the values of X, Y and Z set out as described in the **FORMAT** statement. This has exactly the same effect as the statement

```
    PRINT 15, X, Y, Z
```

The use of other output units is discussed below in Section 9.5.

9.3.2 List-directed WRITE

This form of output is written according to a general format which therefore does not need to be specified by the user. The following two statements send output to the standard output unit in exactly the same way:

```
    WRITE( 6, * )X, Y, Z
    PRINT*, X, Y, Z
```

The **FORMAT** label is replaced by an asterisk. In fact, all our input and output up to now has been list-directed.

9.4 READ

READ, being the converse of **WRITE**, is almost identical to it. There are also three types of input records: unformatted, formatted, and list-directed.

9.4.1 Formatted READ

The main editing codes described above in Section 9.2.1 may be used in **FORMAT** statements associated with **READ**s. In this case the **FORMAT** specifies exactly how the input data is laid out (in a file, for example). For formatted **READ**, the statement is similar to **PRINT**:

        READ n, list of variables separated by commas

where **n** is the label of a **FORMAT** statement.

A very important point to note is that, with formatted **READ**, blanks in the data are by default significant, and are interpreted as zeros.

Example
The program segment

        READ 15, J, K, N, X, Y
        ....

    15   FORMAT(I4, I3, I1, F5.2, F5.3)
           END

with data

    34   12345 .789.1 3

causes the five variables to be assigned the values 3400; 123; 4; 50.78 and 9.103 respectively.

Formatted **READ** is very useful when you don't want to waste space by having blanks or commas between data items. There are also times when you may want to pick specific numbers out of a string of data.

   More generally, you have the option to **READ** from an input unit other than a terminal keyboard (e.g. a data file on a magnetic disk or tape) and if you don't know beforehand exactly how much data there is, an end-of-file condition may be detected by an I/O (Input/Output) status specification. So a more general formatted **READ** could look something like

        READ(INPUT, n, IOSTAT = I) list of variables

where

INPUT is any integer constant or variable representing the input unit where the data may be found. The number of the 'standard input unit' is specific to a particular computer system, and will vary from place to place. It is taken to be 5 in any examples below. Use of other input units is discussed in Section 9.5 on files.

n is a **FORMAT** statement label if the data is formatted, or an asterisk if the data is free formatted (i.e. separated by blanks or commas).

I is any integer variable. The I/O status specification clause, **IOSTAT** = I, enables the program to detect an end-of-file condition without a crash occurring. The value of I will be negative if an end-of-file condition is encountered, but zero if it is not (assuming that there are no other errors). A positive value of I indicates an error before an end-of-file condition.

Example
Suppose, in the example of Section 6.1 (which reads a set of marks), we didn't know how many students there were. The following program will handle this situation:

```
* *** READING AN UNKNOWN AMOUNT OF DATA

*      FIN   : FINAL MARK        / INPUT : UNIT FOR READ
*      IST   : I/O STATUS        / P1    : 1ST PAPER
*      P2    : 2ND PAPER         / REC   : CLASS RECORD
*      STU   : STUDENT COUNTER   / TOT   : TOTAL MARKS

       INTEGER  INPUT
       INTEGER  IST
       INTEGER  STU

       REAL     FIN
       REAL     P1
       REAL     P2
       REAL     REC
       REAL     TOT

       INPUT = 5
       STU = 0
       TOT = 0
       READ( INPUT, *, IOSTAT = IST )REC, P1, P2

    10 IF( IST .EQ. 0 )THEN
          STU = STU + 1
          FIN = (REC + P1 + P2) / 3.0
          TOT = TOT + FIN
          PRINT*, 'STUDENT', STU, ' HAS MARKS', FIN
          READ( INPUT, *, IOSTAT = IST )REC, P1, P2
          GOTO 10
       END IF
       IF( STU .GE. 1 )THEN
          PRINT*, 'CLASS AVERAGE =', TOT / STU
       ELSE
          PRINT*, 'CLASS EMPTY'
       END IF

       STOP
       END
```

Note that two **READ** statements are required, to deal with the case where there is no data at all. This logical structure is called '**READ-AHEAD**'.

Note also the **IF/GOTO** combination for repeating, because the number of repeats is unknown in advance.

The **IOSTAT** specifier is also invaluable in detecting input errors, which can occur, for example, when data is read with an incompatible format. This is one of the commonest sources of error.

9.4.2 List-directed READ

This is the simplest form of input, where the format of the input record does not need to be specified, but is represented by an asterisk in the statement. The following two statements read from the standard input unit in exactly the same way:

```
       READ( 5, * )X, Y, Z
       READ*, X, Y, Z
```

For list-directed input, the items in the input record may be separated by blanks or commas.

9.5 Files

One of the major attributes of modern computers is their ability to store and access large amounts of data fairly quickly. To be able to take full advantage of this powerful facility you need to be acquainted with the concept of files.

For example, you may be conducting an experiment where the voltage in a thermocouple must be recorded every few seconds. For a subsequent analysis of the results, using a suitable computer program, it is inconceivable to have to record the results (there may be hundreds of data items) manually and to enter them afresh each time the program is run. What is far more efficient is to devise some hardware to connect the computer to the experiment so that it can monitor and store the results in a file, which is then available whenever you want to run your analysis program.

Another possibility is that you might need to store the output of one program to be used later as input for another one. An example of this is the numerical solution of a system of differential equations (see Section 15.4), where the numerical output could be stored in a file for later use by a plotter program to produce graphical output.

A third example of the use of files is in order to store sample data for a program which is being tested. This saves you repeatedly entering the data every time the program is run.

A file is a collection of records (lines), each consisting of a number of characters. There are two fundamentally different types of files: sequential and direct access.

9.5.1 Sequential Files

These may be thought of as continuous tapes, where records are located sequentially along the tapes. A particular record can only be found by rewinding the 'tape' and starting from the beginning again. Because of the way information is stored in a file, the records must either all be formatted, or unformatted. To access a file from a program, it must be connected with an **OPEN** statement to a unit which is specified in **READ** and/or **WRITE** statements in the program. An important property of sequential files is that a particular record cannot be replaced without destroying all the subsequent records in the file. For example, the statement

```
OPEN( UNIT = 1, FILE = 'JUNK' )
```

connects a file called 'JUNK' to unit 1. By default, the file is sequential, and its records are formatted. If 'JUNK' does not already exist on the computer system, a new file of that name will be created and retained (saved) after the run successfully terminates. The statement

```
WRITE( 1, 15 )X, Y, Z
```

will then write a record (the first) to the file, containing the values of X, Y and Z as specified by **FORMAT 15**. To read the same record, the same format must be used, but the file must also either be rewound with a **REWIND** statement, which positions the file back at the beginning again, or backspaced one record with a **BACKSPACE** statement, which positions the file back one record. The next program segment writes a record to a file, reads it back, and prints it out.

```
15      FORMAT( ' ', 3F10.4 )
        OPEN( UNIT = 1, FILE = 'JUNK' )
        X = 1.1
        Y = 2.2
        Z = 3.3
        WRITE( 1, 15 )X, Y, Z
        REWIND 1
        READ( 1, 15 )X, Y, Z
        PRINT 15, X, Y, Z
```

Exactly the same effect is achieved if

```
        REWIND 1
```

is replaced by

```
        BACKSPACE 1
```

List-directed input and output may also be used with files, so the **READ** and **WRITE** statements in the above segment may be replaced by

```
        WRITE( 1, * )X, Y, Z
        READ( 1, * )X, Y, Z
```

A file may also consist of unformatted records. The advantage is that this form uses less storage, and is therefore appropriate for handling large amounts of data (for example, when producing data which may be used later by a plotter, as mentioned above). However, unformatted records are written in a machine dependent code, which is unintelligible to the unaided human eye. Such a file must be specified as unformatted, and any **READ/WRITE** statements which access the file must omit a **FORMAT** label. The program segment above can be rewritten for an unformatted file by changing the following statements:

```
        OPEN( UNIT = 1, FORM = 'UNFORMATTED', FILE = 'DUMMY' )
        WRITE( 1 )X, Y, Z
        READ( 1 )X, Y, Z
```

Note that the file must now be specified as unformatted in the **OPEN** statement. Sequential files are specified as formatted by default.

There is a third type of record, which appears in all sequential files, and that is the 'endfile' record, which is a special record to mark the end of the file. This record is detected by the IOSTAT status clause in the **READ** statement (Section 9.4). An endfile record is written by the statement

```
        ENDFILE u
```

where u is the unit connected to the file. This leaves the file positioned after the endfile record, so that no further information may be written to the file. To add new information at the end of the file, the **BACKSPACE** statement must be used, once the end of the file has been found, to position the file before the endfile record. Any subsequent **WRITE**s to the file will destroy the endfile record which should be rewritten with another **ENDFILE** statement (see Exercise 9.3 below).

When a file-handling program terminates after successfully executing, all files connected to it are automatically disconnected. However, it may be convenient to disconnect a file when a program is running. This may be done with the statement

```
        CLOSE( u )
```

where u is the unit connected to the file.

A real example involving reading from and updating files is given in Section 15.4, where the numerical solution of differential equations is discussed.

9.5.2   Direct Access Files

In the case of a direct (or random) access file, as the name implies, a particular record may be read and/or over-written, without affecting subsequent records in the file as in the case of sequential files. This is due to the way in which direct access files are stored on magnetic disks. Direct access files are unformatted by default, and all their records must be the same length. They may not contain an endfile record (see above). The record length is specified in the **OPEN** statement. The length of a formatted record is measured in characters, but the length of an unformatted record is measured in units specific to a particular computer system, usually words, bytes or bits. For example, the statement

```
OPEN( UNIT = 2, ACCESS = 'DIRECT', RECL = 50 )
```

connects an unformatted direct access file to unit 2. Each record is of length 50 units. When writing to the file, the length of each record must therefore not exceed 50 units. It may, however, be less. The statement

```
WRITE( 2, REC = I )X, Y, Z
```

writes to record I, while the statement

```
READ( 2, REC = 6 )A, B, C
```

reads record 6.

Direct access files are useful in a situation where you might need to add extra items of data to a file from time to time, which can then be done without rewriting the whole file. The following example shows a direct access file 'EXPT', which contains the results of an experiment in the form of data pairs (X; Y). These data will be used in Exercise 10.6 as input for a program to find the best straight line through the data. The first record contains the number of data pairs. Subsequent records each hold one data pair. The program below reads a new data pair from the keyboard, writes it to the next record in the file, and updates the first record only (containing the number of data points).

```
OPEN( 1, ACCESS = 'DIRECT', RECL = 20, FILE = 'EXPT' )
READ( 1, REC = 1 )N
READ*, X, Y
N = N + 1
WRITE( 1, REC = N+1 ) X, Y
WRITE( 1, REC = 1 )N

STOP
END
```

Direct access files are also useful when handling linked lists, for example (see Chapter 11).

FORTRAN 77 has one more file-handling statement: **INQUIRE**. As the name implies, this statement enables you to establish the specifications of a file on your computer system. Its main use is in general purpose file-handling programs. For example, the statement

```
INQUIRE( UNIT = 3, ACCESS = A, FORM = F )
```

assigns the string 'SEQUENTIAL' or 'DIRECT' to the character variable A according to the type of the file connected to unit 3, if it is connected. F is a character variable which is given the value 'FORMATTED' or 'UNFORMATTED' as the case may be. Another possibility is

```
INQUIRE( FILE = 'MINE', NUMBER = N, OPENED = LP, RECL = L )
```

where N is a variable which is set to the number of the unit to which 'MINE' is connected (undefined if it is not connected), LP is a logical variable set to .TRUE. if the file is connected to some unit (.FALSE. if not), and L is the record length if the file is connected for direct access.

There is a full description of all the file-handling statements in Appendix A.

9.6   Other Peripheral Devices

The only input/output devices discussed so far have been terminal keyboards, printers and magnetic disks. Other devices, such as magnetic tapes, high-quality printers, plotters of various descriptions, electronic typesetting equipment, etc., may be available on your computer system. These are usually accessed by means of subprograms (see Chapter 12) and/or 'job control' statements peculiar to the operating system at your installation.

9.7   Summary

* A record can be thought of as a line of input/output.

* A **FORMAT** statement specifies the layout of a record.

* The first character in an output record controls the printer carriage.

* **WRITE** is a more general form of **PRINT**.

* Input/output may be formatted, unformatted or list-directed.

* An I/O specifier in a **READ** statement can detect the end of the data.

* A file may be sequential or direct access.

* Sequential files are formatted by default.

* Direct (random) access files are unformatted by default.

* The record length of a direct access file must be specified.

9.8   Exercises

9.1   Give the output of the following two program segments (indicate blanks and new lines carefully):

(a)
```
   5 FORMAT( 1X, 'M=', I3, 'N=', I4, 3X, 'X=', F6.1 /
  $ T3, E11.4 )

     M = 117
     N = - 27
     X = - 0.1235E2
     Y = 1234.567
     PRINT 5, M, N, X, Y
```

(b)
```
   5 FORMAT( I3, 1X, F6.2, F5.3, I2 )
  15 FORMAT( T2, I2, F8.2 / T3, F3.1, I4 )
     READ 5, N, X, Y, J
     PRINT 15, J, X, Y, N
     STOP
     END
```

Data:

```
0146729.123.61035
```

9.2   Show how each of the following numbers will be printed with the editing code shown in brackets (assume that carriage control has been taken care of):

(a) −738 (I4)   (b) +738 (I3)
(c) 38.136 (F7.2)   (d) −100.64 (F6:1)
(e) 9876.545 (E10.4)   (f) −0.000044009 (E9.2)

P.S. The best way to master **FORMAT** is to use it as much as possible!

9.3   You have a formatted sequential file on your computer system called 'VOLTS'. Each record (which is free formatted) contains successive results of an experiment which records the voltage across a thermocouple, and the time of the reading. These are represented by two real variables, the time being given first. Write a program which updates the file by adding one new record to it (without losing all the previous results!). The new results should be keyed in at a terminal. The program should also be able to handle the file initially when it contains no data.

10

Subscripted Variables: Arrays

In real programs we often need to handle a large number of variables in the same way, e.g. to find the mean (average) of a set of numbers. To avoid an enormously clumsy program where perhaps hundreds of variable names are needed, we can use subscripted variables, or arrays. These are variables with components, rather like vectors or matrices, and they are written in the normal way except that the subscripts are enclosed in brackets after the variable name, e.g. $X(3)$, $Y(J+2*N)$.

```
*  ***  EXAMPLE: FIND THE MEAN OF FIVE NUMBERS

        REAL X(5)
15      FORMAT(' ', 'THE MEAN IS', F10.1 //)

        DO 10 I = 1, 5
          READ*, X(I)
10      CONTINUE

        SUM = 0

        DO 20 I = 1, 5
          SUM = SUM + X(I)
20      CONTINUE

        XBAR = SUM / 5.0
        PRINT 15, XBAR

        STOP
        END
```

Data:

5.6
7.2
8.1
3.9
4.0

Memory

X(1): 5.6
X(2): 7.2
X(3): 8.1
X(4): 3.9
X(5): 4.0

Note that the subscripted variables may be easily referenced in the program by changing the subscript in a DO-loop. Admittedly, an array is not strictly necessary here (can you rewrite the program without one?), but this example is deliberately simple to illustrate the basic idea. Arrays are, however, essential in most of the remaining examples in this chapter, and one seldom encounters non-trivial programs without them.

10.1   Basic Rules and Notation

1)   If a variable is to be subscripted (dimensioned), the maximum subscript value must be specified in brackets after the variable name in a **REAL** or **INTEGER** statement placed before the first executable statement in the program. This maximum size is used at the compilation stage to allocate sufficient storage space for the program. Arrays may also be dimensioned in any of the other type specification statements.

2)   Individual members of an array are called elements and are referenced by a subscript, which may be any valid FORTRAN expression. In the unlikely event of the subscript not being integer, it is truncated. E.g. the statement

```
Y = X( 7/3. )
```

in the above program would assign the value of $X(2)$, viz. 7.2, to Y.

3)   The lowest subscript value is 1, by default. This may be altered by defining a range of subscripts in the specification statement. E.g.

```
REAL      A(0:5)
INTEGER B(6)
```

sets up two arrays:

A with real elements $A(0)$, $A(1)$, ..., $A(5)$ and B with integer elements $B(1)$, $B(2)$, ..., $B(6)$.

4)   Arrays may have up to seven dimensions (i.e. seven subscripts) and up to 262143 elements. E.g.

```
INTEGER A(8,8)
```

could define an 8×8 distance array. In this chapter we will only consider arrays with one subscript (one-dimensional arrays). Arrays with more than one subscript are discussed in Chapter 14.

5)   It is not necessary to use all the space allocated for a particular array, but you should **never** try to use **more**.

**** WARNING **** WARNING **** WARNING ****
DO NOT ALLOW SUBSCRIPT VALUES
TO GET OUTSIDE THE RANGE SPECIFIED
IN THE
STATEMENT THAT DIMENSIONS THE ARRAY

Your compiler may gladly accept some such values but will do horrible things to your program with them, or crash it altogether. E.g. consider the arrays dimensioned as follows:

```
REAL X(10)
REAL Y(5)
```

A reference to $X(12)$ in the program (under the ASCII FORTRAN compiler) will find the element two places along from $X(10)$, which will usually be $Y(2)$, since arrays are stored in consecutive memory locations. This will obviously cause subtle errors throughout the program. But assigning a value to $Y(6)$, say, could cause part of the program memory to be overwritten, giving a misleading error message.

6)   An array name may not be referred to without the subscript(s), except in a **PRINT** or **READ** statement (see below).

10.2 Printing in Rows

Arrays enable you to print lists of numbers more economically, with many numbers on a line, rather than one below each other. Anyone who has tried to generate even a short list of prime numbers, for example, will have encountered this problem. The following example shows how to overcome it. Suppose we want to print the integers 1 to 99 in order, with 20 numbers per line in, say, I3 format:

```
        INTEGER NUM(200)
  15    FORMAT( 20I3 )

        DO 70 I = 1, 99
           NUM(I) = I
  70    CONTINUE

        PRINT 15, ( NUM(I), I = 1, 99 )
        STOP
        END
```

Output:

```
 1  2  3  4  5  6  7  8  9 10 11 12 13 14 15 16 17 18 19 20
21 22 23 24 25 26 27 28 29 30 31 32 33 34 35 36 37 38 39 40
41 42 43 44 45 46 47 48 49 50 51 52 53 54 55 56 57 58 59 60
61 62 63 64 65 66 67 68 69 70 71 72 73 74 75 76 77 78 79 80
81 82 83 84 85 86 87 88 89 90 91 92 93 94 95 96 97 98 99
```

10.3 Implied DO-Loop in PRINT

The PRINT 15 statement in the last example contains what is called an implied DO-loop, which is very handy for PRINTing and READing arrays, or parts of arrays. An ordinary DO-loop around the PRINT would not have the same effect (why not?). The general form is:

```
        PRINT n, ( X(i), i = e1, e2 ,e3 )
```

where *n* is the label of a FORMAT statement;
      X is a suitably dimensioned array;
      i, e1, e2, and *e3* are as defined in Section 6.2.

If the entire array is to be printed, then

```
        PRINT n, X
```

is sufficient.
    The rules for an implied DO-loop with READ are identical.

10.4 Mean and Standard Deviation

Suppose we have a set of numbers (results of an experiment, or marks in a test, say) and want to compute their mean and standard deviation. If we have N results (observations) we can represent them with an array X having N elements: $X(1), X(2), ..., X(I), ..., X(N)$.

The mean of this set is defined as $\bar{X} = \sum\limits_{i=1}^{N} x_i / N$ and the

standard deviation s by
$$s^2 = \sum_{i=1}^{n} (x_i - \bar{X})^2 / (N-1).$$

We can compute the mean without an array, by reading each X(I) and adding it to a running total, but since we need the mean before starting to compute s according to our formula, we obviously need to have stored all the observations in an array.

Suppose the data are arranged with more than one number per line in general. We know that there are less than 500 numbers. The total number of numbers, N, appears by itself on the first data line:

```
* *** COMPUTE MEAN AND STD DEVIATION

         REAL X(500)
105      FORMAT( '1', 'MEAN =', T15, F7.1 /
         $' ', 'STD DEVIATION =', T15, F7.1 )

         READ*, N, ( X(I), I = 1, N )
         XBAR = 0
         STD = 0

         DO 10 I = 1, N
            XBAR = XBAR + X(I)
10       CONTINUE

         XBAR = XBAR / N

         DO 20 I = 1, N
            STD = STD + ( X(I) - XBAR ) ** 2
20       CONTINUE

         STD = SQRT( STD / (N - 1) )
         PRINT 105, XBAR, STD

         STOP
         END
```

If the program is to be run with more than 500 data, the array dimension in the first line will have to be changed. This is not a problem in this example, but programs often involve many arrays. Having to change all the dimensions is tedious, and is also an obvious source of error. This can be obviated by the **PARAMETER** statement, which is implemented at compile time, and which allows you to name a constant at the beginning of a program. To use it, replace the **REAL** statement in the above example with the two statements

```
         PARAMETER (MAX = 500)
         REAL X( MAX )
```

This defines MAX as a 'named constant', which is suitable for an array dimension, since this must be a constant and not a variable, except under certain conditions in a subprogram (see Chapter 12). If the value of MAX in the single **PARAMETER** statement is changed, it will take on that value throughout the rest of the program.

Incidentally, **PARAMETER** is useful for defining any other constants you may require in a program, e.g.

```
PARAMETER (PI = 3.1415927, G = 9.8)
```

This guards against an erroneous change later in the program if PI and G were ordinary variables (since a named constant may not have its value changed by the program).

10.5   Sorting Numbers: Bubble Sort

A standard application of arrays is in the problem of sorting a list of numbers into, let us say, ascending order. This might be necessary, for example, before carrying out a linear interpolation on some data (see Exercise 10.7). The basic idea is that the unsorted list is read into an array. The numbers are then ordered by a process which essentially passes through the list many times, swapping consecutive elements that are in the wrong order, until all the elements are in the right order. Such a process is called a Bubble Sort, since the smallest numbers rise to the top of the list, like bubbles of air in water. In fact, the largest number will 'sink' to the bottom of the list after the first pass in the version shown below. There are many other methods of sorting (e.g. the Quick Sort), of varying degrees of efficiency.

A structure plan for a bubble sort is as follows:

    1   Initialize N (length of list),
                    I (number of passes),
                    SWOPS (swop counter)
    2   Read in the list (X)
    3   While SWOPS≠0 and I<N−1 repeat
        3.1   SWOPS = 0
        3.2   Increase I by one
        3.3   J = 1
        3.4   Repeat N−I times
              3.4.1   If X(J)>X(J+1) then
                      3.4.1.1   Swop X(J) and X(J+1)
                      3.4.1.2   Increase SWOPS by one
              3.4.3   Increase J by one
    4   Print the list, and number of passes.

As an example, consider a list of five numbers: 27, 13, 9, 5 and 3. They are initially read into the array X. The computer's memory for this problem is sketched in Table 10.1. Each column shows the memory during each pass. A stroke (/) in a row indicates a change in that variable during the pass as the program works down through the list. The number of tests (comparisons) made on each pass is also shown in the table. If you don't understand the algorithm, work through the table with the structure plan.

Table 10.1 Computer memory during a bubble sort

Pass	1	2	3	4
X(1)	27/13	13/ 9	9/ 5	5/ 3
X(2)	13/27/ 9	9/13/ 5	5/ 9/ 3	3/ 5
X(3)	9/27/ 5	5/13/ 3	3/ 9	9
X(4)	5/27/ 3	3/13	13	13
X(5)	3/27	27	27	27
Tests	4	3	2	1

On the Ith pass there are exactly $N-I$ tests, so the total number of tests is

$$1+2+3+...+(N-1) = N(N-1)/2.$$

So for a list of five numbers there are 10 tests, but for 10 numbers there are 45 tests. The computer time needed goes up as the square of the length of the list.

Suppose we have 100 numbers in the list, to be printed in ascending order, 10 to a line. Assume, for the purposes of neat printout, that the numbers are all integers less than 10000. The program is then as follows:

```
*****  BUBBLE SORT INTO ASCENDING ORDER  ****************************
*                                                                  *
*      I:      PASS COUNTER          / J:      TEST COUNTER         *
*      N:      LENGTH OF LIST        / SWOPS: SWOPS COUNTER         *
*      TEMP: TEMPORARY STORE         / X:      LIST TO BE SORTED    *
********************************************************************
          INTEGER SWOPS
          INTEGER TEMP
          INTEGER X(100)
15        FORMAT( 10I5 )
25        FORMAT( ' ', I5, A )

          N = 100
          SWOPS = 1
          I = 0
          READ*, X

10        IF( SWOPS .NE. 0 .AND. I .LT. N-1 )THEN
             SWOPS = 0
             I = I + 1
             DO 20 J = 1, N-I
                IF( X(J) .GT. X(J+1) )THEN
                   TEMP = X(J)
                   X(J) = X( J+1 )
                   X( J+1 ) = TEMP
                   SWOPS = SWOPS + 1
                END IF
20           CONTINUE

             GOTO 10
          END IF

          PRINT 15, X
          PRINT 25, I, ' PASSES'

          STOP
          END
```

Note that the program uses a variable SWOPS as a 'flag' to detect when the numbers are actually sorted. This could save a great many unnecessary and time-consuming comparisons, and is based on the observation that almost every list of numbers is already partially sorted. They are therefore likely to be sorted long before the maximum number of $N-1$ passes has been made. SWOPS, which counts the number of exchanges made during a pass, must be initialized to 1 to ensure that at least one pass is made. Thereafter, at the beginning of each pass it is set to 0. If it remains 0 during a pass, the list must be sorted, so one of the conditions for further repeats (SWOPS≠0) no longer holds, and the sorting process stops.

10.6 Initializing Arrays: the DATA statement

The **DATA** statement is very useful for assigning initial values to an array, particularly when some of them are the same. This assignment is done by the compiler during compile time. For example, the statements

```
      REAL X(10)
      DATA (X(I), I = 1, 4) / 0, 3 * 1 / X(7) / 2 /
   $ (X(I), I = 9, 10) / 2 * 0 /
```

will assign the values 0, 1, 1, 1, 2, 0, 0 to X(1), X(2), X(3), X(4), X(7), X(9) and X(10) respectively. X(5) and X(6) are initially undefined.

The general syntax is:

```
      DATA var1 / con1 / var2 / con2 / ....
```

where 'var1' is a list of variables which will be given values from the list 'con1', etc. There must be exactly the same number of items in each variable list as in each corresponding list of constants.

The asterisks in the **DATA** statement above are repetition factors to indicate that three values of 1 each, and two of 0 each, are to be assigned.

The entire array may also be initialized by a statement like

```
      DATA X / 5 * 0, 4 * 1, 2 /
```

which assigns 0 to the first 5 elements, 2 to the last, and 1 to the rest.

Non-subscripted variables may also be initialized like this, e.g.

```
      DATA PI, E / 3.1415926, 2.71828 /
```

The **DATA** statements must always appear after all the specification statements in a program.

10.7 Summary

* An array is a collection of subscripted variables with the same name.

* Members of an array are called elements.

* Arrays are useful for representing and processing large amounts of data.

* The maximum required dimension of an array must be declared in a type specification statement at the beginning of the program.

* The subscript of an array element may be any valid arithmetic expression.

* The subscript of an array element may not fall outside the range declared in the specification statement.

* An implied **DO**-loop may be used in a **PRINT** statement to print an array.

* The **PARAMETER** statement may be used to name a constant.

* The **DATA** statement may be used to initialize arrays at compile time.

10.8   Exercises

10.1   If NUM is a FORTRAN integer array which appears in the statement

```
INTEGER NUM( 0:100 )
```

write the lines of coding which will

(a) put the first 100 non-negative integers (0,...,99) in the elements NUM(0),..., NUM(99);

(b) put the first 50 positive even integers (2,...,100) in the elements NUM(1),..., NUM(50).

10.2   Write a FORTRAN program which will read a five-digit number in binary code (e.g. 01100—no blanks between digits) and print out its decimal value (12 in this case). Extend the program to do the reverse, reading in the decimal value (assumed less than 31, say) and printing the binary coded number on one line with no blanks between the digits. *Hint*: store each binary digit in a different element of an array.

10.3   Write a program which puts the first 100 Fibonacci numbers (1, 1, 2, 3, ...) into an array F(1), ..., F(100).

10.4   A prime number is one which is exactly divisible only by itself and unity. Develop a structure plan for the problem of printing all the primes less than 1000 (1 and 2 are generally regarded as primes, and will probably have to be dealt with separately). *Hints*: (1) use an array to store the primes; (2) to save computer time use the fact that if a number has no factors less than its square root, then it has none greater than its square root.

10.5   Write the program for Exercise 10.4.

10.6   In an experiment N pairs of observations $(X_i; Y_i)$ are made. The 'best straight line' that may be drawn through these points (using the method of Least Squares) has intercept A on the y-axis and slope B where

$$B = (S_1 - S_2 S_3/N)/(S_4 - S_2^2/N)$$
$$A = S_3/N - B S_2/N$$
$$S_1 = \Sigma X_i Y_i$$
$$S_2 = \Sigma X_i$$
$$S_3 = \Sigma Y_i$$
$$S_4 = \Sigma X_i^2.$$

The correlation coefficient R is given by

$$R = \frac{N S_1 - S_2 S_3}{\sqrt{N S_4 - S_2^2} \sqrt{N S_5 - S_3^2}}$$

where $S_5 = \Sigma Y_i^2$ ($R = 1$ implies a perfect linear relationship between X and Y). All the summations are over the range $i = 1$ to N. The pairs of observations $(X_i; Y_i)$ are each stored in a record of length 20 in an unformatted direct access file called 'EXPT', set up as in the example in Section 9.5. The number of observations, N, is in the first record of the file. You may assume that $N \leqslant 100$. Write a program to read the data and compute A, B and R.

10.7   If a set of data $(X_i; Y_i)$ are joined by straight lines, the value Y corresponding to a value X which lies on a straight line between X_i and X_{i+1} is given by

$$Y = Y_i + (X - X_i)\frac{(Y_{i+1} - Y_i)}{(X_{i+1} - X_i)}$$

This process is called linear interpolation. Suppose 100 sets of pairs $(X_i; Y_i)$ are stored, in ascending order of X_i, one pair to a record, in an unformatted sequential file called 'RAW'. Write a program which will print an interpolated value of Y given an arbitrary value of X keyed in at the terminal. It is assumed that X is in the range covered by the data. Note that the data must be sorted into ascending order with respect to the X_i values. If this was not so, it would be necessary to sort them beforehand.

11

Character Variables

So far we have used three types of FORTRAN variables: integer, real, and logical. In this chapter we look at a fourth type (mentioned briefly in Chapter 3): character. This enables you to assign literal characters (e.g. names, symbols) to variables in order to print them (e.g. class lists), compare them (e.g. alphabetical word sorts), or manipulate them (ciphers, word processing, graphs, etc.).

11.1   Reading and Printing Names

Our very first example in Chapter 1, to compute and print a student's final course mark, is gravely deficient in that the student's name is neither supplied nor printed. To illustrate the use of character variables, consider a variation on that problem. Suppose the lecturer keeps a file called 'MARKS' with a formatted record for each student's name and marks. The name appears in the first 20 columns, followed by the marks for three tests, all in I4 format. The tests are out of 25, 100, and 50, and count 15%, 50%, and 35% toward the class record respectively. There are 198 students. We want to compute each student's class record as a percentage, and print it out next to the student's name. The only innovation here is the character handling, which is explained in the following sections.

```
        INTEGER       MARK(3)
        CHARACTER*20 NAME
25      FORMAT( A20, 3I4 )
35      FORMAT( 1X, A20, F5.1, '%' )
45      FORMAT( '1NAME', T21, 'CLASS RECORD' / )

        OPEN( UNIT = 1, FILE = 'MARKS' )
        PRINT 45

        DO 10 I = 1, 198
          READ( 1, 25 ), NAME, MARK
          CR = MARK(1) / 25. * 15. + MARK(2) / 100. * 50.
     $       + MARK(3) / 50. * 35.
          PRINT 35, NAME, CR
10      CONTINUE

        STOP
        END
```

The records in 'MARKS' should look as follows:

```
ANDERSON RS            21  99   40
BAKER WZ               25 100   50
....

ZUBB QX                 0  12    3
```

11.2   Basic Rules

The statement

```
CHARACTER*w variable
```

will specify the variable of type character and length *w*, i.e. able to hold a string of up to *w* characters. (For the technically minded, a character takes up one byte (eight bits) of storage.) The string of characters must be input or output using either the A*w* format editing code (or simply the A editing code by itself), or assigned with single quotes. E.g.

```
CHARACTER*5 X
```

specifies X of type character and length five bytes. A five-letter string may be read into X using A or A5 format, or assigned as follows:

```
X = 'PLONK'
```

Note

Blanks are characters, and as such are not ignored by **READ**s with A format.

Characters may be input with **READ*** (list-directed input), in which case the string must be enclosed in apostrophes, and delimited with blanks or commas in the usual way. In this way the delimiting symbols may themselves be read as characters by being enclosed within the apostrophes. If the string is to contain an apostrophe, it must be duplicated.

Character variables which are output with **PRINT*** appear as they do with formatted output.

If a string assigned to a character variable is too long, it is truncated from the right, while if it is too short, it is blank-filled from the right. E.g. the segment

```
CHARACTER*5 A
CHARACTER*4 B

A = 'NAPOLEON'
B = 'HI'
```

will assign the value 'NAPOL' to A and 'HI ' to B.

11.3   Printing a Bar Chart

A standard way of presenting data is by means of a bar chart (or a histogram), where the data is divided into a number of classes, and the size of each class is represented pictorially by a bar. The essence of a program to print a bar chart is to be able to print a line with a variable number of bar symbols (an asterisk, say) in it. This can be done very easily as follows. Suppose that the integer variable CLASS has been assigned somewhere in the program, CLASS being the size of a particular class. The problem is to print CLASS asterisks on the same line, where CLASS should be able to range from 0 to 120:

```
15      FORMAT( ' ', 120A1 ).
        . . . .

        [assign value to CLASS]
        PRINT 15, ( '*', I = 1, CLASS )
```

As it happens, **PRINT*** will work just as well here without the **FORMAT** statement, but **FORMAT** is needed in the next program. We can use this idea in a program to print a full bar chart. Suppose we have counted, in a test, how many students got between 0% and 9.99%, 10% and 19.99%, etc. We would altogether have 11 classes, called **deciles**, in this example (100% and over is a 'decile' by itself). Every test mark falls into one of these classes, so we end up with 11 numbers or frequencies, being the number of results in each decile. To be specific, let us take the following example:

Decile No. [K]	Range	Frequency [CLASS(K)]
0	0%– 9.99%	1
1	10%–19.99%	1
2	20%–29.99%	12
3	30%–39.99%	9
4	40%–49.99%	31
5	50%–59.99%	26
6	60%–69.99%	49
7	70%–79.99%	26
8	80%–89.99%	24
9	90%–99.99%	6
10	100%+	1

These figures mean, for example, that 49 students got marks in the range 60%–69.99%. The following program reads in the 11 frequencies and prints the bar chart:

```
*****  BAR CHART *****
        INTEGER CLASS (0:10)
115     FORMAT( 1X, I2, ' (', I3, '): ', 100A1 )

        READ*, CLASS

        DO 20 K = 0, 10
            PRINT 115, K, CLASS(K), ( '*',   I = 1, CLASS(K) )
20      CONTINUE

        STOP
        END
```

Data:

```
1 0 12 9 31 26 49 26 24 6 1
```

The output looks like this:

```
0 (  1): *
1 (  1):
2 ( 12): ************
3 (  9): *********
4 ( 31): *******************************
```

```
 5 ( 26): ************************
 6 ( 49): *************************************************
 7 ( 26): ************************
 8 ( 24): ***********************
 9 (  6): ******
10 (  1): *
```

Run the program to check that it works. Try it on your own sample data. As an exercise, rewrite it to read the raw test mark and to assign this mark to one of the deciles. Note the absence of any asterisks for decile no. 1. This is because CLASS(1) has the value 0, with the result that the implied **DO**-loop in the **PRINT** statement has an iteration count of 0.

11.4   Sorting Words Alphabetically

Characters may be compared in IF statements, and this is the basis of alphabetical sorting. FORTRAN 77 defines a 'lexical collating sequence' (see Appendix D) such that characters or words are 'less than' those which follow them alphabetically. So, for example, the following logical expressions are all TRUE (note that the blank precedes 'A' in the collating sequence):

```
  'A' .LT. 'B'
 ' A' .LT. 'A'
 'A ' .LT. 'AA'
'CAR' .LT. 'CAT'
'CAT' .LT. 'CATER'
```

Example

Read two five-letter words and print them in alphabetical order.

```
       CHARACTER*5 W1
       CHARACTER*5 W2
15     FORMAT( A5 )
25     FORMAT( 1X, A5 )

       READ 15, W1, W2
       IF( W1 .LT. W2 )THEN
          PRINT 25, W1, W2
       ELSE
          PRINT 25, W2, W1
       END IF

       STOP
       END
```

Data:

```
JONES
JACK
```

The Bubble Sort of Section 10.5 can easily be amended to sort words alphabetically. Suppose we have 100 words each of 10 letters or less. Then, apart from some format changes to deal with the characters, only two other lines need to be changed. Replace

```
       INTEGER TEMP
       INTEGER X(100)
```

by

```
CHARACTER*10 TEMP
CHARACTER*10 X(100)
```

11.5   Order of Merit List

A variation on the Bubble Sort of Chapter 10, which is possible now that you can handle characters, is to produce an order of merit list based on the results of a particular test. Given a set of data, where each student's name and mark appears on one line, the problem is to print the names and marks in descending order of mark.

The Bubble Sort can obviously be used, as long as the names are read into a separate (character) array. But then we must take care to swop names as well as marks each time two marks need to be swopped, otherwise the marks in the final list will be correctly ordered, but not the names! Although this approach works just as well on a large mainframe computer, the extra swopping involved can slow a microcomputer down enormously. For example, to produce an order of merit list for a class of 200 students on an Apple microcomputer using this method takes about 17 minutes! If there are additional data, such as other marks, ages, addresses, telephone numbers, etc., that also need to be swopped each time, the computer time increases even more dramatically.

A more subtle approach is to use the concept of a **pointer**. Let us suppose we have five students in the class. Their names and marks each appear on one data line. Their names are read into a character array NAME, and their marks into an integer array MARK. If the names (in alphabetical order) and marks are

ALICE	54
BRIAN	3
CHARLES	100
DEBBY	47
ETHEL	78

then the arrays NAME and MARK will have the contents

NAME(1): 'ALICE'   MARK(1): 54
NAME(2): 'BRIAN'   MARK(2):   3
NAME(3): 'CHARLES'   MARK(3): 100
NAME(4): 'DERBY'   MARK(4): 47
NAME(5): 'ETHEL'   MARK(5): 78

The master stroke now is to introduce a third array LIST, the successive elements of which, after sorting, will give (point to) the position in the original alphabetical name list of the student who is first, second, etc., in order of merit. To start with, before any sorting has taken place, the values of LIST should simply be

LIST(1): 1
LIST(2): 2
LIST(3): 3
LIST(4): 4
LIST(5): 5

After sorting, we want to find for example that LIST(1) has the value 3, to reflect the fact that the student who is first in order of merit (Charles) is in position three in the original alphabetical list. This will happen if, for successive values of J in the Bubble Sort, we compare

$$\text{MARK(LIST(J))}\quad\text{with}\quad\text{MARK(LIST(J+1))}$$

and swop LIST(J) with LIST(J+1) each time the marks are out of order. Note that neither the marks nor the names are swopped.

Printing NAME(LIST(1)) will then print the name of the top student, whose mark will be in MARK(LIST(1)), and so on. This way, only the elements of LIST are swopped. The original contents of NAME and MARK remain unchanged. In this example, the final values of LIST should be

$$
\begin{aligned}
\text{LIST(1): 3}\\
\text{LIST(2): 5}\\
\text{LIST(3): 1}\\
\text{LIST(4): 4}\\
\text{LIST(5): 2}
\end{aligned}
$$

(Debby is fourth in order of merit and in alphabetical order).

A program to do this for a class of up to 100 students is given below, with some sample data. For this example, the first seven columns on a data line are for the name, and the next three for the mark, which must be right justified.

```
* *** ORDER OF MERIT ***************************************
      CHARACTER*7 NAME(100)
      INTEGER     LIST(100)
      INTEGER     MARK(100)
      INTEGER     SWOPS
      INTEGER     TEMP

5     FORMAT( A7, I3 )
15    FORMAT( ' ', A, 3X, I3 )

      READ*, N
      SWOPS = 1
      I = 0

      DO 30 K = 1, N
        READ 5, NAME(K), MARK(K)
        LIST(K) = K
30    CONTINUE
10    IF( SWOPS .NE. 0 .AND. I .LT. N-1 )THEN
        SWOPS = 0
        I = I + 1

        DO 20 J = 1, N-I
          IF( MARK( LIST(J) ) .LT. MARK( LIST(J+1) ) )THEN
            TEMP = LIST(J)
            LIST(J) = LIST( J+1 )
            LIST( J+1 ) = TEMP
            SWOPS = SWOPS + 1
          END IF
20      CONTINUE

        GOTO 10
      END IF
```

```
      DO 40 K = 1, N
         PRINT 15, NAME( LIST(K) ), MARK( LIST(K) )
40    CONTINUE

      STOP
      END
```

Data:

```
5
ALICE     54
BRIAN      3
CHARLES100
DEBBY     47
ETHEL     78
```

Note

Whenever characters are read as data, the format of the data is crucial. If by mistake NAME is specified as

```
      CHARACTER*8 NAME(100)
```

and A8 format is used, the data being left unchanged, then Charles' name, for example, will be read as 'CHARLES1', which in itself may not be enough to make him lose his head, but what is really serious is that his mark will be read as 000. Using the A*w* format for **READ**, and not simply the A format, does at least minimize the chances of error, since then two mistakes must be made (in the **CHARACTER** and **FORMAT** statements), instead of only one.

11.6 Character Functions, Operations and Substrings

A computer must obviously use a numerical code to represent characters. The intrinsic function **CHAR(I)** returns the single letter character for which I is the ASCII code. Almost all microcomputers use ASCII (American Standard Code for Information Interchange) code, but some mainframes do not. The other commonly used code is EBCDIC (Extended Binary Coded Decimal Interchange Code). ASCII code represents, for example, a blank by the integer 32, 'A' by 65, 'B' by 66, etc. (See Appendix D for a list of ASCII codes.) The following program segment will therefore print the alphabet in upper case letters on one line:

```
5     FORMAT( ' ', 26A1 )
      PRINT 5, ( CHAR( I+64 ), I = 1, 26 )
```

The intrinsic function **ICHAR(X)** returns the ASCII code for X, where X is of type character and length one. E.g.

```
15    FORMAT(1X,I3)
      PRINT 15, ICHAR( '*' )
```

will print the integer 42.

A substring (part of a character string) may be copied or replaced by the assignment statement

```
      VBLE( i:j ) = '.....'
```

where VBLE is a suitably specified character variable. This statement replaces the characters in VBLE from position i to j inclusive by the given literal string (or character variable), which may be empty (as opposed to blank). For example,

```
CHARACTER*10 X
X = 'ABCDEFGHIJ'
X( 4:6 ) = 'xyz'
```

will give X the value 'ABCxyzGHIJ'.

Other possibilities are

```
CHARACTER*9 A
CHARACTER*4 B

A = 'BONAPARTE'
B = A( :4  )
A( 4: ) = 'BON'
```

which results in the value 'BONBON   ' for A and 'BONA' for B. In the first case the substring A(4:) is of length six, from position four of A to the end. The string 'BON' is too short, so it is lengthened to 'BON   '. The last six characters of A ('APARTE') are then replaced by 'BON   '.

Strings of varying length may be concatenated (joined up) with the character operator // as shown in the following segment, which constructs a mnemonic code for a student:

```
CHARACTER*20 INITLS
CHARACTER*20 SURNAM
CHARACTER*7 REGNO
CHARACTER*9 USERID
. . . .

INITLS = 'JK'
SURNAM = 'SMITH'
REGNO = '123456K'
USERID = INITLS( 1:1 ) // SURNAM( 1:1 ) // REGNO
. . . .
```

The value of USERID will be 'JS123456K'.

The intrinsic function **INDEX** may be used to find the first occurrence (if any) of a given substring in a string of characters. In general,

```
i = INDEX( str, sub )
```

returns the position in the string *str* of the first character of the substring *sub*, if the substring occurs in the string, where *str* and *sub* may be character variables, or literal strings, and where *sub* may be a single character. If the substring does not occur in the string, a value of 0 is returned.

The following example illustrates the use of **INDEX**. A line of text is read which contains a surname, followed by the only comma in the line, followed by various other data, e.g.

```
MURPHY, K.O. 1-4-99
```

The output will be the surname only:

```
CHARACTER*1 COMMA
CHARACTER*80 SURNAM
CHARACTER*80 TXT
INTEGER POSCOM

5       FORMAT( A80 )
```

```
15      FORMAT( ' ', A80 )

        COMMA = ','
        READ 5, TXT
        POSCOM = INDEX( TXT, COMMA )
        SURNAM = TXT( 1: POSCOM-1 )
        PRINT 15, SURNAM

        STOP
        END
```

There is one very important restriction in character assignments: a particular character position may not appear (explicitly or implicitly) on both sides of an assignment statement. So the two statements

```
        A = A // 'RHUBARB'
        B( 4:7 ) = B( 7:9 )
```

are not allowed, whereas

```
        B( 4:7 ) = B( 1:3 )
```

is allowed.

The other character functions available in FORTRAN 77 are listed in Appendix B.

11.7 Embedded Format

Character expressions may be used to construct format specifications. This is very useful in cases where the format needs to be changed slightly during a program. Embedded format is illustrated in the next example, which reads an integer and prints it out as an ordinal number with the correct suffix, e.g. 23 is printed as 23RD, but 24 as 24TH.

```
        CHARACTER*20 FT
        CHARACTER*2 INS( 0:9 )
        DATA (INS(I), I = 0, 3) / 'TH', 'ST', 'ND', 'RD' /
     $  (INS(I), I = 4, 9) / 6 * 'TH' /

        FT = '( I5, ''??'' )'
        READ*, I
        LAST = MOD( I, 10 )
        FT( 8:9 ) = INS( LAST )
        PRINT FT, I

        STOP
        END
```

The effect of this is that if the number 3 is input, for example, the string FT will have the value

        (15, 'RD')

which is then used as the format for the **PRINT** statement. Note that the characters RD must be inserted in positions eight and nine of FT since the two duplicated apostrophes in the character assignment statement do not occupy positions in the character variable. Note also the use of the **DATA** statement to initialize the character array INS.

11.8   Summary

* Character variables store literal character strings.

* For the purposes of internal representation, characters are ordered in a lexical collating sequence.

* Character variables may be compared and ordered.

* Character variables may be concatenated.

* Various operations are defined on character substrings.

* Format specifications may be stored in character variables.

11.9   Exercises

11.1   Write a program which reads a sentence of text ending in a full stop, and prints the sentence backwards, without the full stop (assume that the full stop occurs some-where before column 80).

11.2   A formula, called Zeller's Congruence, may be used to compute the day of the week given the date (within a certain range of dates). The formula is

$$f = ([2.6m - 0.2] + k + y + [y/4] + [c/4] - 2c) \text{ modulo } 7,$$

where the square brackets mean 'the integer part of', modulo means 'remainder when divided by', and

> m = month number, with January and February taken as months 11 and 12 of the preceding year, so March is then month 1, and December month 10;
> k = day of the month;
> c = first two digits of the year (i.e. the century number);
> y = year in the century.

E.g., 23rd August 1963 has $m = 6, k = 23, c = 19, y = 63$;
1st January 1800 has $m = 11, k = 1, c = 17, y = 99$.

Write a program to read the date in the usual form (e.g. 31 01 1863 for 31st January 1863) and print out the given date and the day of the week (in words) on which it falls. *Hint*: use a character array for the days of the week. Test your program on some known dates, like today's date, or 7th December 1941 (Pearl Harbour Sunday).

The formula will not work if you go too far back. Shakespeare and Cervantes both died on 23rd April 1616. Shakespeare died on a Tuesday, but Cervantes died on a Saturday! This is because England had not yet adopted the Gregorian calendar and was consequently 10 days behind the rest of the world.

11.3   A class of 100 students write a test. Write a program which prints out the highest mark obtained together with the names of all the students who got that mark (N.B. there may be more than one). Assume that the names appear in the first 20 columns of the data lines, and the marks in the next four, right justified. (*Hint*: it is not necessary to do an order of merit sort, nor to store all the names and marks in arrays. Rather, the program should read through all the marks once, and while doing so it should record in an array the names of all the students who have got the current highest mark.)

11.4   The following extract from *Jabberwocky* by Lewis Carroll must be prepared for enciphering (perhaps not really necessary in this example!):

TWAS BRILLIG AND THE SLITHY TOVES DID GYRE AND GIMBLE IN THE WABE

(punctuation marks have been removed to simplify matters). Write a program to read this single line of text (keyed in at a terminal, and terminated by a slash), remove all the blanks, and print it out in groups of five letters, with a blank between each group, so that the output looks like this:

TWASB RILLI GANDT HESLI THYTO VESDI DGYRE ANDGI MBLEI NTHEW ABE/

11.5 A fair indication of the authorship of prose can sometimes be obtained by calculating the average number of words per sentence (mean sentence length) and the standard deviation of this statistic. I once found, for example, that with samples of about 700 lines, G.K. Chesterton is easily distinguishable from Lord Macaulay, the former having a significantly shorter mean sentence length, with a larger standard deviation. Write a program that reads some text from a sequential file, where each record is formatted 80A1, and computes these two statistics. Assume, to make things a little easier, that words are never separated by more than one blank, that sentences are delimited by full-stops, followed by only one blank, and that full-stops occur nowhere else in the text.

11.6 Languages exhibit a characteristic frequency distribution of single characters if a large enough sample of text is analysed. For example, in Act III of *Hamlet* the blank has a frequency of 19.7%, the 'E' 9.3%, the 'O' 7.3%, while the 'Z' only occurs 14 times out of 35224 characters (Bennett, 1976). (The blank is important because it gives an indication of word length.) Write a program to determine the letter frequency of a sample of text. Assume the text is in a formatted sequential file of unknown length, with no more than 80 characters per record. Also assume that blanks only occur singly.

12

Procedures: Subprograms

In Chapter 4 it was pointed out that the logic of a non-trivial problem should be modularized into separate entities, each carrying out a particular, well-defined task. It often happens that such modules can be used by many different programs, and in fact by different users of the same computing system. FORTRAN 77 enables the user to implement these modules as 'procedures', which may be stored independently on the computer system. Examples are procedures to perform statistical operations, such as finding means and standard deviations, or to sort items into some kind of order, or to find the best straight line through a set of points. This facility also enables the user to access external libraries of procedures, such as the NAG (Numerical Algorithms Group) packages, which enhances one's computing power enormously.

There are four types of procedure:

1) Intrinsic functions, supplied by the FORTRAN 77 compiler, such as SIN, SQRT, LOG, etc.
2) Statement functions.
3) External functions.
4) Subroutines.

Of these, the last three must be supplied by the user, either directly as part of the program, or indirectly from a mass storage device. External functions (often referred to simply as functions) and subroutines are also known as **subprograms**, and subprograms, together with the 'main' program, are known as **program units**. In this chapter we will be concerned mainly with subprograms. However, we will look at statement functions first, as they are relatively easy to handle, and introduce some very important concepts.

12.1 Statement Functions

If a particular expression needs to be evaluated frequently for different values of some variables, it may be defined as a statement function at the head of the program. For example the following program defines a function SEC to be the secant of a given angle, and prints out a table of values:

```
      PARAMETER ( CONV = 3.1415927 / 180. )
      SEC( A ) = 1.0 / COS( A )

      DO 10 I = 0, 180, 20
         ANG = CONV * I
         PRINT*, I, SEC( ANG )
10    CONTINUE

      STOP
      END
```

Note that 90° is avoided, since this will cause an attempted division by 0. Note also that the **PARAMETER** statement may contain an assignment statement if a constant needs to be calculated for the program.

The following rules apply to statement functions (in fact, rules 3 and 4 also apply to function subprograms):

1)   The function must have a one-line definition.
2)   The function name may be any valid FORTRAN variable, except the name of an intrinsic function, like **SIN, SQRT, ABS**, etc.
3)   The type rules apply to the function name and its arguments.
4)   The arguments in the definition (A in the above example) are **dummy arguments**. The same names may be used as variables elsewhere in the program without risk of confusion. The purpose of dummy arguments is simply to define the number and type of function arguments. They are replaced by the **actual** arguments when the function is referenced and executed later on in the program. For example, the following program segment uses a statement function to compute the discriminant in solving the well-known quadratic equation.

```
DISC( A, B, C ) = B ** 2 - 4. * A * C
READ*, P, Q, R
. . . .

IF( DISC( P, Q, R ) .GT. 0 )THEN
    X1 = ( - Q + SQRT( DISC( P, Q, R ) ) ) / 2. / P
    . . . .
```

The dummy arguments in the function definition, A, B and C, inform the compiler that three real arguments are to be used, and that DISC is to be computed according to the rule on the right-hand side. These dummy argument names are compiled into the function definition and are not 'seen' by the rest of the program. Variables with the names A, B and C appearing anywhere else in the program will therefore have no connection at all with the dummy arguments. Any three real variables could have been used, e.g. X, Y and Z. When the function DISC is referenced later in the program, the dummy arguments are replaced by the actual arguments P, Q and R, and DISC is evaluated according to its definition. The function may be used repeatedly in the program. At each reference the dummy arguments in the definition are replaced by the actual arguments used in the reference.

5)   The function must be defined before the first executable statement of the program, but after all the type specification statements. (An executable statement is one which causes some action, like an assignment, or **READ**).

12.1.1   Rotation of Co-ordinate Axes

Statement functions are particularly useful when long arithmetic expressions need to be handled repeatedly. A good example is the rotation of a Cartesian co-ordinate system. If such a system is rotated counterclockwise through an angle of t radians, the new co-ordinates $(x'; y')$ of a point referred to the rotated axes are given by

$$x' = x \cos t + y \sin t$$
$$y' = -x \sin t + y \cos t,$$

where $(x; y)$ are its co-ordinates before rotation of the axes. The following statement functions could be used to define the new co-ordinates:

```
XNEW( X, Y, T ) = X * COS( T ) + Y * SIN( T )
YNEW( X, Y, T ) = - X * SIN( T ) + Y * COS( T )
```

12.2　Function Subprograms

The first example is an integer function FACT(N) to compute N-factorial ($N! = 1 \times 2 \times 3 \ldots \times N$). It is shown here with a main program that uses it to compute 11! (the total number of possible batting orders for a cricket team). The operation of the function subprogram is discussed below:

```
* *** FACT : FACTORIAL FUNCTION
* *** N     : NUMBER
      INTEGER N
      INTEGER FACT

5     FORMAT( I4, A, I9 )

      N = 11
      PRINT 5, N, '! = ', FACT( N )

      STOP
      END

      INTEGER FUNCTION FACT( K )
**********************************************************************
*        COMPUTES N-FACTORIAL                                       *
**********************************************************************

      FACT = 1

      DO 10 I = 1, K
         FACT = FACT * I
10    CONTINUE

      RETURN
      END
```

The output of this program is:

```
11! =   39916800
```

The following points apply equally to functions and subroutines, except where the context indicates otherwise:

1)　The whole program now consists of two distinct program units: the main program (also the 'calling' program here, because the function name is mentioned in it), and the function subprogram. The main program, which may be optionally named with the non-executable **PROGRAM** statement (this serves no purpose other than to identify the program to the reader), must always appear first, followed by the subprograms, in any order, although alphabetical order is recommended for the sake of clarity. Note also that the box of asterisks after the function name makes it easy to find in a large program, and describes its purpose clearly. The general structure is as follows:

```
      PROGRAM PLONK
      . . . .
      . . . .                    main program

      STOP
      END
```

```
SUBROUTINE PLANK( arguments, separated by commas )
....
....    (subroutines will be dealt with in §12.3)

RETURN
END

FUNCTION PLINK( arguments, separated by commas )
....
....

RETURN
END
```

2)   The main and subprograms are compiled and stored *separately*, and therefore all variables named inside a subprogram are independent from the main program (and from any other subprograms). So the same variable names could be used if necessary, without fear of confusion. For example, the variable I could also have been used in the calling program as an index in a DO-loop.

3)   External functions are used (referenced) in the same way as the intrinsic functions described in Chapter 5. Names of intrinsic functions (**MOD, EXP, COS**, etc.) may be used as names of external functions only if they are specified in an **EXTERNAL** statement as described below in Section 12.5.

4)   The *only* communication between the function and the calling program is through the argument list (i.e. the items in brackets after the function name), and the name of the function. The arguments in the function definition are 'dummy' arguments, as discussed above, i.e. they do not need to have the same names in the function and the calling program. When the function is called (by mentioning its name in the calling program) the values of the arguments are effectively copied from the calling program into the function. So the value in N (in the above example) is 'copied' into K. On return to the calling program, this value is effectively copied back again, i.e. K into N. (What actually happens is that the storage addresses of the arguments are passed through to the subprogram; the effect is the same.)

5)   Since the function name in the above example is a FORTRAN variable, its name implies **INTEGER** type. It may also be specified with any of the other five types: **REAL, DOUBLE PRECISION, COMPLEX, LOGICAL** or **CHARACTER**. In this case, the function name must be declared in a specification statement in the calling program, and its type must also be specified in the function definition. If the function is of type **CHARACTER** its length may be specified in the usual way. Alternatively, a variable length may be specified as (*). In this case the function will have the actual length as specified in the calling program, which may be different in different program units. E.g. the function

```
CHARACTER*(*) FUNCTION CODE( X, Y, Z )
```

may be referenced as **CHARACTER*5 CODE** from one program unit, but as **CHARACTER*20 CODE** from another.

6)   If the function arguments are arrays, they must be dimensioned in *both* function and calling program. If arguments are specified with a type in the calling program, they must be specified with the *same* type in the subprogram. In other words, the arguments must have the same type and dimension in the calling and subprogram, whether by specification or by default (see below).

7)   All functions and subroutines must appear after the **END** statement of the main program (alphabetical order is suggested).

8)   Subprograms may call other subprograms. However, they may not call themselves, either directly, or indirectly (this is known as recursion).

9) In the unlikely event that a function has no arguments, the brackets must still be written where it would be appropriate to mention the arguments, e.g.

```
FUNCTION FUNNY( )
```

10) In the case of functions only, a single value, which is associated with the function name, is computed and returned to the calling program. The function name is therefore treated as a variable in the function program, where it must appear at least once on the left-hand side of an assignment statement. Where the function name is referenced within the subprogram, it must appear without brackets or arguments.

11) The effect of the **RETURN** statement is to transfer control back to the calling program, to the point where the function was referenced.

12.2.1   Length of a File

In this example, the function LENGTH finds the number of records (formatted or unformatted) in a sequential file. The arguments are the name of the file and the input unit number. The file name and unit number are keyed in at a terminal. The function is shown with a test calling program:

```
      CHARACTER*20 FNAME

      READ*, FNAME, INP
      L = LENGTH( FNAME, INP )
      . . . .

      STOP
      END

      INTEGER FUNCTION LENGTH( NAME, NIT )
**********************************************************************
*       FINDS THE LENGTH OF THE SEQUENTIAL FILE name, READ ON
*       UNIT nit
**********************************************************************
      CHARACTER*20 NAME
15    FORMAT( A )

      OPEN( UNIT = NIT, FILE = NAME )
      LENGTH = 0
      IOS = 0
      READ( NIT, 15, IOSTAT = IOS )

10    IF( IOS .EQ. 0 )THEN
         READ( NIT, 15, IOSTAT = IOS )
         LENGTH = LENGTH + 1
         GOTO 10
      END IF

      CLOSE ( NIT )
      RETURN
      END
```

Note that **READ** without any variables skips past a record.

12.2.2   The Heaviside Unit Function

The Heaviside Unit Function $H(x)$ occurs often in electrical and civil engineering, and is defined to be 1 if its argument x is greater than or equal to 0, or 0 otherwise. It is also called the unit step function, and represents a switch being thrown at $x = 0$. The following section of coding shows how to define and use it as a function subprogram.

```
      PROGRAM HEAVY
      INTEGER H
      ....

      READ*, X
      Y = EXP( X ) * H( X )
      ....

      END

      INTEGER FUNCTION H( J )
***********************************************************************
*        SETS H=1 IF J>=0, H=0 OTHERWISE                              *
***********************************************************************
      REAL J

      IF( J .GE. 0 )THEN
         H = 1
      ELSE
         H = 0
      END IF

      RETURN
      END
```

Note that H is specified of type integer in the calling program, and also in the function definition, and that the argument J is specified of type real in the subprogram to match the real argument X in the calling program. The programmer could of course have used X or A or any other variable name as an argument in the function subprogram.

12.2.3   Position of Largest Item in a List

In this example, the function MAXPOS returns the position of the largest element of an array of 10 elements. The argument of the function is the entire array.

```
      REAL X(10)

      READ*, X
      PRINT*, 'POSITION OF LARGEST ITEM IS', MAXPOS( X )

      STOP
      END

      INTEGER FUNCTION MAXPOS( A )
***********************************************************************
      RETURNS THE POSITION OF THE LARGEST ELEMENT OF THE ARRAY A

***********************************************************************
      REAL A(10)
```

```
      AMAX = A(1)
      MAXPOS = 1

      DO 20 I = 2, 10
        IF( A(I) .GT. AMAX )THEN
          AMAX = A(I)
          MAXPOS = I
        END IF
20    CONTINUE

      RETURN
      END
```

12.2.4   Adjustable Array Dimension

Our function MAXPOS is rather limited, because we can only use it in a program that handles an array of exactly 10 elements. We can in fact write a function that handles arrays of all sizes, by having an adjustable dimension specified in the function subprogram, but then we must pass the actual size of the array in the calling program through as an argument to the function. The function subprogram would be changed as follows:

```
      INTEGER FUNCTION MAXPOS( A, N )
**************************************************************
*     RETURNS THE POSITION OF THE LARGEST ELEMENT OF THE ARRAY A
*
**************************************************************
      REAL A(N)

      AMAX = A(1)
      MAXPOS = 1

      DO 20 I = 2, N
        IF( A(I) .GT. AMAX )THEN
          AMAX = A(I)
          MAXPOS = I
        END IF
20    CONTINUE

      RETURN
      END
```

The only change in the calling program is to specify the value of N and to include it in the function argument list:

```
      READ*, N, ( X(I), I = 1, N )
      PRINT*, 'POSITION OF LARGEST ITEM IS', MAXPOS( X, N )
```

Note

1)   The specification statement in the calling program must provide a high enough dimension to make sure that there is enough space for any size array X that the user might require.

2)   A peculiar feature of FORTRAN can cause problems when multi-dimensional arrays are passed as arguments into subprograms where they are specified with adjustable dimensions. This is discussed in Chapter 14.

Example

Define a function to compute the mean of a set of observations stored in an array.

```
      PROGRAM CHECK
      REAL MEAN
      REAL X(1000)

      READ*, N, ( X(I), I = 1, N )
      XBAR = MEAN( X, N )
      ....

      STOP
      END

      REAL FUNCTION MEAN( A, N )
*******************************************************************
*        COMPUTES THE MEAN OF THE ELEMENTS OF A(N)               *
*******************************************************************
      REAL A(N)

      SUM = 0

      DO 90 I = 1, N
         SUM = SUM + A(I)
90    CONTINUE

      MEAN = SUM / N

      RETURN
      END
```

Note that this is a real function, so the variable MEAN must be specified of type **REAL** (since MEAN would normally be of type **INTEGER**).

12.2.5   Assumed-size Arrays

This is an alternative to an adjustable dimension. An array which is a dummy argument of a subprogram may be dimensioned with an asterisk in the subprogram. So in the above example, the statement

```
      REAL A(N)
```

in the function MEAN may be replaced by

```
      REAL A(*)
```

This is called an 'assumed-size' array declaration, because the array size is undefined, yet assumed to be large enough for any references to the array. In this case, the dummy array name cannot appear in an input/output list.

12.3   Subroutine Subprograms

Everything in the previous section about functions applies also to subroutines, except that no value is associated with a subroutine name—all input and output is through the arguments—and hence the name must never be specified in a type statement. As an example, let us write a subroutine that will swop the values of two given variables (this might be useful in a sorting program). The complete program is as follows:

```
A = 3
B = 7
CALL SWOP( A, B )
PRINT*, A, B

STOP
END

SUBROUTINE SWOP( X, Y )
*******************************************************************
*       EXCHANGES THE CONTENTS OF X AND Y (REALS)                *
*******************************************************************
TEMP = X
X = Y
Y = TEMP

RETURN
END
```

Note

1)   The output will be the numbers 7.0 and 3.0 (in that order). Note that the values are swopped in the subroutine, and that the swopped values are copied back: X into A and Y into B.

2)   The subroutine is invoked with a **CALL** statement in the calling program, and **RETURN**s to the statement after the **CALL** statement in the calling program.

3)   A subroutine name is subject to the same rules as a variable, i.e. up to six alphanumeric characters, starting with a letter.

4)   A subroutine need not have any arguments, in which case the name is written without brackets, e.g.

```
CALL SUB
```

5)   A subroutine should be used instead of a function whenever more than one value needs to be computed and returned to the calling program.

The following example shows a subroutine which computes the mean and standard deviation of a set of numbers stored in an array.

```
REAL   X(1000)

READ*, N, ( X(I), I = 1, N )
CALL MEAN( X, N, AVG, SDEV )
PRINT*, AVG, SDEV
....

STOP
END

SUBROUTINE MEAN( A, N, AV, SD )
*******************************************************************
*       COMPUTES MEAN AND STD DEVIATION OF ELEMENTS OF A(N)      *
*******************************************************************
REAL   A(*)
```

```
        SUM = 0

        DO 90 I = 1, N
           SUM = SUM + A(I)
90      CONTINUE

        AV = SUM / N
        SUMSQ = 0

        DO 80 I = 1, N
           SUMSQ = SUMSQ + ( A(I) - AV ) ** 2
80      CONTINUE

        SD = SQRT( SUMSQ / (N - 1) )

        RETURN
        END
```

Once the subroutine has been tested, it is completely 'portable'. The 18 lines comprising the subroutine may be stored in a file and physically inserted after the **END** of any calling program that needs to compute the mean and standard deviation of any set of numbers read into a real array, as long as that array is suitably dimensioned in the calling program.

As another example, consider a subroutine to print a variable number of the same characters on a line. The user may specify how many of which character are to be printed. In this particular example, 72 hash symbols will be printed:

```
        CHARACTER*1 SYMBOL
5       FORMAT( I3, A1 )

        READ 5, N, SYMBOL
        CALL LINE( SYMBOL, N )

        STOP
        END

        SUBROUTINE LINE( SYMBOL, N )
****************************************************************************
*       PRINTS N SINGLE CHARACTER SYMBOLS ON A LINE                       *
****************************************************************************
        CHARACTER*1 SYMBOL
5       FORMAT( 120A )

        PRINT 5, ( SYMBOL, I = 1, N )
        RETURN
        END
```

Data:

```
 72#
```

Note that SYMBOL must be declared **CHARACTER*1** in the subroutine as well as in the calling program. This applies to any special type declarations.

When a dummy argument is a character array, a complication arises because the *number* of elements, as well as the *length* of each element, must be considered, as the following segment indicates:

```
CHARACTER*2 A(10)
....

CALL MURKY( A )
....

END

SUBROUTINE MURKY( X )
CHARACTER*4 X(5)
....

END
```

The array A consists of 10 elements, each of two characters, so it has a total length of 20 characters. X has five elements, each of four characters, also giving it a total length of 20. The correspondence, however, is not between elements, but between individual characters. E.g. the first character in the second element of A will correspond to the third character in the first element of X. So if A(1) and A(2) have the values 'AH' and 'SO' respectively, X(1) will have the value 'AHSO' on entry.

12.4   The SAVE Statement

Variables in a subprogram which do not appear as dummy arguments, or in **COMMON** statements (see below), are called 'local' variables. These are undefined on entry into the subprogram, as one might expect. However, they are also usually undefined on re-entry, no matter what values they may have taken on previous calls to the subprogram. There are times when it would be useful for these values to be retained between calls.

The **SAVE** statement, which is a specification statement, and must appear before any **DATA** statements or statement functions, will cause the values of local variables to be retained between calls to the subprogram. It takes two forms:

```
SAVE
```

which retains the values of all local variables, and

```
SAVE var1, var2, ...
```

which retains the values of only the local variables listed.

For example, the following function returns the position of the next occurrence of a character CHAR in a line TEXT of no more than LEN characters. On return, the next occurrence (POS) of CHAR is saved for the next call. If the end of the line is reached, a value of zero is returned. Note that POS must be initialized with a DATA statement, which is implemented only once, at compile time.

```
      INTEGER FUNCTION NEXT( TEXT, CHAR, LEN )

      CHARACTER*1 CHAR
      CHARACTER*1 TEXT(LEN)
      INTEGER POS
      SAVE POS
      DATA POS / 1 /

10    IF( TEXT( POS ) .NE. CHAR .AND. POS .LE. LEN )THEN
         POS = POS + 1
         GOTO 10
```

```
END IF

IF( POS .GT. LEN )THEN
   NEXT = 0
ELSE
   NEXT = POS
   POS = POS + 1
END IF


RETURN
END
```

12.5   Procedures as Arguments: EXTERNAL and INTRINSIC

A procedure name may be passed to another procedure as an argument with the **EXTER-NAL** or **INTRINSIC** statements. **INTRINSIC** also enables you to define a function subprogram with the same name as an intrinsic function. There are three basic rules.

1)   If an external procedure name (or a dummy procedure) is to be used as an argument of a subprogram, it must be declared in an **EXTERNAL** specification statement in the calling program, if the context requires it (see below).
2)   If you want to write a function with the same name as an intrinsic function, the function name must appear in an **EXTERNAL** statement. E.g.

```
EXTERNAL SIN
```

means that SIN is now an external subprogram (supplied by the user), and that the usual intrinsic function **SIN** is no longer available to the program unit.
3)   If an intrinsic function name is to be used as an argument of a subprogram, its specific (*not* generic) name must be declared in an **INTRINSIC** specification statement in the calling program. The intrinsic functions for type conversion, string comparision and for finding maxima and minima may not be passed as arguments.

When a procedure name is used as an actual argument, the name must always appear in an **EXTERNAL** or **INTRINSIC** statement in the calling program. However, the corresponding dummy argument, which is now a 'dummy procedure', must only appear in an **EXTERNAL** statement in the subprogram if the context requires it. The compiler recognizes a dummy argument as a dummy procedure if it appears in a **CALL** statement, or if it is followed by a left bracket and is not an array name. Only if these conditions do not apply must the dummy procedure appear in an **EXTERNAL** statement. E.g.

```
EXTERNAL MEAN
INTRINSIC SIN
....

CALL ANOVA( A, B, MEAN, SIN )
....

END
SUBROUTINE ANOVA( X, Y, SUB, F )
EXTERNAL F
....

CALL SUB( X, Y, F )
....
```

```
END
SUBROUTINE SUB( A, B, FUNG )
....

CALL BUS( P, FUNG( Z ) )
....

END
```

The intrinsic function **SIN** must be declared as such in the main program, since it is an argument in the call to ANOVA. However, once the function has been passed to ANOVA, it becomes a dummy procedure (F), its previous history as an intrinsic function being unknown to ANOVA. It must therefore appear in an **EXTERNAL** statement since it is an actual argument in a call to SUB. Inside SUB the function (FUNG at this stage of its interesting and varied career as a procedure name!) is recognized as such since it is followed by a left parenthesis and is not an array name. Therefore it must not appear in an **EXTERNAL** statement inside SUB. Similarly, since SUB appears in a **CALL** statement inside ANOVA it must not be specified in an **EXTERNAL** statement.

The use of **EXTERNAL** and **INTRINSIC** is illustrated in an example of numerical integration in Chapter 15.

12.6   The COMMON Statement

Variables in a subprogram are local, as we have already seen, i.e. they are hidden from other subprograms. However, it may sometimes be useful for variables to be 'shared' by some subprograms, by using **COMMON** blocks of storage which may be accessed by a group of subprograms. Such storage is called 'global'. E.g. suppose in a mechanics problem we need to use the (integer) mass M of an object, and the gravitational acceleration G in a number of subprograms. The non-executable statement

```
COMMON / PARAM / M, G
```

at the head of the program unit will allocate the names M and G to the first two variables in the **COMMON** block named PARAM (PARAM stands for any name of the user's choice). Now if M and G are assigned in any program unit which references the **COMMON** block named PARAM, they will be accessible with those values in any other subprogram which references the **COMMON** block of the same name.

For example, the statements

```
COMMON / PARAM / M, G
M = 100
G = 9.8
```

in subprogram SUB1 and the statement

```
COMMON / PARAM / M, G
```

in subprogram SUB2 will cause the variables M and G in SUB2 to have the values 100 and 9.8 respectively.

There is a rather subtle source of error here. Suppose by mistake SUB2 above has

```
COMMON / PARAM / G, M
```

(the wrong way round). The contents of G (which is 100 in integer representation) is interpreted as a real number now, and its value comes out as 0.21895289E-44 (on a Sperry mainframe), while M (which should be 9.8 if the second **COMMON** variable is treated as real) turns out as 17798948454 when it is regarded as an integer. So muddling up your **COMMON** variables, or mismatching their type, can cause big problems!

The basic rules for **COMMON** are as follows. The general syntax for naming **COMMON** blocks is

```
COMMON / blockl / listl / block2 / list2 ....
```

where the variables in list1 are allocated to block1, etc. The variables in the list are allocated to *consecutive* storage locations in the named block. E.g.

```
COMMON / TOM / A, B, C(100) / DICK / X, Y
COMMON / TOM / D(20)
```

Note that the list for a named block (TOM in this case) may be continued in a separate **COMMON** statement. Arrays may be dimensioned in a **COMMON** statement, or before the array name is specified in **COMMON**, but not after. The **COMMON** block names (TOM and DICK here) are global and should not be used for any other purpose in the program. The rules for block names are the same as for variable names.

One **COMMON** block has no name, and is called the **blank COMMON** block. E.g.

```
COMMON D, E, F(100)
COMMON / HARRY / R, S / / T, U, V
```

will allocate the variables D, E, T, U and V and the array F to blank **COMMON** (the double slash in the second statement indicates blank **COMMON**).

Character variables must not be mixed with variables of another type in a **COMMON** block. This is because there are basically two types of storage, numeric and character, which may not be used in the same **C OMMON** block.

In a subprogram a dummy argument may not appear in a **COMMON** list. In a function subprogram the function name may not appear in a **COMMON** list.

The length (in terms of words of storage) of a particular block must be the same in all program units which reference that block. This should never cause problems if variables in a given block have the same names in all program units.

Variables in a named **COMMON** block will become undefined on exit from a subprogram which is not referenced directly or indirectly by another program unit specifying the same block, unless the block name appears in a **SAVE** statement. Variables in blank **COMMON** never become undefined. Since the main program references all subprograms directly, or indirectly, variables listed in **COMMON** blocks in the main program never become undefined. E.g.

```
PROGRAM MAIN
COMMON / GLOB / ...
....

CALL SUB
....

END
SUBROUTINE SUB
COMMON / GLOB / ... / LOC / ...
....

CALL BUS
....
```

```
END

SUBROUTINE BUS
COMMON / LOC / ...
....

END
```

The variables in LOC will be defined on exit from BUS, but undefined on exit from SUB. The variables in GLOB will be defined on exit from BUS and SUB. The statement

```
SAVE / LOC /
```

in subroutine SUB will retain the values of the variables in the block LOC on exit from SUB. On a subsequent call to SUB, therefore, they will be defined.

Variables in named **COMMON** blocks may be initialized with **DATA** statements in a special subprogram called a **BLOCK DATA** subprogram, which may contain only type specification statements and the **PARAMETER, DATA** and **COMMON** statements, i.e. no executable statements. The **BLOCK DATA** subprogram may be named with an optional name, which is global and should not be used for any other purpose. There may be only one unnamed **BLOCK DATA** subprogram in a program. Blank **COMMON** may not be initialized in this way. E.g.

```
BLOCK DATA INIT
INTEGER MAX
PARAMETER ( MAX = 100 )
REAL VARS (MAX)
COMMON / STATES / VARS
DATA ( VAR(I), I = 1, MAX ) / MAX * 0.0 /
END
```

Examples of where **COMMON** can be useful are given below and in Chapter 15.

There is an ongoing discussion among programmers as to whether **COMMON** should be used instead of subprogram arguments in transferring information between program units. Balfour and Marwick (1979) give a number of reasons (pp. 146, 147) why **COMMON** should not be used, mainly with regard to program structure and style. These should be noted by the serious programmer.

There are cases, however, in many real applications where it is almost inconceivable not to use **COMMON**. Such examples cannot be included in a book of this nature, but the scale of the problems can be illustrated by the extract below from the DRIVER interactive modelling package (Furniss, 1977). This package, which has been implemented on a number of mainframes, runs a model subroutine written by the user to update a dynamical system defined by state variables and parameters for a given number of time-steps (the basic concepts of such a system are shown in the highly over-simplified example in Chapter 15 of a predator–prey model). DRIVER has some 50 subroutines to keep track of initial and current state variable values, parameter values and output specifications (output may be tabular and/or graphical, and may be sent to the printer and/or a file). In addition, 'commands' may be issued interactively involving the state variables and parameters, which may be referenced by symbolic local names. This necessitates the setting up of a complicated 'command dictionary' and search procedures. The following **COMMON** declarations appear in most of the subroutines:

```
C ********* COM - COMMON BLOCK DECLARATIONS,USED IN MOST ROUTINES
C            COMMON BLOCK
C      FIRST THE ITEMS THAT ARE ACCESSED BY MODEL
       COMMON /PARAM/ PARVAL(250)
       COMMON /VARIA/ VARVAL(150)
       COMMON /FUNC/ LENTHS(40),XAR(24,40),YAR(24,40)
C            THEN NAMES
       REAL INVAL(150)
       CHARACTER*8 PARNAM(250),VARNAM(150)
       CHARACTER*30 FILNAM
       CHARACTER*8 ANSWA,PRTFIL
       COMMON /REFINF/ PARNAM,VARNAM,FILNAM,PRTFIL
C            THEN THE COMMAND DICTIONARY
       CHARACTER*4 WDMAIN(67),WDFUN(17),WDREP(17),WDPLOT(37),
      *WDTABL(37),WDFIN(37)
       COMMON /COMDIC/ WDMAIN,WDFUN,WDREP,WDPLOT,WDTABL,WDFIN
       INTEGER VLMAIN(67),VLFUN(17),VLREP(17),VLPLOT(37),VLTABL(37)
      *VLFIN(37)
       COMMON /COMDIC/ VLMAIN,VLFUN,VLREP,VLPLOT,VLTABL,VLFIN
       COMMON /COMDIC/ MNMAIN,MNFUN,MNREP,MNPLOT,MNTABL,MNFIN
       COMMON /COMDIC/ M2MAIN,M2FUN,M2REP,M2PLOT,M2TABL,M2FIN
C            AND THE REFILE PROPER
       COMMON /REFINF/ ICYCLE,NOFUNC,NOPAR,NPLOTS,NPRINT,NOVAR,
      *IOPTYP,IOPINT(2),IPRINT(10),IPLOTS(8)
       CHARACTER*1 SYMBOL(150)
       COMMON /REFINF/ INVAL,SYMBOL,SCALE(150),BOUNDS(2,150)
       COMMON /REFINF/ NVARPT,IVARPT(150),LINCNT,MNP,MNP2,MNV,MNV2
       INTEGER PPOS(377),VPOS(223)
       COMMON /REFINF/ PPOS,VPOS
```

Values of the variables and parameters are stored in the **COMMON** blocks PARAM and VARIA, while their symbolic names are stored as character variables in the block REFINF, which contains other input/output details as well. The block COMDIC contains the command dictionary information. It is difficult to see how such a program could be written without **COMMON**!

12.7   Graphs on the Line Printer

If you do not have graphics facilities on your computer you can still plot reasonable graphs on the screen or line printer. The subroutine GRAPH below in this section prints a graph of a function F(X) with the y-axis (dependent variable) running across the screen, and the x-axis (independent variable) running down the screen. The subroutine is as simple as possible. No labels or gradations on the axes are printed. You might like to fill in these details as a project. It would also be useful to have the x- and y-values printed out on either side of the graph. The routine cannot handle graphs that curve back on themselves (see Chapter 14 for a more general graphing example).

The user of GRAPH must supply a function subprogram to define the function being graphed, the lowest and highest x-values (XMIN and XMAX), the increment on the x-axis between plotted points (DX), the lowest and highest function values (FMIN and FMAX), the extreme column positions between which the graph must be printed (LEFT and RIGHT), and the plotting symbol (SYMBOL). All the arguments are real except LEFT and RIGHT (integers), and SYMBOL (one-letter character). The function name, since it is an actual argument in the reference to GRAPH, must appear in an **EXTERNAL** or **INTRINSIC** statement in the calling program.

The scaling transformation in GRAPH probably requires some explanation. The user decides on the upper and lower bounds for F(X):

$$FMIN \leqslant F(X) \leqslant FMAX,$$

i.e.
$$0 \leqslant F(X) - FMIN \leqslant FMAX - FMIN.$$

But this range must be transformed into a range of (RIGHT−LEFT), which is the full width of the plotted y co-ordinates, i.e.

$$0 \leqslant (RIGHT-LEFT)(F(X)-FMIN) \leqslant (RIGHT-LEFT)(FMAX-FMIN),$$

i.e.
$$0 \leqslant \frac{(RIGHT-LEFT)(F(X)-FMIN)}{(FMAX-FMIN)} \leqslant (RIGHT-LEFT)$$

Finally, the range must be shifted to start in column LEFT:

$$LEFT \leqslant LEFT + \frac{(RIGHT-LEFT)(F(X)-FMIN)}{(FMAX-FMIN)} \leqslant RIGHT$$

So if LEFT = 10 and RIGHT = 60, as in the sample run below, the expression between the inequality symbols will be in the range 10−60, and will give the column in which the plotting symbol must be printed.

In this example, GRAPH is shown in operation with the current $i(t)$ undergoing damped oscillations, as discussed in Section 6.5.

```
PARAMETER (PI = 3.1415927)
INTEGER CYCLES
INTEGER PERCY
REAL I
REAL L
EXTERNAL I
COMMON / ELEC / A, Fl, L, R

Q = 1E-5
R = 1
C = 1E-5
L = 0.002
CYCLES = 2
PERCY = 10
FO = SQRT( 1 / (L * C) ) / (2 * PI)
Fl = SQRT( 1 / (L * C) - R ** 2 / (4 * L ** 2) ) / (2 * PI)
A = 2 * PI * FO ** 2 * Q / Fl
DT = 0.5 / (PERCY * Fl)
TMIN = 0
TMAX = CYCLES / Fl
FMIN = -1E-1
FMAX = 1E-1
IL = 10
IR = 60

CALL GRAPH( TMIN, TMAX, DT, FMIN, FMAX, I, IL, IR, '*' )

STOP
END
```

```
      SUBROUTINE GRAPH( XMIN, XMAX, DX, FMIN, FMAX, F, LEFT,
     $ RIGHT, SYMBOL )
* *** GRAPHING ON THE LINE PRINTER OR SCREEN *********************
*     ARGUMENTS DESCRIBED IN TEXT                               *
****************************************************************

      CHARACTER*1 LINE(80)
      CHARACTER*1 SYMBOL
      INTEGER POINT
      INTEGER RIGHT

5     FORMAT( ' ', 80A1 )

      DO 10 I = 1, 80
        LINE(I) = ' '
10    CONTINUE

      DO 20 I = LEFT, RIGHT
        LINE(I) = '-'
20    CONTINUE

      SCALE = (RIGHT - LEFT) / (FMAX - FMIN)
      X = XMIN
      POINT = NINT( LEFT + SCALE * (F( X ) - FMIN) )
      LINE( POINT ) = SYMBOL
      PRINT 5, LINE

      DO 30 I = LEFT, RIGHT
        LINE(I) = ' '
30    CONTINUE

40    IF( X .LE. XMAX )THEN
        IF( X. GT. XMIN )PRINT 5, LINE
        LINE( POINT ) = ' '
        LINE( LEFT ) = ':'
        X = X + DX
        POINT = NINT( LEFT + SCALE * (F( X ) - FMIN) )
        LINE( POINT ) = SYMBOL
        GOTO 40
      END IF

      RETURN
      END

      REAL FUNCTION I( T )
* *** CURRENT IN R-L-C CIRCUIT, CAPACITOR INITIALLY CHARGED ******

      PARAMETER (PI = 3.1415927)
      REAL L
      COMMON / ELEC / A, Fl, L, R

      I = A * EXP( - R * T / (2 * L) ) * SIN( 2 * PI * Fl * T )

      RETURN
      END
```

The output is:

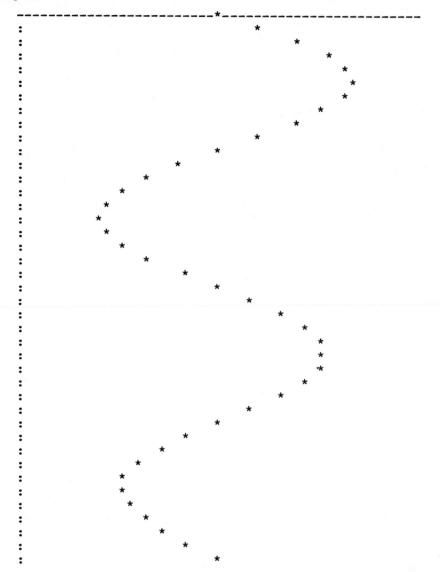

12.8   External Libraries

As mentioned above, the subprogram facilities of FORTRAN 77 enable you to access external libraries of general purpose subprograms, usually in the form of subroutines. A detailed understanding of how a particular subroutine (or package, as it is often called) works, while desirable, is not essential. All you need to know is how the arguments are defined, and what (system dependent) job control statements are needed to link the package to your program. For example, there is a NAG (Numerical Algorithms Group) package called C02AEF for finding all the roots of a polynomial with real coefficients. The appropriate NAG Manual will inform you that its specification is

```
SUBROUTINE CO2AEF( A, N, REZ, IMZ, TOL, IFAIL )
```

where the arguments have the following meanings:

A (real array, dimension N): set on entry by the user to the coefficients of the polynomial;
N (integer): the number of coefficients of the polynomial;
REZ (real array, dimension N): set on exit to the real parts of the roots;
IMZ (real array, dimension N): set on exit to the imaginary parts of the roots;
TOL (real): a machine dependent tolerance to specify the accuracy of the method;
IFAIL (integer): set to 0 or 1 on entry by the user; set on exit to 0 unless an error has been detected.

To use the subroutine in a program, it must simply be referenced in a **CALL** statement in the usual way (and attached to your program by some job control statements).

12.9 Summary

* Good structured programming requires real problem-solving programs to be broken down into independent procedures.

* There are four types of procedure: intrinsic functions, statement functions, external functions and subroutines.

* External functions and subroutines are called subprograms.

* The main program and subprograms are called program units.

* Statement functions have one-line definitions.

* Communication between program units is mainly through argument lists.

* Actual argument values are copied into dummy arguments when a procedure is referenced.

* Arrays may be given adjustable dimensions in a subprogram only if they are passed as arguments.

* The values of local variables in a subprogram may be retained between calls with the **SAVE** statement.

* Use **INTRINSIC** in a calling program when an intrinsic function's specific name is to be used as an actual argument in a procedure reference.

* Use **EXTERNAL** in a calling program when a procedure name appears as an actual argument, or when it appears as a dummy argument and is not identified by the context as a function or subroutine.

* Named and blank **COMMON** make global storage available.

* Character variables may not be mixed with any other type of variable in a **COMMON** statement.

* Named **COMMON** blocks may be initialized with a **BLOCK DATA** subprogram.

* External libraries of general purpose subprograms are available on many computer systems.

12.10   Exercises

12.1   Write a program which uses the Newton quotient

$$[f(x+h)-f(x)]/h$$

to estimate the first derivative of $f(x)=x^3$ at $x=1$, using successively smaller values of h: 1, 1/2, 1/4, 1/8, ... Use a statement function for $f(x)$.

12.2   Write your own FORTRAN function E(X) to compute the exponential function directly from the series

$$\exp(x) = 1+x+x^2/2!+x^3/3!+ \ ....$$

The series should terminate when the last term is less than 1E−6.

12.3   Write a function subprogram FACT(N) which returns $N!$ (N−factorial).

12.4   Write a function subprogram BIN(N, R) which returns the binomial coefficient,

$$n! / [r!(n-r)!]$$

You should avoid computing each factorial directly. Make use of the fact that cancellations occur. E.g. if $n=5$ and $r=2$, the binomial coefficient may be calculated directly as

$$(5\times4)/(1\times2).$$

12.5   Write a subroutine QUAD(A, B, C, X1, X2, J) which computes the roots of the quadratic equation

$$ax^2+bx+c=0$$

The arguments A, B, C (which may take any values) are the coefficients of the quadratic, and X1, X2 are the two roots (if they exist), which may be equal. J is a 'flag' which must be set by the subroutine as follows:

$J = \ -1$: imaginary roots (discriminant<0);
$J = \quad 0$: no solution ($a=b=0$, $c\neq0$);
$J = \quad 1$: one root ($a=0$, $b\neq0$, so the root is $-c/b$);
$J = \quad 2$: two roots (which could be equal, but see Section 9.5);
$J = \ 99$: any x a solution ($a=b=c=0$).

Write a main program which reads some sample values of a, b, and c, and uses the subroutine to print the root(s), together with an appropriate message according to the value of J. The point about using a flag like J is that the subroutine can be safely used with any set of data. Appropriate actions may be programmed in the calling program according to the value of J.

12.6   Rewrite the program in Section 7.11 using a function subprogram for the charge Q, with a named **COMMON** block for the constants C, R and V.

12.7   What is the output from the following program (run it if you are not sure)?

```
REAL   A(2)

A(1)  = 1
A(2)  = 2
CALL PLONK( A, B )
PRINT*, A, B
STOP
END
```

```
      SUBROUTINE PLONK(X, A)
************************************************************
      REAL X(2)

      A = X(1) + X(2)
      X(2) = A
      RETURN
      END
```

12.8   If a random variable X is distributed normally with zero mean and unit standard deviation, the probability that $0 \leq X \leq x$ is given by the standard normal function $\phi(x)$. This is usually looked up in tables, but it may be approximated as follows:

$$\phi(x) = 0.5 - r(at + bt^2 + ct^3),$$

where $a = 0.4361836$
$b = -0.1201676$
$c = 0.937298$
$r = \exp(-0.5x^2) / \sqrt{2\pi}$
$t = 1 / (1 + 0.3326x)$

Write a function subprogram to compute this function, and use it in a program to print out values of $\phi(x)$ for $0 \leq x \leq 4$ in steps of 0.1.

13

Simulation

One of the most powerful applications of modern computers is in the field of **simulation**, where aspects of reality that appear to be based on random processes, or that are too complicated to understand properly, may be represented using random numbers. Examples are radioactive decay, bacteria division and traffic flow. The essence of such programs is that the programmer is unable to predict beforehand exactly what the output will be, and this is true to the area of the real world being simulated. For example, when you spin a coin, you do not know exactly what the result will be.

13.1 Pseudo-Random Number Generators

The basis of any simulation is a random number generator, of which there are many examples in the literature. The one used here is a function subprogram called URAND (listed in Section 13.9), which returns a uniformly distributed random number in the range 0 to 1 (exclusive). It is called as follows:

```
R = URAND( IY )
```

where R is the name of any real variable that is to be set to a random number. IY stands for any integer, and is called the **seed** of the random process. It must be set to some arbitrary positive value at the start of the simulation program. When URAND is called, the value of IY is changed to a random integer, and this is scaled down to a positive real number less than 1. In all the simulation examples that follow, it is assumed that the coding for URAND has been inserted after the **END** of the main program.

If a random number from a normal distribution with given mean and standard deviation is needed, the function GRAND (listed in Section 13.10) may be used as follows:

```
R = GRAND( IY, STDEV, AMEAN )
```

where IY is the seed, the STDEV and AMEAN have the obvious meanings.

13.2 Example: Spinning a Coin

When a fair (unbiased) coin is spun, the probability of getting heads or tails is 0.5 (50%). Since the value of URAND is equally likely to be anywhere in the interval (0;1) we can call it heads if URAND is less than 0.5, and tails if it is greater than 0.5 (statisticians will tell you that it can never be exactly 0.5). The following program simulates an 'experiment' in which a fair coin is spun 10 times:

```
          READ*, IY

          DO 90 I = 1, 10
            R = URAND( IY )
            IF( R .LT. 0.5 )THEN
               PRINT*, 'HEADS'
            ELSE
               PRINT*, 'TAILS'
            END IF
90        CONTINUE

          STOP
          END

          FUNCTION URAND( IY )
          .... (see Section 13.9)
```

Data:

23041983   (initial seed: any positive value will do)

Note

1) The output will be a random sequence of 'HEADS' and 'TAILS'.
2) If the program is rerun with a *different* initial seed, the output will be a *different* sequence of 'HEADS' and 'TAILS'.
3) The seed IY should not be changed by an assignment statement in the program, since URAND changes it randomly to another integer, and a further change by the program will interfere with the random sequence.

13.3 Example: Rolling a Fair Die

When a fair die (plural 'dice') is rolled, the number uppermost is equally likely to be 1, 2, 3, 4, 5, or 6. The following example simulates 30 rolls of a die, prints the results out on one line, and estimates from the simulation the probability of throwing a six.

```
          INTEGER NUM(30)
15        FORMAT( 1X, 30I2 / '0PROB(6) =', F7.2 )

          READ*, ISEED
          N6 = 0

          DO 90 I = 1, 30
            P = URAND( ISEED )
            NUM(I) = INT( P * 6 ) + 1
            IF( NUM(I) .EQ. 6 ) N6 = N6 + 1
90        CONTINUE

          PROB6 = FLOAT( N6 ) / 30
          PRINT 15, NUM, PROB6
          STOP
          END
```

Data:

1983

The output is as follows:

    6 5 5 5 5 3 2 2 6 6 4 4 4 1 2 2 5 3 5 1 5 6 5 1 4 6 2 5 1 1

PROB(6) =   .17

Exercise
Run the program with different initial seeds and observe that the results are always slightly
different, just as you would expect if you performed a real experiment a number of times.
Get the program to simulate more rolls of the die each time, and see what happens to the
estimated probability of getting a six.

13.4   A Random Walk

Suppose a drunken sailor has to negotiate a jetty toward his ship. The jetty is 50 steps long
and 20 wide. A mate places him in the middle of the jetty at the quay end, and points him
toward the ship. Suppose at every step he has a 60% chance of lurching toward the ship, but
a 20% chance of lurching to the left or right (he manages to be always facing the ship). If he
reaches the ship end of the jetty he is hauled aboard by waiting mates. The problem is to
simulate his progress along the jetty, and to estimate his chances of getting to the ship
without falling into the sea. To do this correctly, we must simulate one 'walk' along the
jetty, ascertain whether or not he reaches the ship, and then repeat this simulation 1000
times, say. The proportion of simulations that end with the sailor safely in the ship will be
an estimate of his chances of making it to the ship. For a given walk we assume that if he has
not either reached the ship or fallen into the sea after, say 10000 steps, he dies of thirst on
the jetty.
   To represent the jetty, we set up an X, Y co-ordinate system (where X and Y are
measured in steps) with the X-axis running along the middle of the jetty from the quay to
the ship, and with the origin at the quay end. The sailor starts his walk from the origin. The
structure plan and program for this problem are as follows:

    1   Initialize variables
    2   Repeat 1000 simulated walks down the jetty
        2.1   Start at the land end of the jetty
        2.2   While still on jetty AND still alive repeat
              2.2.1   Get a random number
              2.2.2   If r < 0.6 then
                      2.2.2.1   Move forward (shipward)
                      Otherwise if r < 0.8 then
                      2.2.2.2   Move port
                      Otherwise
                      2.2.2.3   Move starboard
        2.3   If he got to the ship then
              2.3.1   Increase relevant counter
              3   Compute and print probability of reaching ship.

```
*****  RANDOM WALK SIMULATION  *************************************
*      NSAFE : NO. OF TIMES HE MAKES IT                           *
*      NSIM  : NO. OF SIMULATIONS                                 *
*****  NSTEP : NO. OF STEPS ON A GIVEN WALK  **********************

       READ*, ISEED
       NSAFE = 0
       NSIM = 1000
       NSTEP = 0

* ***  TRY NSIM RANDOM WALKS

       DO 20 ISIM = 1, NSIM
         X = 0
         Y = 0
         NSTEP = 0

* ***      LURCH UNTIL HE ARRIVES, OR FALLS OFF, OR DIES

10         IF( X .LE. 50 .AND. ABS( Y ) .LE. 10
     $    .AND. NSTEP .LT. 10000 )THEN
             NSTEP = NSTEP + 1
             R = URAND( ISEED )
             IF( R .LT. 0.6 )THEN
               X = X + 1
             ELSE IF( R .LT. 0.8 )THEN
               Y = Y + 1
             ELSE
               Y = Y - 1
             END IF
             GOTO 10
           END IF

* ***      DID HE ACTUALLY MAKE IT?

           IF( X .GT. 50 ) NSAFE = NSAFE + 1
20         CONTINUE

       PHOME = FLOAT( NSAFE ) / NSIM
       PRINT*, 'PROB OF REACHING SHIP IS', PHOME

       STOP
       END
```

13.5   Time of Day as a Seed

A cunning way to get the initial seed for a simulation is to use the computer's internal clock. Since you could never run the program at exactly the same time on different days, you would always be certain to get a different initial seed. Try to find out whether your computer system's internal clock can be accessed from inside a FORTRAN program while it is running.

13.6   Dealing a Bridge Hand

The next program, which is similar to one by Kemeny and Kurtz (1967), simulates a deal c
13 cards from a pack of 52 playing cards (the jokers have been removed). The names of th
four suits are read as characters into SUIT, and the 13 face values from 'TWO' to 'ACE' ar
read into VALUE. To deal one card, a random number in the range 0 to 51 is generatec
i.e. the 52 cards are represented uniquely by the numbers 0 to 51. The main problem is tha
a given card may only be dealt once. To ensure this, an array LIST is set up, with all i
elements initially 0 (meaning no cards have been dealt yet). When a random number NUM
comes up, LIST(NUM) is checked. If it is still 0, that card has not been dealt, so NUM i
put into the next element of HAND, and LIST(NUM) is set to −1, indicating that NUM
has been dealt. If LIST(NUM) already has the value −1 when NUM comes up, it mean
that that card has already been dealt, so another random number is generated. This proces
is repeated 13 times, until the array HAND contains 13 unique numbers in the range 0 to 5
(the first column of numbers in the sample output below). This part of the program may b
structure planned as follows:

> Repeat 13 times
> 1   Get a random number R.
> 2   Convert it to an integer NUM in range 0 to 51.
> 3   While LIST(NUM) = −1 repeat
>   3.1   Get another random number and convert it to NUM
> 4   Assign NUM to next element of HAND.
> 5   Set LIST(NUM) to −1.

To print the hand of cards, each element of HAND is subjected to integer division by 1:
The quotient (KS) will be in the range 0 to 3 (won't it?) and gives the suit. The remainde
(KV) will be in the range 0 to 12, and gives the face value. E.g. the number 35 on divisio
by 13 gives a quotient of 2 (SPADES), and a remainder of 9 (JACK), as shown in the firs
line of output below.

The program is given below. The data, apart from the seed for URAND, consists of 1
lines: 13 faces values and four suits. The data is followed by a sample run. If you run thi
program as it stands, you should get a different hand, since you are highly unlikely to us
the same seed as I did.

```
*****  SIMULATES A DEAL OF 13 PLAYING CARDS  *********************
       CHARACTER*8  SUIT( 0:3 )
       CHARACTER*5  VALUE( 0:12 )
       INTEGER      HAND(13)
       INTEGER      LIST( 0:51 )
       DATA ( LIST(I), I = 0, 51 ) / 52 * 0 /

5      FORMAT( A )
15     FORMAT( ' ', 3A, T30, I2, T40, I2, T45, I2 )

* ***  READ IN FACE VALUES
       READ 5, VALUE
* ***  READ IN SUITS
       READ 5, SUIT
       READ*, ISEED

* ***  DEAL 13 CARDS
       DO 90 ICARD = 1, 13
         R = URAND( ISEED )
         NUM = INT( 52 * R )
```

```
* ***       IF IT'S BEEN DEALT ALREADY, GET ANOTHER NUMBER
70          IF( LIST(NUM) .EQ. -1 )THEN
               R = URAND( ISEED )
               NUM = INT( 52 * R )
               GOTO 70
            END IF

* ***       IF IT HASN'T BEEN DEALT, DEAL IT NOW
            HAND( ICARD ) = NUM
            LIST( NUM ) = -1
* ***       NOW IT CAN'T BE DEALT AGAIN
90          CONTINUE

* *** PRINT THE 13 CARDS
            DO 80 ICARD = 1, 13
               KS = HAND(ICARD) / 13
               KV = MOD( HAND(ICARD), 13 )
               PRINT 15, VALUE(KV), ' OF ', SUIT(KS), HAND(ICARD), KS, KV
80          CONTINUE

            STOP
            END
Data:
.... (initial seed)

TWO
THREE
FOUR
FIVE
SIX
SEVEN
EIGHT
NINE
TEN
JACK
QUEEN
KING
ACE
SPADES
HEARTS
DIAMONDS
CLUBS
```

Output from a sample run looks like this (headings for the last three columns have been inserted into the text):

	HAND(ICARD)	KS	KV
JACK OF DIAMONDS	35	2	9
KING OF SPADES	11	0	11
NINE OF SPADES	7	0	7
TEN OF DIAMONDS	34	2	8
ACE OF HEARTS	25	1	12
JACK OF HEARTS	22	1	9
TEN OF SPADES	8	0	8
ACE OF DIAMONDS	38	2	12
THREE OF HEARTS	14	1	1
THREE OF CLUBS	40	3	1
FOUR OF DIAMONDS	28	2	2
KING OF DIAMONDS	37	2	11
FIVE OF DIAMONDS	29	2	3

You may feel that the method of 'shuffling' the cards, with the **IF/GOTO 70** combination, is inefficient, because as more cards get dealt, so the number of calls to URAND goes up and up. The following program segment shuffles all 52 cards, and replaces the nine lines under "DEAL 13 CARDS". With a few ammendments, a deal of all four hands can now be printed (HAND must be dimensioned with 52 elements in this case).

```
*  ***  SHUFFLE THE PACK

         DO 70 I = 1, 52
            HAND(I) = I - 1
70       CONTINUE

         DO 90 I = 1, 52
            R = URAND( ISEED )
            NUM = INT( 52 * R ) + 1
            ITEMP = HAND(NUM)
            HAND(NUM) = HAND(I)
            HAND(I) = ITEMP
90       CONTINUE
```

Note that NUM is now in the range 1 to 52 since it represents the position of a card rather than the card itself.

   You could test which of the two shuffling methods is more efficient by incrementing a counter each time URAND is called. A number of sample runs would then be needed to get an estimate of the average number of calls to URAND.

13.7   Traffic Simulation

A major use of simulation in large cities is to model the traffic flow, so as to be able to try out different traffic light patterns on the computer before imposing them on the real traffic. This has been done, for example, in the city of Leeds, in the United Kingdom. In this section we look at a small part of this problem: how to simulate the flow of a single line of traffic through one set of traffic lights. We make the following assumptions:

1)   Traffic travels straight, without turning.
2)   The probability of a car arriving at the lights in any one second is independent of what happened during the previous second. This is called a Poisson process. This probability (call it p) may be estimated by watching cars at the intersection and monitoring their arrival pattern. In this simulation, we take $p = 0.3$ (this is entirely arbitrary).

3)   When the lights are green, assume the cars move through at a steady rate of, say, eight every 10 seconds (this can also be estimated in reality).
4)   In this simulation, we will take the basic time interval to be 10 seconds, so we want a printout showing the length of the queue (if any) of traffic at the lights every 10 seconds, starting at the end of the first 10-second period.
5)   We will set the lights red or green for variable multiples of 10 seconds.

The program below simulates a queue of traffic at a set of traffic lights, according to the assumptions stated above. The program has two subroutines. LIGHTS decides when the traffic lights change, and QUEUE prints a row of asterisks every 10 seconds, where one asterisk represents one car in the queue.
   The output that follows is for one sample simulation of 50 10-second periods. Each line of output gives the number of the period, the colour of the lights, and the representation of the queue. From the output, it appears that a traffic jam is building up with the particular red/green period given as data (40 seconds red, 20 seconds green). Running more simulations will confirm whether this is so. We could also compute some statistics such as the mean length of the queue. However, we cannot compute the mean time spent waiting in the queue from this type of simulation. The example in the next section handles that problem.

```
*****  TRAFFIC SIMULATION  *********************************************
*         COLOUR : LOGICAL VBLE FOR LIGHTS (T = GREEN, F = RED)        *
*         CARS   : NO. OF CARS IN QUEUE / GTIMER : TIMER FOR GREEN     *
*         N      : NO. OF SIMULATIONS    / RTIMER : TIMER FOR RED      *
*****  TGREEN : PERIOD FOR GREEN        / TRED   : PERIOD FOR RED  ****

          LOGICAL   COLOUR
          INTEGER   CARS
          INTEGER   GTIMER
          INTEGER   N
          INTEGER   RTIMER
          INTEGER   TGREEN
          INTEGER   TRED

          P = 0.3
          READ*, ISEED
          READ*, N, TRED, TGREEN

*  ***  N SIMULATIONS, EACH OF 50 10-SEC PERIODS
          DO 30 I = 1, N
             CARS = 0
             RTIMER = 0
             GTIMER = 0
             COLOUR = .FALSE.

*  ***      SIMULATE 50 10-SEC PERIODS
             DO 20 J = 1, 50

*  ***         SIMULATE ARRIVAL OF CARS IN 10-SEC PERIOD
                DO 10 L = 1, 10
                   R = URAND( ISEED )
                   IF( R .LT. P ) CARS = CARS + 1
   10           CONTINUE

                IF( COLOUR )THEN
*  ***             LIGHTS GREEN
                   CARS = CARS - 8
```

```
               IF( CARS .LT. 0 )CARS = 0
               CALL QUEUE( COLOUR, J, CARS )
               CALL LIGHTS( TGREEN, GTIMER, COLOUR )
            ELSE
* ***          LIGHTS RED
               CALL QUEUE(COLOUR, J, CARS)
               CALL LIGHTS(TRED, RTIMER, COLOUR)
            ENDIF

   20     CONTINUE

   30 CONTINUE

      STOP
      END

      SUBROUTINE LIGHTS( T, TIMER, COLOUR )
*****************************************************************
*     TIMER FOR LIGHTS IS INCREMENTED                          *
*     COLOUR IS CHANGED WHEN TIMER = T (PERIOD OF LIGHTS)      *
*     TIMER IS THEN RESET TO ZERO                              *
*****************************************************************

      LOGICAL COLOUR
      INTEGER T
      INTEGER TIMER

      TIMER = TIMER + 1
      IF( TIMER .EQ. T )THEN
* ***    CHANGE LIGHTS AND RESET TIMER
         COLOUR = .NOT. COLOUR
         TIMER = 0
      ENDIF

      RETURN
      END

      SUBROUTINE QUEUE(COLOUR, J, CARS)
*****************************************************************
*     PRINTS NUMBER OF 10-S INTERVAL (J),
*             COLOUR OF LIGHTS (C),
*             AND ROW OF *s REPRESENTING LENGTH OF QUEUE
*****************************************************************

      LOGICAL     COLOUR
      INTEGER     CARS
      CHARACTER*1 C

   15 FORMAT( I3, 2X, A1, 2X, 120A1 )

      C = 'R'
      IF( COLOUR )C = 'G'
      PRINT 15, J, C, ( '*', K=1, CARS )

      RETURN
      END
```

Data:

```
.... (initial seed)
1 4 2
```

The output from a sample run is shown below:

```
 1   R   **
 2   R   ******
 3   R   **********
 4   R   *************
 5   G   *******
 6   G   ****
 7   R   ****
 8   R   *******
 9   R   **********
10   R   ************
11   G   *******
12   G   **
13   R   *****
14   R   ********
15   R   ***********
16   R   ***************
17   G   **********
18   G   *****
19   R   **********
20   R   ************
21   R   *************
22   R   ********************
23   G   **************
24   G   ********
25   R   ***********
26   R   *************
27   R   ****************
28   R   *********************
29   G   ***************
30   G   ********
31   R   *********
32   R   ***********
33   R   ************
34   R   *****************
35   G   *********
36   G   *****
37   R   ******
38   R   *********
39   R   **************
40   R   ******************
41   G   ***************
42   G   **********
43   R   ***************
44   R   ********************
45   R   **********************
46   R   **************************
47   G   ********************
48   G   **************
49   R   ******************
50   R   ********************
```

13.8   Queues

In this section we look at how to simulate a simple first-in first-out (FIFO) queue. There are now two random processes involved: the arrival of users, and the service of users, both of which we assume to be Poisson distributed. These processes may be represented by two random variables: the inter-arrival time (*IAT*) between users joining the end of the queue, and the service time (*ST*) for the user at the front of the queue. Let us suppose that these random variables are distributed as follows (e.g. based on a survey in a Post Office):

IAT (seconds)	Prob (frequency)	Prob (cumulative)
10	0.10	0.10
15	0.25	0.35
20	0.30	0.65
25	0.25	0.90
30	0.10	1.00

ST (seconds)	Prob (frequency)	Prob (cumulative)
5	0.08	0.08
10	0.14	0.22
15	0.18	0.40
20	0.24	0.64
25	0.22	0.86
30	0.14	1.00

We define the following additional terms:

A: clock time of arrival
E: clock time of entry into service
L: clock time of leaving service $(L = E + ST)$
T: user's time in system $(T = L - A)$
W: user's wait time $(W = E - A)$.

The purpose of the simulation is to estimate a user's mean time in the system and mean wait time, to see if these are acceptable. If they are not, attempts can be made to improve the service. The structure plan is as follows:

1   Repeat for each user
   1.1   Generate *IAT* according to Poisson distribution
   1.2   Update arrival time
   1.3   Determine when user enters service as follows:
      If he arrives after previous user has left then
         1.3.1   He enters service immediately
      Else
         1.3.2   He waits until previous user leaves
   1.4   Generate *ST* according to Poisson distribution
   1.5   Determine when he leaves service
   1.6   Add wait time and time in system to running total
2   Compute mean wait time and mean time in system for all users.

It is an interesting problem to determine the length of the queue the moment after each user joins it. To do this we need to record all the leave times in a list (array), and use a term *H* which identifies the user at the front of the queue. The following section should then be added to the structure plan:

      1.7   While arrival time $> = H$s leave time repeat
          1.7.1   Increment *H* by one
      1.8   Determine length of queue between *H* and current user

The program below simulates the service of 50 users in a FIFO queue, and prints out the variables defined above for each user:

```
*****  SIMULATION OF A FIFO QUEUE  ********************************
*                                                                *
*       ARR    : CLOCK TIME OF ARRIVAL                           *
*       ENT    : CLOCK TIME OF ENTRY INTO SERVICE                *
*       HEAD   : USER AT FRONT OF QUEUE                          *
*       IAT    : INTER-ARRIVAL TIME                              *
*       LEAVE  : CLOCK TIME OF LEAVING SERVICE (LIST)            *
*       MNTIS  : MEAN USER TIME IN SYSTEM                        *
*       MNWAIT : MEAN USER WAIT TIME                             *
*       NUM    : NUMBER OF USERS (ASSUMED LESS THAN 100)         *
*       RND    : RANDOM NUMBER                                   *
*       SEED   : SEED FOR URAND                                  *
*       ST     : SERVICE TIME                                    *
*       TIS    : USER TIME IN SYSTEM                             *
*       WAIT   : USER WAIT TIME                                  *
******************************************************************

        INTEGER ARR
        INTEGER ENT
        INTEGER HEAD
        INTEGER IAT
        INTEGER LEAVE( 0:100 )
        INTEGER NUM
        INTEGER SEED
        INTEGER ST
        INTEGER TIS
        INTEGER WAIT
        INTEGER USER
        REAL    MNTIS
        REAL    MNWAIT
        REAL    RND

5       FORMAT( 4I5, I4, I7, I6, 2I5 )
15      FORMAT( '1USER   IAT   ARR   ENT   ST   LEAVE   WAIT   TIS   LEN'
       $ / )
25      FORMAT( '0MEAN USER TIME IN SYSTEM:', T28, F6.1 /
       $' MEAN USER WAIT TIME:', T28, F6.1 )

        ARR = 0
        HEAD = 1
        LEAVE(0) = 0
        MNTIS = 0
        MNWAIT = 0
        NUM = 50
        READ*, SEED
        PRINT 15
```

```
         DO 100 USER = 1, NUM
* ***    GENERATE INTER-ARRIVAL TIME
         RAN = URAND( SEED )
         IF( RAN .LT. 0.1 )THEN
           IAT = 10
         ELSE IF( RAN .LT. 0.35 )THEN
           IAT = 15
         ELSE IF( RAN .LT. 0.65 )THEN
           IAT = 20
         ELSE IF( RAN .LT. 0.90 )THEN

           IAT = 25
         ELSE
           IAT = 30
         END IF

         ARR = ARR + IAT
         IF( ARR .GE. LEAVE( USER - 1 ) )THEN
           ENT = ARR
         ELSE
           ENT = LEAVE( USER - 1 )
         END IF

* ***    NOW GENERATE SERVICE TIME
         RAN = URAND( SEED )
         IF( RAN .LT. 0.08 )THEN
           ST = 5
         ELSE IF( RAN .LT. 0.22 )THEN
           ST = 10
         ELSE IF( RAN .LT. 0.40 )THEN
           ST = 15
         ELSE IF( RAN .LT. 0.64 )THEN
           ST = 20
         ELSE IF( RAN .LT. 0.86 )THEN
           ST = 25
         ELSE
           ST = 30
         END IF

         LEAVE( USER ) = ENT + ST
         WAIT = ENT - ARR
         TIS = LEAVE( USER ) - ARR
         MNTIS = MNTIS + TIS
         MNWAIT = MNWAIT + WAIT

* ***    DETERMINE LENGTH OF QUEUE
10       IF( ARR .GE. LEAVE( HEAD ) )THEN
           HEAD = HEAD + 1
           GOTO 10
         END IF

         LENG = USER - HEAD + 1
         PRINT 5, USER, IAT, ARR, ENT, ST, LEAVE( USER ),
     $  WAIT, TIS, LENG
100   CONTINUE
```

```
MNTIS = MNTIS / NUM
MNWAIT = MNWAIT / NUM
PRINT 25, MNTIS, MNWAIT

STOP
END
```

A sample run produces the following output:

USER	IAT	ARR	ENT	ST	LEAVE	WAIT	TIS	LEN
1	20	20	20	25	45	0	25	1
2	15	35	45	25	70	10	35	2
3	25	60	70	20	90	10	30	2
4	25	85	90	25	115	5	30	2
5	20	105	115	20	135	10	30	2
6	15	120	135	15	150	15	30	2
7	20	140	150	25	175	10	35	2
8	10	150	175	25	200	25	50	2
9	20	170	200	15	215	30	45	3
10	20	190	215	20	235	25	45	3
11	25	215	235	25	260	20	45	2
12	15	230	260	30	290	30	60	3
13	10	240	290	30	320	50	80	3
14	25	265	320	30	350	55	85	3
15	30	295	350	25	375	55	80	3
16	10	305	375	25	400	70	95	4
17	25	330	400	15	415	70	85	4
18	25	355	415	25	440	60	85	4
19	15	370	440	15	455	70	85	5
20	15	385	455	20	475	70	90	5
21	25	410	475	30	505	65	95	5
22	20	430	505	30	535	75	105	5
23	15	445	535	30	565	90	120	5
24	30	475	565	25	590	90	115	4
25	10	485	590	10	600	105	115	5
26	25	510	600	25	625	90	115	5
27	15	525	625	25	650	100	125	6
28	20	545	650	25	675	105	130	6
29	15	560	675	20	695	115	135	7
30	15	575	695	20	715	120	140	7
31	25	600	715	25	740	115	140	6
32	25	625	740	25	765	115	140	6
33	15	640	765	20	785	125	145	7
34	25	665	785	15	800	120	135	7
35	15	680	800	20	820	120	140	7
36	15	695	820	30	850	125	155	7
37	25	720	850	15	865	130	145	7
38	25	745	865	25	890	120	145	7
39	30	775	890	30	920	115	145	7
40	10	785	920	15	935	135	150	7
41	15	800	935	20	955	135	155	7
42	30	830	955	30	985	125	155	7
43	20	850	985	10	995	135	145	7
44	20	870	995	5	1000	125	130	7
45	30	900	1000	15	1015	100	115	7

```
46   15  915 1015   20    1035    100  120    8
47   10  925 1035   25    1060    110  135    8
48   15  940 1060   10    1070    120  130    8
49   20  960 1070   25    1095    110  135    8
50   25  985 1095   20    1115    110  130    8
```

```
MEAN USER TIME IN SYSTEM:   102.6
MEAN USER WAIT TIME:         80.7
```

13.9   Listing of URAND

```
      REAL FUNCTION URAND(IY)
      INTEGER IY
*
*   URAND IS A UNIFORM RANDOM NUMBER GENERATOR BASED ON THEORY
*   AND SUGGESTIONS GIVEN BY KNUTH (1969).  THE INTEGER
*   IY SHOULD BE INITIALIZED TO AN ARBITRARY INTEGER PRIOR TO THE
*   FIRST CALL TO URAND.  THE CALLING PROGRAM SHOULD NOT ALTER THE
*   VALUE OF IY BETWEEN SUBSEQUENT CALLS TO URAND.  VALUES OF URAND
*   WILL BE RETURNED IN THE INTERVAL (0,1).
*
      INTEGER IA, IC, ITWO, M2, M, MIC
      DOUBLE PRECISION HALFM
      REAL S
      DATA M2/ 0/, ITWO/ 2/

*   IF FIRST ENTRY, COMPUTE MACHINE INTEGER WORD LENGTH
      IF( M2 .EQ. 0 )THEN
        M = 1
10       IF( M .GT. M2 )THEN
         M2 = M
         M = ITWO * M2
         GOTO 10
        END IF
        HALFM = M2
*
*   COMPUTE MULTIPLIER AND INCREMENT FOR LINEAR CONGRUENTIAL METHOD
        IA = 8 * INT(HALFM * ATAN(1.D0) / 8.D0) + 5
        IC = 2 * INT(HALFM * (0.5D0 - SQRT(3.D0) / 6.D0)) + 1
        MIC = (M2 - IC) + M2
*
*   S IS THE SCALE FACTOR FOR CONVERTING TO FLOATING POINT
        S = 0.5 / HALFM
      END IF
*
*   COMPUTE NEXT RANDOM NUMBER
      IY = IY * IA
*
*   THE FOLLOWING STATEMENT IS FOR COMPUTERS WHICH DO NOT ALLOW
*   INTEGER OVERFLOW ON ADDITION
      IF( IY .GT. MIC ) IY = (IY - M2) - M2
*
      IY = IY + IC
```

```
*
*    THE FOLLOWING STATEMENT IS FOR COMPUTERS WHERE THE
*    WORD LENGTH FOR ADDITION IS GREATER THAN FOR MULTIPLICATION
         IF( IY / 2 .GT. M2 ) IY = (IY - M2) - M2
*
*    THE FOLLOWING STATEMENT IS FOR COMPUTERS WHERE INTEGER OVERFLOW
*    AFFECTS THE SIGN BIT
         IF( IY .LT. 0 ) IY = (IY + M2) + M2
         URAND = FLOAT(IY) * S

         RETURN
         END
```

Note that the **DATA** statement assigns the values 0 and 2 to the variables M2 and ITWO respectively at compile time. This enables the subprogram to detect the first call of URAND, since M2 is changed during the first call. Note also that the references to the generic names of intrinsic functions (**ATAN, INT** and **SQRT**) with double precision arguments return double precision values.

13.10   Listing of GRAND

```
         FUNCTION GRAND(IY, STDEV, AMEAN)

*    A ROUTINE TO GENERATE PSEUDO RANDOM NUMBERS FROM A GAUSSIAN
*    DISTRIBUTION WITH A MEAN OF AMEAN AND A STANDARD DEVIATION OF
*    STDEV AS SPECIFIED BY THE USER.
*    THE ROUTINE MAKES USE OF THE FACT THAT THE DISTRIBUTION OF
*    SAMPLE MEANS IS GAUSSIAN.   SAMPLE MEANS OF 12 UNIFORMLY
*    DISTRIBUTED PSEUDO RANDOM NUMBERS ARE TAKEN AND TRANSFORMED
*    TO THE DESIRED DISTRIBUTION.
*    THE REPRODUCABILITY OF THE VALUES RETURNED WILL BE AFFECTED BY
*    ANY USE THAT IS MADE OF URAND IN THE INTERIM.
*    THIS ROUTINE REFERENCES URAND TO GENERATE THE UNIFORMLY
*    DISTRIBUTED RANDOM NUMBERS

         GRAND = 0.0

         DO 10 I = 1,12
            GRAND = GRAND + URAND(IY)
10       CONTINUE

         GRAND = (GRAND - 6.0) * STDEV + AMEAN

         RETURN
         END
```

13.11   Summary

* The random number generator URAND returns a uniformly distributed random number in the range (0;1), and is the basis of the simulations discussed in this chapter.

* URAND will generate a different random sequence each time a program is run if a different initial seed is used each time.

* On some computer systems, the time of day may be used to seed the random number generator initially.

* The randomness is *pseudo* because the same initial seed will always produce the same sequence of numbers.

13.12   Exercises

13.1   Extend the card dealing example of Section 13.6 to deal all four hands of cards, and to sort each hand before printing. *Hint*: use the second method outlined in that example to shuffle all 52 cards, and then copy each hand into another array for sorting in a Bubble Sort subroutine.

13.2   In a game of BINGO the numbers 1 to 99 are drawn at random from a bag. Write a program to simulate the draw of the numbers (each number can only be drawn once), printing the drawn numbers nine to a line.

13.3   URAND can be used to estimate π as follows. Write a program which generates random points in a square of length 2, say, and which counts what proportion of these points fall inside the circle of unit radius that fits exactly into the square. This proportion will be the ratio of the area of the circle to that of the square. Hence estimate π. (This is not a very efficient way to compute π!)

13.4   The aim of this exercise is to simulate bacteria growth. Suppose that a certain type of bacterium divides or dies according to the following assumptions: (1) during a fixed time interval, called a generation, a single bacterium divides into two identical replicas with probability p; (2) if it does not divide during that interval, it dies (ceases to be, shuffles off this mortal coil); (3) the offspring (called daughters) will divide or die during the next generation, independently of the past history (there may well be no offspring, in which case the colony becomes extinct).

Start with a single individual and write a program which simulates a number of generations. Take $p = 0.75$. The number of generations which you can simulate will depend on your computer system. Carry out a large number (e.g. 100) of such simulations. The probability of ultimate extinction, $p(E)$, may be estimated as the fraction of simulations that end in extinction. You can also estimate the mean size of the nth generation from a large number of simulations (theory says that it should be $(2p)^n$.

Statistical theory asserts that the expected value of the extinction probability $p(E)$ is whichever is the smaller of 1, and $(1-p)/p$. So for $p = 0.75$, $p(E)$ is expected to be 1/3. But for $p \leqslant 0.5$, $p(E)$ is expected to be 1, which means that extinction is certain (a rather unexpected result). You can use your program to test this theory by running it for different values of p, and estimating $p(E)$ in each case.

13.5   Dribblefire Jets Inc. (Kass, 1977) make two types of aeroplane, the two-engined DFII, and the four-engined DFIV. The engines are terrible and fail with probability 0.5 on a standard flight (the engines fail independently of each other). The manufacturers claim that the planes can fly if at least half of their engines are working, i.e. the

DFII will crash only if both its engines fail, while the DFIV will crash if all four, or if any three, engines fail.

You have been commissioned by the Civil Aviation Bureau to ascertain which of the two models is less likely to crash. Since parachutes are expensive, the cheapest (and safest!) way to do this is to simulate a large number of flights of each model. For example, two calls of URAND could represent one standard flight of the DFII: if both random numbers are less than 0.5 then that flight crashes, otherwise it doesn't. Write a program which simulates a large number of flights of both models, and estimate the probability of a crash in each case. If you can run enough simulations, you should get a rather unexpected result. (Incidentally, the probability of n engines failing on a given flight is given by the binomial distribution, but you do not need to use this fact in the simulation.)

13.6 Two players, A and B, play a game called 'Eights'. They take it in turns to choose a number 1, 2 or 3, which may not be the same as the last number chosen (so if A starts with 2, B may only choose 1 or 3 at the next move). A starts first, and may choose any of the three numbers for the first move. After each move, the number chosen is added to a running total. If the total reaches 8 exactly the player whose turn it was wins the game. If a player makes the total go over 8, the other player wins. For example, suppose A starts with 1 (total 1), B chooses 2 (3), A chooses 1 (4) and B chooses 2 (6). A would like to play 2 now, to win, but he can't because B cunningly played it on the last move, so A chooses 1 (7). This is even smarter, because B is forced to play 2 or 3, making the total go over 8, thereby losing.

Write a simulation program to estimate each player's chances of winning if they always play at random.

14

Matrices and their Applications

In this chapter we look at how to use a computer to solve problems involving matrices, with examples from linear algebra, networks, population dynamics, building science and Markov processes.

The programming introduced here follows on from Chapter 10, where arrays with only one subscript were discussed (such arrays are also called lists or vectors). In this chapter we deal with arrays having more than one subscript, or multi-dimensional arrays. Although up to seven subscripts may be used, we will discuss only two-dimensional arrays here, since these occur most often. An array with two subscripts can represent a table of numbers, since one subscript (usually the first) can label the rows in the table, while the second subscript labels the columns. This is also the convention adopted for matrices. Tables and matrices look exactly the same, but since matrices are used in mathematical applications, we will deal with them separately.

14.1 Tables

Suppose we have a class of four students, each with two test marks (the numbers have been kept trivially small for the sake of illustration). Each student's marks will be on one input record. We want to represent the whole class' marks as a table in the computer's memory. We will need an array, which could be declared as follows:

```
INTEGER MARK( 4,2 )
```

Since the first subscript runs from 1 to 4 it must clearly label the student number, while the second runs from 1 to 2 and must label the test. So the mark obtained by student number 3 in the first test will be stored in element MARK(3,1) (we hope!). To ensure the marks are stored in the correct elements, we could use:

```
INTEGER MARK( 4,2 )
....

DO 50 I = 1, 4
    READ*, ( MARK( I,J ),   J = 1, 2 )
50  CONTINUE
....

END
```

Data:

```
13 65
26 98
3 16
19 56
```

Alternatively, we could use a nested implied DO-loop:

```
      INTEGER MARK( 4,2 )
      READ*, ( (MARK( I,J ),  J = 1, 2),  I = 1, 4 )
      ....

      END
```

Data:

```
13 65
26 98
3 16
19 56
```

It is instructive to understand how multi-dimensional arrays are stored in FORTRAN 77. They are allocated consecutive storage locations in such a way that the *first* subscript varies *most rapidly*, and the last least rapidly. So the elements of MARK in the above example are actually stored in the order

MARK(1,1)
MARK(2,1)
MARK(3,1)
MARK(4,1)
MARK(1,2)
MARK(2,2)
MARK(3,2)
MARK(4,2)

If large arrays have to be handled it is therefore more efficient for this order to be followed in input/output, i.e. the first subscript changing fastest, the second changing second fastest, and the last changing slowest.

14.2   Graphs Again

The subroutine GRAPH2 in this section is more general than GRAPH in Section 12.7, since it can in principle handle any shape graph. The dummy arguments of GRAPH2 have the following meanings. The user must specify how many points (N) are to be plotted. These points are to be stored in the two one-dimensional arrays X and Y, where X(I) and Y(I) are the x and y co-ordinates of the ith point to be plotted. These arrays must be set up by the user before entry. The user also supplies the smallest and largest x co-ordinates for the plot (XF and XL), the lowest and highest y co-ordinates (YD and YU), the plotting symbol (PLOT), which must be specified CHARACTER*1, and a title, which must be CHARACTER*80.

GRAPH2 prints a horizontal x-axis over MAXCOL (65) columns and a vertical y-axis down MAXROW (20) rows. These values are set in PARAMETER statements in the routine. The x and y co-ordinates of the ith point are scales into the range 1−MAXCOL and 1−MAXROW respectively, using a similar transformation to the one in Section 12.7. The plotting symbol is then assigned to the appropriate row (IY) and column (IX) of a two-dimensional character array P. P is printed by rows to give the graph.

The sample run below shows how GRAPH2 may be used to plot the damped oscillations discussed in Section 6.5.

```
*  ***  GENERAL GRAPHING OF DAMPED OSCILLATIONS ***  *

          INTEGER CYCLES
          INTEGER PERCY
          REAL I
          REAL L
          REAL X( 100 )
          REAL Y( 100 )
          CHARACTER*80 TITLE
          CHARACTER*1 PLOT

          Q = 1E-5
          R = 1
          C = 1E-5
          L = 0.002
          CYCLES = 2
          PERCY = 10
          NPTS = CYCLES * PERCY + 1
          PI = 3.1415927
          FO = SQRT( 1 / (L * C) ) / (2 * PI)
          F1 = SQRT( 1 / (L * C) - R ** 2 / (4 * L ** 2) ) / (2 * PI)
          A = 2 * PI * FO ** 2 * Q / F1
          T = 0
          X(1) = T
          DT = 1.0 / (PERCY * F1)

          DO 10 K = 1, NPTS
            I = A * EXP( - R * T / (2 * L) ) * SIN( 2 * PI * F1 * T )
            Y(K) = I
            T = T + DT
            X(K + 1) = T
10        CONTINUE

          TITLE = '            CURRENT IN A RLC CIRCUIT INITIALLY CHARGED
          PLOT = '*'
          XF = 0
          XL = CYCLES / F1
          YD = -1E-1
          YU = 1E-1
          CALL GRAPH2( X, Y, NPTS, XF, XL, YD, YU, PLOT, TITLE )

          STOP
          END

          SUBROUTINE GRAPH2( X, Y, N, XF, XL, YD, YU, SYMBOL, TITLE )
*  ***  GENERAL GRAPHING ROUTINE: ARGUMENTS DESCRIBED IN TEXT

          PARAMETER (MAXROW = 20)
          PARAMETER (MAXCOL = 65)
          REAL X(N)
          REAL Y(N)
          CHARACTER*1 P( MAXROW, MAXCOL )
          CHARACTER*1 SYMBOL
          CHARACTER*80 TITLE
```

```
5         FORMAT( '1', A80 / )
15        FORMAT( T2, 80A1 )
          DO 10 I = 1, MAXROW
             DO 20 J = 1, MAXCOL
                P(I, J) = ' '
20           CONTINUE
10        CONTINUE

          DO 60 I = 1, MAXROW
             P(I, 1) = ':'
60        CONTINUE

          DO 70 J = 1, MAXCOL
             P(MAXROW, J) = '-'
70        CONTINUE

          DO 30 I = 1, N
             IX = NINT( (X(I) - XF) * (MAXCOL - 1) / (XL - XF) + 1 )
             IY = NINT( (Y(I) - YU) * (MAXROW - 1) / (YD - YU) + 1 )
             P(IY, IX) = SYMBOL
30        CONTINUE

          PRINT 5, TITLE

          DO 40 I = 1, MAXROW
             PRINT 15, ( P(I, J), J = 1, MAXCOL )
40        CONTINUE

          RETURN
          END
```

```
         CURRENT IN A RLC CIRCUIT INITIALLY CHARGED
:
:
:
:
:        *
:           *
:
:  *              *
:                                      *    *
:                                   *
:                                        *
*
:           *
:                    *
:
:
:
:
:
:
:
:
*--------------------------------------------------------------
```

14.3   Matrices

A **matrix** is a two-dimensional array (i.e. a table) which may be used in a wide variety of representations. For example, a distance array representing the lengths of direct connections in a network is a matrix. We will deal mainly with square matrices in this chapter (i.e. matrices having the same number of rows as columns), although in principle a matrix can have any number of rows or columns. A matrix with only one column is also called a vector.

A matrix is usually denoted by a bold capital letter, e.g. **A**, and each entry or element of the matrix is denoted by the small letter of the same name followed by two subscripts, the first indicating the row of the element, and the second indicating the column. So a general element of the matrix **A** is called a_{ij}, meaning it may be found in row i and column j. If **A** has three rows and three columns (3×3 for short) it will look like this in general:

$$\begin{bmatrix} a_{11} & a_{12} & a_{13} \\ a_{21} & a_{22} & a_{23} \\ a_{31} & a_{32} & a_{33} \end{bmatrix}$$

If, for example,

$$\mathbf{A} = \begin{bmatrix} 6 & 2 & 0 \\ -1 & 4 & 7 \\ 5 & 1 & 13 \end{bmatrix}$$

then $a_{21} = -1$; $a_{23} = 7$; $a_{31} = 5$; and so on.

14.3.1   Matrix Multiplication

Various mathematical operations are defined on matrices. Multiplication is probably the most important such operation, and is used widely in such areas as network theory, solution of linear systems of equations, transformation of co-ordinate systems, and population modelling. The rule of multiplying matrices looks a little weird at first, but will be justified by the applications that follow.

When two matrices, **A** and **B**, are multiplied together, their product is a third matrix, which we may as well call **C**. The operation is written as

$$\mathbf{C} = \mathbf{AB} \quad ,$$

and the general element c_{ij} of **C** is formed by taking the scalar product of the ith row of **A** with the jth column of **B**. It follows then that **A** and **B** can only be successfully multiplied (in that order) if the number of columns in **A** is the same as the number of rows in **B**.

Definition

If **A** is a $n \times m$ matrix, and **B** is a $m \times p$ matrix, their product **C** will be a $n \times p$ matrix defined so that the general element c_{ij} of **C** is given by

$$c_{ij} = \sum_{k=1}^{m} a_{ik} b_{kj} \quad .$$

Note that in general **AB** is not equal to **BA** (matrix multiplication is not commutative).

Examples

$$\begin{bmatrix} 1 & 2 \\ 3 & 4 \end{bmatrix} \begin{bmatrix} 5 & 6 \\ 0 & -1 \end{bmatrix} = \begin{bmatrix} 5 & 4 \\ 15 & 14 \end{bmatrix}$$

$$\begin{bmatrix} 1 & 2 \\ 3 & 4 \end{bmatrix} \begin{bmatrix} 2 \\ 3 \end{bmatrix} = \begin{bmatrix} 8 \\ 18 \end{bmatrix}$$

As another example, consider the system of three simultaneous equations,

$$\begin{aligned} 2x - 4y + 3z &= -9 \\ 3x \quad\ - z &= 4 \\ 2x + 5y + z &= 11 \end{aligned}$$

If we define the matrix **A** as

$$\mathbf{A} = \begin{bmatrix} 2 & -4 & 3 \\ 3 & 0 & -1 \\ 2 & 5 & 1 \end{bmatrix}$$

and the vectors **X** and **B** as

$$\mathbf{X} = \begin{bmatrix} x \\ y \\ z \end{bmatrix} \qquad \text{and} \qquad \mathbf{B} = \begin{bmatrix} -9 \\ 4 \\ 11 \end{bmatrix}$$

the definition of matrix multiplication allows us to represent the above three equations as

$$\begin{bmatrix} 2 & -4 & 3 \\ 3 & 0 & -1 \\ 2 & 5 & 1 \end{bmatrix} \begin{bmatrix} x \\ y \\ z \end{bmatrix} = \begin{bmatrix} -9 \\ 4 \\ 11 \end{bmatrix}$$

or even more concisely as the single matrix equation

$$\mathbf{AX} = \mathbf{B}.$$

This neat representation hints at a way of solving the equations, viz.

$$\mathbf{X} = \mathbf{A}^{-1}\mathbf{B},$$

where $\mathbf{A}^{-1}$ is the matrix inverse of **A** (see Section 14.7 for a method of calculating a matrix inverse).

Matrices can obviously be represented in FORTRAN with two-dimensional arrays. Operations on matrices, like multiplication, are most conveniently handled by using subroutines (which must dimension the arrays they use in the subroutine). To avoid needing a different subroutine for each size of matrix, it is better to specify the *largest* dimension you might need, say MAX, as well as the *actual* dimensions (which must not exceed MAX) used in the particular problem. These dimensions must all be passed over to the subroutine in the argument list. Matrices must be dimensioned to the *same* maximum dimensions in the calling program and the subroutine, otherwise you cannot expect the computer to store the elements correctly.

The subroutine below is a general routine which can be used to multiply matrices of any size. It checks that the two matrices to be multiplied are of compatible dimensions, and if they are not, it prints an error message. The routine is shown in use with a sample calling program which reads two 2×2 matrices, **X** and **Y**, and prints their product, **Z**. The variables IX and IY represent the number of rows in **X** and **Y**, and JX and JY the number of columns. The matrices are declared 3×3 in the main program, so MAX is set to 3.

```
*****  SAMPLE PROGRAM TO TEST MATRIX MULTIPLICATION **************
       REAL      X( 3,3 )
       REAL      Y( 3,3 )
       REAL      Z( 3,3 )
       INTEGER   IX
       INTEGER   IY
       INTEGER   JX
       INTEGER   JY
       INTEGER   MAX

15     FORMAT( 3F6.1 )

       MAX = 3
       READ*, IX, JX, ( (X( I,J ),  J = 1, JX),  I = 1, IX )
       READ*, IY, JY, ( (Y( I,J ),  J = 1, JY),  I = 1, IY )

       CALL MULT( X, Y, Z, MAX, IX, JX, IY, JY )

       DO 20 I = 1, IX
          PRINT 15, ( Z( I,J ),  J = 1, JY )
20     CONTINUE

       STOP
       END

       SUBROUTINE MULT( A, B, C, MAX, IA, JA, IB, JB )
*****  PERFORMS MATRIX MULTIPLICATION:   C = AB ******************
       REAL   A( MAX,MAX )
       REAL   B( MAX,MAX )
       REAL   C( MAX,MAX )

       IF( JA .NE. IB )THEN
          PRINT*, 'MATRICES ARE NOT COMPATIBLE'
       ELSE
          M = JA

          DO 10 I = 1, IA

             DO 20 J = 1, JB
                C( I,J ) = 0

                DO 30 K = 1, M
                   C( I,J ) = C( I,J ) + A( I,K ) * B( K,J )
30              CONTINUE

20           CONTINUE

10        CONTINUE

       END IF

       RETURN
       END
```

Data:

```
2 2            (dimensions of X)
1 2
3 4
2 2            (dimensions of Y)
5 6
0 -1
```

The output from this example is the 2×2 matrix

```
 5.0    4.0
15.0   14.0
```

To appreciate the importance of specifying the correct dimensions in the subroutine, it helps to sketch the memory layout of one of the arrays, and to keep track of how the matrix elements are passed as arguments in the above example. As mentioned above, FORTRAN 77 stores multi-dimensional arrays linearly, by columns:

Calling Program	*Subroutine*	
REAL X(3,3)	**REAL A(MAX,MAX)** /	**REAL A(IA,JA)**
	i.e. A(3,3)	/ i.e. A(2,2)
X(1,1) : 1 -------------	A(1,1) : 1	/ A(1,1) : 1
X(2,1) : 3 -------------	A(2,1) : 3	/ A(2,1) : 3
X(3,1) : 0 -------------	A(3,1) : 0	/ A(1,2) : 0
X(1,2) : 2 -------------	A(1,2) : 2	/ A(2,2) : 2
X(2,2) : 4 -------------	A(2,2) : 4	/ ????????
X(3,2) : 0 -------------	A(3,2) : 0	
. . . . etc		

The column under A (MAX,MAX) shows the correct position. All the subscripts match up between main program and subprogram, so that X(1,2) for example is correctly copied into A(1,2). However, the column under A(IA,JA) shows what happens when the actual matrix size (IA × JA) is incorrectly used to dimension the equivalent array in the subroutine. In this case the array dimensions are not the same as they are in the calling program, and so obviously the subscripts do not all match up correctly now. X(1,2) is now incorrectly copied into A(2,2) which consequently has the value 2 instead of 4, and to make matters even worse (if that is possible) the value of X(2,2) appears to get lost altogether!

As an important postscript to handling multi-dimensional arrays with adjustable dimensions, it should be stressed that arrays can *only* be given adjustable dimensions in a subroutine IF THE ARRAYS ARE PASSED THROUGH AS ARGUMENTS OF THE SUBROUTINE.

It is also instructive to examine some alternatives to the statements handling the matrix output in the above example, i.e.

```
      DO 20 I = 1, IX
         PRINT 15, ( Z( I,J ),   J = 1, JY )
20    CONTINUE
```

If instead of this we wrote

```
      DO 10 I = 1, IX

         DO 20 J = 1, JY
            PRINT 15, Z( I,J )
20       CONTINUE

10    CONTINUE
```

the output would be

```
  5.0
  4.0
 15.0
 14.0
```

since the **PRINT** statement is executed four times, and the **FORMAT** statement opens a new output record each time. On the other hand, if we wrote

```
PRINT 15, ( ( Z( I,J ), J = 1, JY ), I = 1, IX )
```

the output would be

```
  5.0    4.0   15.0
 14.0
```

because **PRINT** is executed only once now. However, the specification 3F6.1 only allows three items into the output record, so a new record is opened for the fourth item.

14.4   Networks

In our first application of matrix multiplication we consider a problem which at first glance appears to have nothing to do with matrix multiplication.

14.4.1   A Spy Ring

Suppose five spies in an espionage ring have the code names Alex, Boris, Cyril, Denisov, and Eric (whom we can number for the sake of argument with the subtle codes of A, B, C, D, and E respectively). The hallmark of a good spy network is that each agent is not able to contact all the others. The arrangement for this particular group is:

> Alex can contact only Cyril (and NOT vice-versa);
> Boris can contact only Alex or Eric (”);
> Denisov can contact only Cyril (”);
> Eric can contact only Cyril or Denisov (”).

The need for good spies to be versed in matrix theory becomes apparent when one spots that the possible paths of communication can be represented by a 5×5 matrix, with rows representing transmitting agents, and columns representing receiving agents, thus:

	A	B	C	D	E
A	0	0	1	0	0
B	1	0	0	0	1
C	0	0	0	0	0
D	0	0	1	0	0
E	0	0	1	1	0

We will call this matrix **A**. It clearly represents a **directed network** with the spies at the **nodes**, and with **arcs** all of length one, where a network is a collection of points, called nodes, joined by lines, called arcs. In a directed network, movement is only possible along the arcs in *one* direction (see Fig. 14.1).

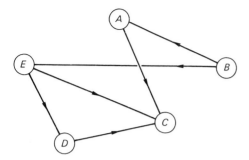

Fig. 14.1 The network represented by the matrix **A**

The matrix **A** may also be thought of as an 'adjacency' matrix, with 1 in row i and column j if there is an arc from node i to node j, or 0 in that position if there is no arc between those two nodes. The diagonal elements of **A** (i.e. a_{11}, a_{22}, etc.) are all 0, because good spies do not talk to themselves (since they might then talk in their sleep and give themselves away).

Now let us multiply this matrix **A** by itself (why not?) and see what happens. We note incidentally, before we embark on this awesome task, that each 1 in **A** represents a single path of length *one* arc in the network (path here means a direct link between two agents). Well, if we do the multiplication, we get

$$\begin{bmatrix} 0 & 0 & 1 & 0 & 0 \\ 1 & 0 & 0 & 0 & 1 \\ 0 & 0 & 0 & 0 & 0 \\ 0 & 0 & 1 & 0 & 0 \\ 0 & 0 & 1 & 1 & 0 \end{bmatrix} \times \begin{bmatrix} 0 & 0 & 1 & 0 & 0 \\ 1 & 0 & 0 & 0 & 1 \\ 0 & 0 & 0 & 0 & 0 \\ 0 & 0 & 1 & 0 & 0 \\ 0 & 0 & 1 & 1 & 0 \end{bmatrix}$$

$$= \begin{bmatrix} 0 & 0 & 0 & 0 & 0 \\ 0 & 0 & 2 & 1 & 0 \\ 0 & 0 & 0 & 0 & 0 \\ 0 & 0 & 0 & 0 & 0 \\ 0 & 0 & 1 & 0 & 0 \end{bmatrix} \text{, which is called } \mathbf{A}^2.$$

Row 2 and column 3 have been highlighted in the two versions of **A** above to help interpret **A**^{2} (which is understood as the matrix **A** multiplied by itself). The element 2 in **A**^{2} (row 2, column 3) results when row 2 of **A** is multiplied term by term with column 3, and the products added. This gives us the scalar product

$$1 \times 1 + 0 \times 0 + 0 \times 0 + 0 \times 1 + 1 \times 1 = 2.$$

The first 1×1 arises because there is a path from node 2 to node 1, which we will denote by (2−1), followed by a path (1−3), giving a composite path (2−1−3) of length two (i.e. from Boris to Cyril via Alex). The second 1×1 arises because there is a path (2−5) followed by a path (5−3), giving a second composite path (2−5−3) of length two (i.e. from Boris to Cyril again, but via Eric this time). It is clear therefore that the entries in **A**^{2} represent the number of paths of length *two* between the various nodes in the network (on the strict understanding that all the arcs are of length one). There are therefore only four paths of length two: two from Boris to Cyril, as we have seen, one from Boris to Denisov, and one from Eric to Cyril (a path of length two in the spy context means one intermediary).

Having got so much interesting information from A^2, the obvious thing to do now is to multiply the matrix A^2 by A again, to form the third power of A, viz. A^3. If you do this correctly, you will get for your trouble the rather dull matrix

$$A^3 = \begin{bmatrix} 0 & 0 & 0 & 0 & 0 \\ 0 & 0 & 1 & 0 & 0 \\ 0 & 0 & 0 & 0 & 0 \\ 0 & 0 & 0 & 0 & 0 \\ 0 & 0 & 0 & 0 & 0 \end{bmatrix} .$$

The single 1 in A^3 tells us now that there is only one path of length *three* in the network (i.e. with *two* intermediaries) and that it is from Boris to Cyril. Drawing the network, or alternatively examining the appropriate row and column in A^2 and A that give rise to this one entry in A^3, reveals that the actual path is Boris—Eric—Denisov—Cyril.

If we now compute A^4, we will find that every element is 0 (we call such a matrix the **null** matrix), signifying that there are no paths of length four in the network, which can be verified by inspection. All higher powers of A will also obviously be null, since if there are no paths of length four there can hardly be any that are longer!

In general, therefore, the element in row i and column j of the kth power of an adjacency matrix A (a matrix where $a_{ij} = 1$ if there is an arc of any length between node i and node j, and $a_{ij} = 0$ if there is no arc) is equal to the number of paths, consisting of k arcs, linking node i to node j.

Coming back to our spy network, since the elements of A are the number of paths of length *one*, and the elements of A^2 are the number of paths of length *two*, etc., then clearly the sum of all these powers of A will tell us how many paths of any length there are altogether between the various nodes. We can therefore define a **reachability** matrix R for this 5×5 network:

$$R = A + A^2 + A^3 + A^4 .$$

R is also a 5×5 matrix, and its elements give the total number of paths of communication between the agents. Doing the calculation eventually gives us

$$R = \begin{bmatrix} 0 & 0 & 1 & 0 & 0 \\ 1 & 0 & 3 & 1 & 1 \\ 0 & 0 & 0 & 0 & 0 \\ 0 & 0 & 1 & 0 & 0 \\ 0 & 0 & 2 & 1 & 0 \end{bmatrix} .$$

So we can read off from the reachability matrix R the fact that there are, for example, three different paths of communication between Boris and Cyril, but only two between Eric and Cyril (the actual lengths of these paths have already been calculated in finding the powers of A). The name reachability is used because the non-zero elements of R indicate which agents may contact which, directly or indirectly, or for a distance network, which nodes may be reached from each node.

14.4.2   The Reachability Matrix

In general, the reachability matrix R of an $n \times n$ network may be defined as the sum of the first $(n-1)$ powers of the adjacency matrix A associated with the network. You may be wondering why we can stop at the $(n-1)$th power of A? The elements of A^{n-1} will be the number of paths that have $(n-1)$ arcs, i.e. that connect n nodes (since each arc joins two nodes). Since there are no further nodes that can be reached, it is not necessary to raise A to the nth power. However, A^n does reveal an interesting property of networks, which you may have guessed, and we will look at this in the next section.

The program that follows computes the reachability matrix **R** for any network of up to ten nodes, given the number of nodes, n, and the adjacency matrix **A** as data, i.e. it computes

$$R = A + A^2 + A^3 + \ldots + A^{n-1}.$$

The program computes the powers of **A** successively, adding them to **R** each time. It uses the matrix multiplication subroutine MULT developed in Section 14.3, and two new subroutines, COPY and SUM, which are discussed below. The matrices **B**, **C**, and **D** are used for intermediate storage.

```
*****  TO COMPUTE THE REACHABILITY MATRIX OF A NETWORK ************

           PARAMETER ( MAX = 10 )

           REAL      A( MAX,MAX )
           REAL      B( MAX,MAX )
           REAL      C( MAX,MAX )
           REAL      D( MAX,MAX )
           REAL      R( MAX,MAX )
           INTEGER N

15         FORMAT( 10F4.0 )

           READ*, N, ( (A( I,J ),  J = 1, N),   I = 1, N )
           CALL COPY( A, B, MAX, N, N )
           CALL COPY( A, R, MAX, N, N )

*  ***  WE WANT N-1 POWERS BUT ALREADY HAVE THE 1ST ONE
           DO 10 I = 1, N-2
              CALL MULT( A, B, C, MAX, N, N, N, N )
              CALL COPY( C, B, MAX, N, N )
              CALL SUM( B, R, D, MAX, N )
              CALL COPY( D, R, MAX, N, N )
10         CONTINUE

           DO 20 I = 1, N
              PRINT 15, ( R( I,J ),  J = 1, N )
20         CONTINUE

           STOP
           END

           SUBROUTINE COPY( A, B, MAX, IA, JA )
*  ***  COPIES A (IAxJA) INTO B AND LOSES PREVIOUS B **************
           REAL   A( MAX, MAX )
           REAL   B( MAX, MAX )

           DO 10 I = 1, IA
              DO 20 J = 1, JA
                 B( I,J ) = A( I,J )
20            CONTINUE
10         CONTINUE

           RETURN
           END

           SUBROUTINE MULT( A, B, C, MAX, IA, JA, IB, JB )
*****  as in §14.3  ***********************************************
```

```
          SUBROUTINE SUM( A, B, C, MAX, N )
* ***  PUTS SUM OF SQUARE MATRICES A & B INTO C,   LOOSING OLD C ***
          DIMENSION A(MAX, MAX), B(MAX, MAX), C(MAX, MAX)
          REAL   A( MAX, MAX )
          REAL   B( MAX, MAX )
          REAL   C( MAX, MAX )

          DO 10 I = 1, N
            DO 20 J = 1, N
              C( I,J ) = A( I,J ) + B( I,J )
20          CONTINUE
10        CONTINUE

          RETURN
          END
```

Note that the maximum matrix dimension (MAX) is set in a **PARAMETER** statement, which makes for very easy editing if a larger dimension is ever required.

The subroutine COPY replaces a matrix **B**, of any dimensions, by a matrix **A** of the same dimensions. It is tempting to try to write a simpler main program, without all the calls to COPY, and with the call to MULT replaced by something like

```
          CALL MULT( A, C, C, MAX, N, N, N, N )
```

since all we are trying to do is to multiply **A** by the previous product each time. However, this is incorrect programming, since on return from MULT the dummy arguments **A** and **B** cannot be copied back into the same array **C**.

The subroutine SUM adds two square matrices of any size, **A** and **B** (by adding elements in the same row and column of each matrix) and stores the sum in **C**.

14.4.3   Cycles

If any elements of A^n, where **A** is the $n \times n$ adjacency matrix of a network, are non-zero, what does this imply? A non-zero element in A^n means a path of length n, i.e. a path linking $n+1$ nodes. Since the network has only n nodes, we are drawn to the inescapable conclusion that in this case the network has a cycle (a path which passes through a particular set of nodes indefinitely).

So we have a neat test for cycling in a network: if A^n is null, there are no cycles; if it is not null, there are cycles. Indeed, since we need to compute all the intermediate powers of **A** in order to get A^n we can spot cycles that do not involve all of the nodes before we have got A^n. If any smaller power of **A** has at least one non-zero on its main diagonal, the network will have at least one cycle, since a path that starts and ends at the same node must be cyclic.

We can therefore extend the test for cycling stated above to the following:

IF   any of the matrices A^2, A^3, . . . , A^{n-1} has a non-zero entry anywhere on a main diagonal,

OR A^n has a non-zero entry anywhere at all,

THEN   the network has at least one cycle, defined by the positions of the non-zero entries,

ELSE   it has no cycles.

Postscript
If **A** has no rows that are full of zeros (i.e. each node has an exit), or no columns full of zeros (i.e. each node can be reached) then there must be a cycle (if not, there may still be one, but we can't be sure).

14.5   Leslie Matrices

Another very interesting and useful application of matrices is to population dynamics, but we will need to do some preliminary work before we can see where the matrices come in. The rabbit population model of Section 9.1 can be made a lot more realistic if we allow some rabbits to die from time to time. The approach we are going to adopt requires that we divide the rabbit population up into a number of age classes, where the members of each age class are one time unit older than the members of the previous class, the time unit being whatever is convenient for the population being studied (days, months, years, etc.). If X_i is the size of the ith age class, we define a survival factor P_i as the proportion of the ith class that survive to the $(i+1)$th age class (i.e. the proportion that 'graduate') and F_i as the mean fertility of the ith class, i.e. the number of newborn individuals expected to be produced during one time interval by each member of the ith class at the beginning of the interval (only females count in biological modelling, since there are always enough males to go round!).

Suppose for our modified rabbit model we have three age classes, with X_1, X_2, and X_3 members respectively. We will call them young, middle-aged, and old-aged for convenience. (We could easily have more age classes — see the example at the end of this section — but we want to keep the problem fairly simple.) We will take our time unit as one month, so X_1 are the number that were born during the current month, and which will be considered as youngsters at the end of the month, X_2 are the number of middle-aged rabbits at the end of this month, and X_3 the number of oldsters. Suppose that the youngsters cannot reproduce, so that $F_1 = 0$. The fertility rate for middle-aged rabbits is 9, so $F_2 = 9$, while that of oldsters is 12, so $F_3 = 12$. The probability of survival from youth to middle-age is one third, so $P_1 = 1/3$, while no less than half the middle-aged rabbits live to become oldsters, so $P_2 = 1/2$. With this information we can quite easily compute the changing population structure month by month, as long as we have the population breakdown to start with. First we calculate how many babies are born in the current month. Let us call this number NEW for the moment, and not X_1 yet:

$$\text{NEW} = \text{F2*X2} + \text{F3*X3} . \tag{1}$$

At the end of the current month, most lucky middle-aged rabbits get promoted to oldsters, so the new value for X_3 will be given by

$$\text{X3} = \text{P2*X2} . \tag{2}$$

Similarly, some youngsters will get to experience the delights of middle-age:

$$\text{X2} = \text{P1*X1} . \tag{3}$$

Finally, now that we have used the current value of X_1, we can update it:

$$\text{X1} = \text{NEW} . \tag{4}$$

Note that we took care to compute the new arrivals in equation (1) from the values of X_2 and X_3 before they were updated in equations (2) and (3). This effectively implies that the gestation period is one month. Also it would be incorrect to use X_1 on the left-hand side of equation (1) because then we would be using the wrong value of X_1 in equation (3).

We are assuming for the sake of illustration that all old-aged rabbits die at the end of the month. This can be corrected in two ways. The members of the third age class could be defined as those rabbits which are three months and older at the end of the current month, in which case we would need to introduce a P_3, being the probability that an oldster does not die that month. The example on the American robin at the end of this section uses this device. Alternatively, one can simply have more age classes, although this will require more biological data. When this type of model was tried out on elephants in the Kruger National

Park, it was found that 60 age classes were sufficient, with a time unit of one year, since very few elephants lived beyond the age of 60 years.

If we have some values of X_1, X_2 and X_3 to start with, we can write a program that uses the above scheme to update the age classes month by month, for as long as we like, and so project the rabbit population into the future. In the program below, we start the model with one old rabbit, and no others, so $X_1=0$, $X_2=0$, and $X_3=1$. The printout after the program gives the population structure and the total population over a period of 24 months.

```
*****  ADVANCED RABBIT POPULATION MODEL BASED ON 3 AGE CLASSES ****
       INTEGER   T
       REAL      F2
       REAL      F3
       REAL      NEW
       REAL      P1
       REAL      P2
       REAL      X1
       REAL      X2
       REAL      X3
       REAL      XTOTAL

15     FORMAT( I4, 4F12.1 )
25     FORMAT( ' MONTH', T12, 'YOUNG', T23, 'MIDDLE', T38, 'OLD',
       $T50, 'TOT'/)
       READ*, X1, X2, X3
       F2 = 9.
       F3 = 12.
       P1 = 1 / 3.
       P2 = 0.5
       XTOTAL = X1 + X2 + X3
       T = 0
       PRINT 25
       PRINT 15, T, X1, X2, X3, XTOTAL
       DO 10 T = 1, 24
          NEW = F2 * X2 + F3 * X3
          X3 = P2 * X2
          X2 = P1 * X1
          X1 = NEW
          XTOTAL = X1 + X2 + X3
          PRINT 15, T, X1, X2, X3, XTOTAL
10     CONTINUE

       STOP
       END
```

Data:

0 0 1

Output:

MONTH	YOUNG	MIDDLE	OLD	TOT
0	.0	.0	1.0	1.0
1	12.0	.0	.0	12.0
2	.0	4.0	.0	4.0
3	36.0	.0	2.0	38.0
4	24.0	12.0	.0	36.0
5	108.0	8.0	6.0	122.0
6	144.0	36.0	4.0	184.0
7	372.0	48.0	18.0	438.0
8	648.0	124.0	24.0	796.0
9	1404.0	216.0	62.0	1682.0
10	2688.0	468.0	108.0	3264.0
11	5508.0	896.0	234.0	6638.0
12	10872.0	1836.0	448.0	13156.0
13	21900.0	3624.0	918.0	26442.0
14	43632.0	7300.0	1812.0	52744.0
15	87444.0	14544.0	3650.0	105638.0
16	174696.0	29148.0	7272.0	211116.0
17	349596.0	58232.0	14574.0	422401.9
18	698975.9	116532.0	29116.0	844623.9
19	1398179.8	232992.0	58266.0	1689437.8
20	2796119.6	466059.9	116496.0	3378675.5
21	5592491.2	932039.9	233030.0	6757560.9
22	11184718.3	1864163.7	466019.9	13514901.8
23	22369712.3	3728239.4	932081.9	27030033.3
24	44739136.5	7456570.7	1864119.7	54059826.5

If you look carefully at the output you may spot that after some months the total population doubles every month. But what you probably won't spot is that the numbers in the three age classes tend to a limiting ratio of 24:4:1. This can be demonstrated very clearly if you run the model with an initial population structure having this limiting ratio, e.g. $X_1 = 24$; $X_2 = 4$; $X_3 = 1$. We will come back to this intriguing result at the end of this section.

Well, what has all this got to do with matrices? Everything, as we shall see in a moment. If we denote the current month by t, and next month by $t+1$, we can refer to this month's youngsters as X_1 (t), and to next month's as X_1 $(t+1)$, and similarly for the other two age classes. The scheme of equations (1) to (4) for updating the population can then be written as three equations:

$$
\begin{aligned}
X_1(t+1) &= 0 &+& F_2X_2(t) &+& F_3X_3(t) \\
X_2(t+1) &= P_1X_1(t) &+& 0 &+& 0 \\
X_3(t+1) &= 0 &+& P_2X_2(t) &+& 0
\end{aligned}
$$

The obvious thing to do now is to define a population vector $\mathbf{X}$ (t), with three components, $X_1(t)$, $X_2(t)$, and $X_3(t)$, representing the three age classes of the rabbit population in month t. The above three equations specify how to get from $\mathbf{X}(t)$ to $\mathbf{X}(t+1)$, and using this vector, with a matrix for the coefficients on the right-hand side, we can easily rewrite the equations as

$$
\begin{bmatrix} X_1 \\ X_2 \\ X_3 \end{bmatrix}_{t+1} = \begin{bmatrix} 0 & F_2 & F_3 \\ P_1 & 0 & 0 \\ 0 & P_2 & 0 \end{bmatrix} \begin{bmatrix} X_1 \\ X_2 \\ X_3 \end{bmatrix}_{t}
$$

where the subscript at the bottom of the vectors indicates the month. We can write this even more concisely as the matrix equation

$$X(t+1) = LX(t) \quad , \tag{5}$$

where **L** is the matrix

$$\begin{bmatrix} 0 & 9 & 12 \\ 1/3 & 0 & 0 \\ 0 & 1/2 & 0 \end{bmatrix}$$

in this particular case. **L** is called a **Leslie Matrix**. A population model can always be written in the form of equation (5) if the concepts of age classes, fertility, and survival factors, as outlined above, are used.

Now that we have established a matrix representation for our population model, we can easily write a program using matrix multiplication and repeated applications of equation (5):

$$X(t+2) = LX(t+1),$$
$$X(t+3) = LX(t+2), \text{ etc.}$$

However, we need only one vector **X** in the program (a 3×1 array will do) because after each matrix multiplication we can copy the product back into **X**. The following program will produce exactly the same output as the previous one, but is totally general, in that it can deal with a population with up to ten age classes. Note that a one-dimensional array X(10) can be used in place of the square array X(10,10) to save storage space, but then MULT and COPY will have to be rewritten, since these routines assume square two-dimensional arrays for maximum dimensioning. The function POPTOT is used to compute the total population size each month.

```
*****  COMPUTES POPULATION STRUCTURE USING LESLIE MATRIX **********

       PARAMETER (MAX = 10)

       REAL      L( MAX,MAX )
       REAL      P( MAX,MAX )
       REAL      X( MAX,MAX )
       INTEGER   N
       INTEGER   T

15     FORMAT( ' MONTH', T12, 'YOUNG', T23, 'MIDDLE', T38, 'OLD',
      $T50, 'TOT'/)
25     FORMAT( I4, 10F12.1 )

       T = 0
       M = 1
       READ*, N, ( X( K,1 ),  K = 1, N )
       READ*, ( (L( K,J ),   J = 1, N),   K = 1, N )
       PRINT 15
       PRINT 25, T, ( X( K,1 ), K = 1, N ), POPTOT( X, MAX, N )

       DO 10 T = 1, 24
          CALL MULT( L, X, P, MAX, N, N, N, M )
          CALL COPY( P, X, MAX, N, M )
          PRINT 25, T, ( X( K,1 ),  K = 1, N ), POPTOT( X, MAX, N )
10     CONTINUE

       STOP
       END
```

```
        SUBROUTINE COPY( A,  B,  MAX,  IA,  JA )
*****   as  in  §14.4.2  ****************************************

        SUBROUTINE MULT( A,  B,  C,  MAX,  IA,  JA,  IB,  JB )
*****   as  in  §14.3  ******************************************

        FUNCTION POPTOT( X,  MAX,  N )
*****   SUMS ALL ELEMENTS IN 1ST COLUMN OF X ********************
        REAL X( MAX,MAX )

        POPTOT = 0

        DO 10 K = 1,  N
            POPTOT = POPTOT + X( K,1 )
10      CONTINUE

        RETURN
        END
```

Data:

```
3
0 0 1
0 9 12
0.333333 0 0
0 0.5 0
```

We have already observed that after sufficient time has elapsed, the total population doubles each month. This factor is called the growth factor, and is a property of the particular Leslie Matrix being used (for those who know about these things, it is the dominant eigenvalue of the matrix). The growth factor is two in this example, but if the values in the Leslie Matrix are changed, the long-term growth factor changes too (try it and see!).

We have also noted that the values of X_1, X_2, and X_3 reach a limiting ratio of 24:4:1. This limiting ratio is called the stable age distribution of the population, and again it is a property of the Leslie Matrix (in fact, it is the eigenvector belonging to the dominant eigenvalue of the matrix). Different population matrices lead to different stable age distributions. The interesting point about all this is that any given Leslie Matrix always eventually gets a population into the *same* stable age distribution, which increases eventually by the *same* growth factor each month, *whatever the initial population is.* For example, if you run the above model with any other initial population, it will always get into a stable age distribution of 24:4:1 with a growth factor of two (try it and see).

A Leslie Matrix may be constructed for any population, with any number of age classes, and always has the same characteristic structure. For example, the American robin has been modelled along these line. Seven age classes, $X_1, X_2, \ldots, X_7$ are defined, with a time unit of one year, the seventh class representing all the robins that are more than six years old. The general structure of the Leslie Matrix is:

$$
\begin{bmatrix}
0 & F_2 & F_3 & F_4 & F_5 & F_6 & F_7 \\
P_1 & 0 & 0 & 0 & 0 & 0 & 0 \\
0 & P_2 & 0 & 0 & 0 & 0 & 0 \\
0 & 0 & P_3 & 0 & 0 & 0 & 0 \\
0 & 0 & 0 & P_4 & 0 & 0 & 0 \\
0 & 0 & 0 & 0 & P_5 & 0 & 0 \\
0 & 0 & 0 & 0 & 0 & P_6 & P_7
\end{bmatrix}
$$

The F_i and P_i have the same meaning as before, and P_7 is the proportion of robins aged seven years and older that survive each year. A study of these birds published in 1945, cited by Spain (1982), gives the following values for the Leslie Matrix:

$$\begin{bmatrix} 0.000 & 1.400 & 2.100 & 1.600 & 1.400 & 1.100 & 1.000 \\ 0.355 & 0 & 0 & 0 & 0 & 0 & 0 \\ 0 & 0.461 & 0 & 0 & 0 & 0 & 0 \\ 0 & 0 & 0.433 & 0 & 0 & 0 & 0 \\ 0 & 0 & 0 & 0.364 & 0 & 0 & 0 \\ 0 & 0 & 0 & 0 & 0.300 & 0 & 0 \\ 0 & 0 & 0 & 0 & 0 & 0.200 & 0.100 \end{bmatrix}$$

Sample values of the seven age classes X_1 to X_7 are 1400, 497, 229, 99, 36, 10 and 6 respectively.

14.6   Markov Chains

Often a process that we wish to model may be represented by a number of possible discrete (i.e. discontinuous) states that describe the process. For example, if we are spinning a coin, then the process is adequately represented by the two states 'heads' and 'tails' (and nothing in between). If the process is random, as it is with spinning coins, there is a certain probability of being in any of the states at a given moment, and also a probability of changing from one state to another. If the probability of moving from one state to another depends only on the present state, and not on any previous state, the process is called a **Markov chain**. The progress of the drunk sailor in Chapter 13 is an example of a Markov chain. A variation on this example is given below. Markov chains are used widely in such diverse fields as biology and business decision making, to name just two areas. We will give two simple examples to illustrate the concept.

14.6.1   Weather 'Prediction'

The first example (Kemeny and Kurtz, 1967) is taken from the Land of Oz, where the weather on a given day may be in one of three states: Rainy, Fair, or Snowy. We can represent these states by a three component vector $X(t)$, where $X_1(t)$, $X_2(t)$, and $X_3(t)$ are the probabilities of the weather being Rainy, Fair, or Snowy respectively, on day t. Obviously, the components of $X(t)$ must sum to one, since the weather can be in no other state. The weather is 'controlled' by the Wizard, who operates on a fairly random basis, like most wizards. His rule appears to be that if it is rainy today, it will be the same tomorrow one half of the time, and equally likely to be fair or snowy the rest of the time. If it is fair today, the weather tomorrow is equally likely to be rainy or snowy (two fair days in a row are unheard of in Oz). If it is snowy today, it will be the same tomorrow one half of the time, and equally likely to be rainy or fair the rest of the time.

In the last three sentences, we have stated the **transition** probabilities of moving from any one state today to any other state tomorrow. These probabilities are best expressed in the form of a **transition probability matrix, P**, where **P** is

		Today		
		Rainy	Fair	Snowy
	Rainy	0.5	0.5	0.25
Tomorrow	Fair	0.25	0.0	0.25
	Snowy	0.25	0.5	0.5

Note that the columns of P add up to one. What is the weather likely to do tomorrow? The chances of it being rainy tomorrow are 0.5 if it rained or was fair today, and 0.25 if it snowed today (top row of **P**). Thus, if time t is today, the probability of it being rainy tomorrow, represented by $X_1(t+1)$, is given by

$$X_1(t+1)=0.5X_1(t)+0.5X_2(t)+0.25X_3(t) \quad . \quad (1)$$

Similarly, the chances of it being fair or snowy tomorrow are given respectively by equations (2) and (3):

$$X_2(t+1)=0.25X(t)+0+0.25X_3(t) \quad , \quad (2)$$
$$X_3(t+1)=0.25X_1(t)+0.5X_2(t)+0.5X_3(t) \quad . \quad (3)$$

We can write equations (1) to (3) in matrix form, as we did with the rabbit population model:

$$\begin{bmatrix} X_1 \\ X_2 \\ X_3 \end{bmatrix}_{t+1} = \begin{bmatrix} 0.5 & 0.5 & 0.25 \\ 0.25 & 0.0 & 0.25 \\ 0.25 & 0.5 & 0.5 \end{bmatrix} \begin{bmatrix} X_1 \\ X_2 \\ X_3 \end{bmatrix}_{t}$$

or more concisely,

$$X(t+1)=PX(t).$$

By applying equation (4) repeatedly, we can find the long range weather prospects,

$$X(t+2)=PX(t+1),$$
$$X(t+3)=PX(t+2), \text{etc.},$$

provided we know the state of the weather on a given day. Suppose it is rainy today. Then $X_1(0)=1$, since it is certain, while $X_2(0)=0$ and $X_3(0)=0$. Using these starting values, we can generate the probability states of the weather for as long as we like.

The computing is almost identical to that required in the previous section for generating the rabbit population structure over a number of months. In fact the same program may be used, with only minor changes to the **FORMAT** statements. Starting with a rainy day at time $t=0$, as suggested above, the program gives the following output for the next week:

Day	Rainy	Fair	Snowy
0	1.0000	.0000	.0000
1	.5000	.2500	.2500
2	.4375	.1875	.3750
3	.4063	.2031	.3906
4	.4023	.1992	.3984
5	.4004	.2002	.3994
6	.4001	.2000	.3999
7	.4000	.2000	.4000

We see from the output that the probabilites 'converge' to the limiting probabilities $X_1=0.4$; $X_2=0.2$; $X_3=0.4$. In fact, they converge to the *same* limit, for a given transition probability matrix **P**, *whatever the initial state happens to be* (try this out on different initial states). The limiting probabilities in this example mean that in the long run it rains 40% of the time, and snows 40% of the time, while the weather is fair on average one day in five.

14.6.2   A Random Walk

The second example (Kemeny and Kurtz, 1967) is a variation on the random walk problem. A street has six intersections. A drunk wanders down the street. His home is at intersection 1 and his favourite bar at intersection 6. At each intersection other than home or bar he moves in the direction of the bar with probability 2/3, and in the direction of home with probability 1/3. He never wanders down a side street. If he reaches his home or the bar, he disappears into it, never to reappear (when he disappears, we say in the jargon that the Markov process is 'absorbed').

We would like to know: what are the chances of him ending up at home or in the bar, if he starts at a given corner (other than home or bar, obviously)? He can clearly be in one of six states, with respect to his random walk, which can be conveniently labelled by the intersection number, where state 1 means 'Home', and state 6 means 'Bar'. We can express this Markov process by the following transition probability matrix:

| | | Present state (corner) | | | | | |
		Home	2	3	4	5	Bar
	Home	1	1/3	0	0	0	0
	2	0	0	1/3	0	0	0
Next	3	0	2/3	0	1/3	0	0
state	4	0	0	2/3	0	1/3	0
(corner)	5	0	0	0	2/3	0	0
	Bar	0	0	0	0	2/3	1

The entries for *Home — Home* and *Bar — Bar* are both 1, because he stays put there with certainty (probability 1).

We can compute the probability states in the same way as we did for the land of Oz, forming the new state vector from the old one each time:

$$X(t+1) = PX(t) \quad .$$

If we suppose the man starts at intersection 2, the initial probabilities will be: (0; 1; 0; 0; 0; 0). Using this starting vector, we generate the following states in the future:

Time	Home	2	3	4	5	Bar
0	.0000	1.0000	.0000	.0000	.0000	.0000
1	.3333	.0000	.6667	.0000	.0000	.0000
2	.3333	.2222	.0000	.4444	.0000	.0000
3	.4074	.0000	.2963	.0000	.2963	.0000
4	.4074	.0988	.0000	.2963	.0000	.1975
5	.4403	.0000	.1646	.0000	.1975	.1975
6	.4403	.0549	.0000	.1756	.0000	.3292
7	.4586	.0000	.0951	.0000	.1171	.3292
8	.4586	.0317	.0000	.1024	.0000	.4073
9	.4692	.0000	.0553	.0000	.0683	.4073
10	.4692	.0184	.0000	.0596	.0000	.4528
11	.4753	.0000	.0322	.0000	.0397	.4528
12	.4753	.0107	.0000	.0347	.0000	.4793
13	.4789	.0000	.0187	.0000	.0231	.4793
14	.4789	.0062	.0000	.0202	.0000	.4947
15	.4810	.0000	.0109	.0000	.0135	.4947
16	.4810	.0036	.0000	.0117	.0000	.5037
. . . .						
30	.4838	.0001	.0000	.0003	.0000	.5158
. . . .						
40	.4839	.0000	.0000	.0000	.0000	.5161
. . . .						
50	.4839	.0000	.0000	.0000	.0000	.5161

By running the program for long enough, we soon find the limiting probabilities: he ends up at home about 48% of the time, and at the bar about 52% of the time. Perhaps this is a little surprising: from the transition probabilities, we might have expected him to get to the bar rather more easily. It just goes to show that you should never trust your intuition when it comes to statistics!

Note that the Markov chain approach is not a simulation: one gets the 'theoretical' probabilities each time (this can all be done mathematically, without a computer). But it is interesting to confirm the limiting probabilities by simulating the drunk's progress, using a random number generator (see Exercise 14.4 below).

14.7   Solution of Simultaneous Linear Equations

A problem that often arises in scientific applications is the solution of a system of simultaneous linear equations. As an example, let us take the system of three equations

$$2x-y+z=4$$
$$x+y+z=3$$
$$3x-y-z=1 \quad .$$

One way of solving a system like this is by **Gauss reduction**, which goes as follows. Write the coefficients of the left-hand side as a matrix, with the right-hand side constants as a vector on the right of the matrix, separated by a vertical line, thus:

$$\left[\begin{array}{ccc|c} 2 & -1 & 1 & 4 \\ 1 & 1 & 1 & 3 \\ 3 & -1 & -1 & 1 \end{array}\right]$$

This is simply shorthand for the original set. As long as we perform only 'row operations' on the numbers, we can omit the symbols x, y and z each time. We can refer to the array of coefficients as a matrix $\mathbf{A}$, where $a_{11}=2$, $a_{12}=-1$, etc., and to the right-hand side as a vector $\mathbf{B}$, where $b_1=4$, etc.

In Gauss reduction we start with the first row (R_1), and call it the **pivot row**. We call the element a_{11} the **pivot element**. Divide the whole pivot row by the pivot element, so the array now looks like:

$$\left[\begin{array}{ccc|c} 1 & -1/2 & 1/2 & 2 \\ 1 & 1 & 1 & 3 \\ 3 & -1 & -1 & 1 \end{array}\right]$$

Rows R_2 and R_3 are now called **target rows**. The object is to get zeros in all the target rows below (and above if necessary) the pivot element. Take the target row R_2. Replace each element in the row by itself minus the corresponding element in the pivot row. The array now looks like this:

$$\left[\begin{array}{ccc|c} 1 & -1/2 & 1/2 & 2 \\ 0 & 3/2 & 1/2 & 1 \\ 3 & -1 & -1 & 1 \end{array}\right]$$

Now take the target row R_3. To reduce a_{31} to zero with an operation involving the pivot row requires replacing the target row by itself minus the pivot row multiplied by a_{31} (bearing in mind for the subsequent computer solution that this operation can change the value of a_{31} itself!):

$$\left[\begin{array}{ccc|c} 1 & -1/2 & 1/2 & 2 \\ 0 & 3/2 & 1/2 & 1 \\ 0 & 1/2 & -5/2 & -5 \end{array}\right]$$

We now designate R_2 as the pivot row, and a_{22} as the pivot element. The whole procedure is repeated, except that the target rows are now R_1 and R_3, and the object is to get zeros in these two rows above and below the pivot element. The result is:

$$\begin{bmatrix} 1 & 0 & 2/3 & 7/3 \\ 0 & 1 & 1/3 & 2/3 \\ 0 & 0 & -8/3 & -16/3 \end{bmatrix}$$

Now take R_3 as the pivot row, with a_{33} as the pivot element, and R_1 and R_2 as target rows. After repeating similar operations on them, the array finally looks like:

$$\begin{bmatrix} 1 & 0 & 0 & 1 \\ 0 & 1 & 0 & 0 \\ 0 & 0 & 1 & 2 \end{bmatrix}$$

Since we have retained the mathematical integrity of the system of equations by performing operations on the rows only, this is equivalent to

$$x+0y+0z=1$$
$$0x+ y+0z=0$$
$$0x+0y+ z=2 \quad.$$

The solution may therefore be read off as $x=1; y=0; z=2$.

The subroutine GAUSS below performs a Gauss reduction on a system of N linear equations with coefficients in the array A, and right-hand side constants in the array B. The solutions are returned in the array X. The array G is used for 'working space', and contains the elements of the reduction process. Although it is not needed by the main program, G must be passed as an argument to the subroutine in order to have an adjustable dimension. The subroutine is shown in operation with a test main program, which will work for a system of up to 10 equations. For larger systems, only the **PARAMETER** statement needs to be changed.

```
        PARAMETER (MAX = 10)
        REAL A( MAX, MAX )
        REAL B( MAX )
        REAL G( MAX, MAX+1 )
        REAL X( MAX )

15      FORMAT( ' ', 4F8.2 )

        READ*, N, ( ( A( I, J ), J = 1, N ), I = 1, N )
        READ*, ( B( I ), I = 1, N )

        CALL GAUSS( A, B, G, X, N, MAX )

        PRINT 15, ( X( I ), I = 1, N )

        STOP
        END


        SUBROUTINE GAUSS( A, B, G, X, N, MAX )
* ***   LHS COEFFS IN A, RHS IN B, SOLUTION IN X

        REAL A( MAX, MAX )
        REAL B( MAX )
        REAL G( MAX, MAX+1 )
        REAL X( MAX )
```

```
* *** INSERT A INTO FIRST N COLUMNS OF G

      DO 10 I = 1, N

        DO 20 J = 1, N
          G( I, J ) = A( I, J )
20        CONTINUE

10    CONTINUE

* *** INSERT B INTO (N+1)TH COLUMN OF G

      DO 30 I = 1, N
        G( I, N+1 ) = B( I )
30    CONTINUE

* *** NOW FOR THE GAUSS REDUCTION ...
* *** MAKE EACH ROW THE PIVOT ROW IN TURN,
* *** AND DIVIDE EACH ELEMENT IN PIVOT ROW BY THE PIVOT ELEMENT

      DO 40 IP = 1, N
        PIV = G( IP, IP )

        DO 50 J = 1, N+1
          G( IP, J ) = G( IP, J ) / PIV
50        CONTINUE

* ***     THEN REPLACE EVERY OTHER ROW (CALLED TARGET ROWS) BY
* ***     TARGET ROW MINUS PIVOT ROW MULTIPLIED BY ELEMENT IN
* ***     TARGET ROW AND PIVOT COLUMM

        DO 60 IT = 1, N

          IF( IT. NE. IP )THEN
          TARCO = G( IT, IP )

            DO 70 J = 1, N+1
              G( IT, J ) = G( IT, J ) - G( IP, J ) * TARCO
70            CONTINUE

          END IF

60        CONTINUE

40    CONTINUE

* *** FINALLY COPY (N+1)TH COLUMN OF G INTO X
      DO 80 I = 1, N
        X( I ) = G( I, N+1 )
80    CONTINUE

      RETURN
      END
```

Unfortunately things can go wrong with the Gauss reduction as implemented in our subroutine:

1) The pivot element could be zero. This happens quite easily when the coefficients are all integers. However, rows of the array can be interchanged (see Exercise 14.5) without changing the system of equation. So a non-zero pivot element can often be found in this way (but see the next two cases).

2) A row of zeros could appear right across the array (in which case a non-zero pivot element cannot be found). In this case the system of equations is indeterminate and the solution can only be determined down to as many arbitrary constants as there are rows of zeros.

3) A row of the array could be filled with zeros, except for the extreme right-hand element. In this case the equations are inconsistent, which means that there are no solutions.

It is a nice programming project to extend the above subroutine to deal with these three cases.

Gauss reduction can also be used to invert a matrix. Suppose we want to invert the matrix

$$A = \begin{bmatrix} 2 & 2 & 2 \\ 3 & 2 & 2 \\ 3 & 2 & 3 \end{bmatrix}$$

Construct the array $A \mid I$, i.e.

$$\left[\begin{array}{ccc|ccc} 2 & 2 & 2 & 1 & 0 & 0 \\ 3 & 2 & 2 & 0 & 1 & 0 \\ 3 & 2 & 3 & 0 & 0 & 1 \end{array} \right]$$

where I is the **identity matrix**, and perform a Gauss reduction until the identity matrix has appeared to the left of the vertical line, so that the array looks as follows:

$$\left[\begin{array}{ccc|ccc} 1 & 0 & 0 & -1 & 1 & 0 \\ 0 & 1 & 0 & 3/2 & 0 & -1 \\ 0 & 0 & 1 & 0 & -1 & 1 \end{array} \right]$$

The entity to the right of the line is the inverse of A. If A is not invertible, the process breaks down, and a row of zeros appears.

14.8 Calculation of Volume of Excavation

A problem that arises in the building industry is the calculation of the volume of earth to be excavated on a site. We assume that the excavation is to have a rectangular level base and vertical sides. The area to be excavated is surveyed, and the heights of the ground above the excavation base are found, on a 10 metre square grid, let us say. So a section of a plan of such an excavation could look something like this:

	A	B	C
3	395	386	356
2	295	285	248
1	245	310	300

The numbers are the heights above the excavation base in centimetres. Consider the square bounded by A_3, B_3, A_2 and B_2. The volume of the vertical square prism excavated beneath it is the horizontal plan area times the average height of the corners above the base, i.e.

Volume $= 10\times10\times(3.95+3.86+2.85+2.95)/4$ cubic metres.

We could do this for every vertical square prism to be excavated and add up all the volumes so calculated. However, an easier way presents itself if we notice that some corner heights are used in four squares, some in two squares, and some in only one, as shown below:

Grid point	Corner height	No. of squares (n) corner appears in	$n\times$ corner height
A_3	3.95	1	3.95
B_3	3.86	2	7.72
C_3	3.56	1	3.56
A_2	2.95	2	5.90
B_2	2.85	4	11.40
C_2	2.48	2	4.96
A_1	2.45	1	2.45
B_1	3.10	2	6.20
C_1	3.00	1	3.00
			TOTAL:49.14

From this table, the volume to be excavated may be calculated as

$10\times10\times49.14/4 = 1228.5$ cubic metres.

In general, the corner heights may obviously be represented by a matrix $\mathbf{H}$, say, where a praticular height is given h_{ij}, and where i and j label the rows and columns of the grid respectively. Let us suppose there are m rows and n columns in the grid. The contributions of the heights to the total volume are as follows:

Corners in 1 square: $h_{11}+h_{1n}+h_{m1}+h_{mn}$

Corners in 2 squares: $2\sum_{i=2}^{m-1}[h_{i1}+h_{in}]+2\sum_{j=2}^{n-1}[h_{1j}+h_{mj}]$

Corners in 4 squares: $4\sum_{i=2}^{m-1}\sum_{j=2}^{n-1}h_{ij}$

This sort of calculation is what computers were invented for. The program below computes the volume of excavation under an M×N grid, where the maximum size of M and N is 10.

```
      PARAMETER (MAX = 10)
      REAL H( MAX, MAX )

15    FORMAT( A, F8.2 )

      READ*, M, N
      READ*, ( ( H( I, J ), J = 1, N ), I = 1, M )

      PRINT 15, ' VOLUME EXCAVATED:', EXVOL( H, MAX, N, M )

      STOP
      END
```

```
REAL FUNCTION EXVOL( H, MAX, M, N )
REAL H( MAX, MAX )
DATA V1, V2, V4 / 3 * 0.0 /

V1 = H( 1, 1 ) + H( 1, N ) + H( M, 1 ) + H( M, N )

      DO 10 I = 2, M-1
        V2 = V2 + 2 * ( H( I, 1 ) + H( I, N ) )
10    CONTINUE

      DO 20 J = 2, N-1
        V2 = V2 + 2 * ( H( 1, J ) + H( M, J ) )
20    CONTINUE

      DO 30 I = 2, M-1

        DO 40 J = 2, N-1
          V4 = V4 + 4 * H( I, J )
40      CONTINUE

30    CONTINUE

EXVOL = 100 * (V1 + V2+ V4) / 4.0

RETURN
END
```

14.9   Area of a Site

A problem which arises in land surveying is the calculation of the area of a plot of ground. Assuming the sides of the plot to be straight, this amounts to finding the area of an irregular polygon, i.e. an n-sided figure with straight sides. Although the computation that is described below doesn't actually use matrices directly, the algorithm used exploits a mathematical property of matrices: the determinant.

Considering the 3×3 matrix

$$\mathbf{A} = \begin{bmatrix} a_{11} & a_{12} & a_{13} \\ a_{21} & a_{22} & a_{23} \\ a_{31} & a_{32} & a_{33} \end{bmatrix} \quad ,$$

its determinant D is defined as

$$\begin{aligned} D = &a_{11}(a_{22}a_{33} - a_{23}a_{32}) \\ &+ a_{12}(a_{23}a_{31} - a_{21}a_{33}) \\ &+ a_{13}(a_{21}a_{32} - a_{22}a_{31}) \end{aligned}$$

Now consider the triangle in Fig 14.2.

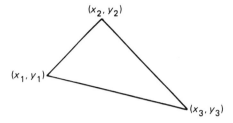

Fig. 14.2

If the positions of its vertices are represented by Cartesian co-ordinates in the usual way, the area of the triangle may be given as

$$\text{Area} = 0.5 \times Det \begin{bmatrix} 1 & 1 & 1 \\ y_1 & y_2 & y_3 \\ x_1 & x_2 & x_3 \end{bmatrix}$$

where Det stands for determinant (this is not too difficult to prove: drop perpendiculars from the vertices to the x-axis and use the areas of the resulting trapezia in the figure to find the area of the triangle).

The point about this is that a polygon with N vertices may be broken up into N-2 triangles sharing a common vertex by drawing lines from the common vertex to each other vertex in turn, as shown in Fig. 14.3.

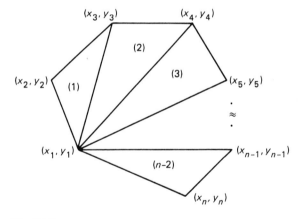

Fig. 14.3

The area of the ith triangle (numbered from the left) in the composite figure is thus

$$0.5 \times Det \begin{bmatrix} 1 & 1 & 1 \\ y_1 & y_{i+1} & y_{i+2} \\ x_1 & x_{i+1} & x_{i+2} \end{bmatrix}$$

as can easily be seen by writing out the expression for the areas of a 6-sided polygon, for example. The area of the N-sided polygon thus formed is the sum of the areas (∗) for i running from 1 to N−2. The formula works, by the way, even if some of the interior angles of the polygon are reflex (>180°). This is because the sign of a determinant changes if two rows or columns are interchanged (puzzle that one out if you like!).

The program that follows computes the area of a polygon, where the only restriction on the data is that the co-ordinates of the vertices must be given in order as one moves round the figure in a clockwise sense. The sample data in the program is for a seven-sided figure with one reflex angle, the area of which is 4 units (you can verify the result by drawing the figure on squared paper).

```
      PARAMETER (MAX = 7)
      REAL A(3,3)
      REAL X(MAX)
      REAL Y(MAX)

      DATA A(1,1), A(1,2), A(1,3) / 3 * 1.0 /
      DATA X / 0.0, -1.0, 0.0, 1.0, 1.0, 2.0, 2.0 /
      DATA Y / 0.0, 1.0, 2.0, 2.0, 1.0, 1.0, 0.0 /

15    FORMAT( A, F8.1 )

      AREA = 0
      A(2,1) = X(1)
      A(3,1) = Y(1)

      DO 10 I = 1, MAX-2
         A(2,2) = Y(I+1)
         A(3,2) = X(I+1)
         A(2,3) = Y(I+2)
         A(3,3) = X(I+2)
         AREA = AREA + 0.5 * DET3( A )
10    CONTINUE

      PRINT 15, ' AREA:', AREA

      STOP
      END

      REAL FUNCTION DET3( A )
* *** COMPUTES THE DETERMINANT OF A 3x3 MATRIX A

      REAL A(3,3)

      D1 = A(1,1) * ( A(2,2) * A(3,3) - A(2,3) * A(3,2) )
      D2 = A(1,2) * ( A(2,3) * A(3,1) - A(2,1) * A(3,3) )
      D3 = A(1,3) * ( A(2,1) * A(3,2) - A(2,2) * A(3,1) )
      DET3 = D1 + D2 + D3

      RETURN
      END
```

14.10   Rotation of a Co-ordinate System

When a Cartesian co-ordinate system is rotated counterclockwise through an angle a the new co-ordinates (x', y') of a point in the rotated system are given by

$$x' = x \cos(a) + y \sin(a)$$
$$y' = -x \sin(a) + y \cos(a)$$

where (x, y) are its co-ordinates before rotation. In Section 12.1 we saw how to compute the new co-ordinates using a statement function. However, this transformation may be written more concisely using matrix multiplication:

$$X' = A X$$

where $A = \begin{bmatrix} \cos(a) & \sin(a) \\ -\sin(a) & \cos(a) \end{bmatrix}$

and $X = \begin{bmatrix} x \\ y \end{bmatrix}$, $X' = \begin{bmatrix} x' \\ y' \end{bmatrix}$

The program below computes and prints out the new co-ordinates of five points on the x-axis after a rotation of 30°. It could form the basis of a more general graphics program to rotate a figure on a screen by transforming the co-ordinates of each point in the figure. Note that only the first columns of B and C are used since they represent the column vectors X and X'.

```
        INTEGER PTS
        PARAMETER (PTS = 5)
        PARAMETER (MAX = 2)
        PARAMETER (CONV = 3.1415927 / 180)
        REAL A( MAX,MAX )
        REAL B( MAX,MAX )
        REAL C( MAX,MAX )
        REAL X(PTS)
        REAL Y(PTS)

        DATA X / 1.0, 2.0, 3.0, 4.0, 5.0 / Y / 5 * 0.0 /

15      FORMAT( 2F8.4 )

        ANG = CONV * 30
        M = 1

C ***   SET UP TRANSFORMATION MATRIX
        A( 1,1 ) = COS( ANG )
        A( 1,2 ) = SIN( ANG )
        A( 2,1 ) = - A( 1,2 )
        A( 2,2 ) = A( 1,1 )

        DO 10 I = 1, PTS
           B( 1,1 ) = X(I)
           B( 2,1 ) = Y(I)
           CALL MULT( A, B, C, MAX, MAX, MAX, MAX, M )
           PRINT 15, C( 1,1 ), C( 2,1 )
10      CONTINUE

        STOP
        END

        SUBROUTINE MULT( A, B, C, MAX, IA, JA, IB, JB )
* ***   as in §14.3 ***
```

The output (the x' and y' co-ordinates of each point) is:

```
 .8660  -.5000
1.7321 -1.0000
2.5981 -1.5000
3.4641 -2.0000
4.3301 -2.5000
```

14.11   Summary

* A matrix or table may be represented in FORTRAN by a two-dimensional array.

* A matrix may be input/output in various ways: nested implied DO-loops, implied DO-loop within a DO-loop, nested DO-loops.

* The elements of a matrix are stored by column, i.e. so that the first subscript changes fastest, and the last subscript changes slowest.

* If a matrix is an argument of a subprogram, it must be dimensioned with the same (maximum) dimension in the subprogram as in the main program.

14.12   Exercises

14.1   Write a subroutine TRANS (A, MAX, N) which replaces the N×N matrix **A** by its transpose, where N ≤ MAX. *Hint*: the following coding will *not* do the job (why not)?

```
     DO 10 I = 1, N
       DO 20 J = 1, N
         A(I, J) = A(J, I)
20       CONTINUE
10     CONTINUE
```

14.2   Run the Leslie matrix model of the American robin in Section 14.5 using the populations values suggested and see if you can find the stable age distribution.

14.3   Compute the limiting probabilities for the drunk in Section 14.6 when he starts at each of the remaining intersections in turn, and confirm that the closer he starts to the bar, the more likely he is to end up there.

14.4   Write a program to *simulate* the drunk's progress down the street. Start him at a given intersection, and generate a random number to decide whether he moves towards the bar or home, according to the probabilities in the transition matrix (i.e. if the random number is ≤ 2/3 he moves toward the bar, unless he is already at home or the bar, in which case that random walk ends, otherwise he moves towards home). For each simulated random walk, record whether he ends up at home or in the bar. Repeat a large number of times. The proportion of walks that end up in either place should approach the limiting probabilities computed using the Markov model in Exercise 14.3.

14.5   Write a subroutine to interchange rows I and J of an array A with N columns and of maximum dimensions MAX. The routine should be invoked with a statement like

```
     CALL ROWSWP( A, N, MAX, I, J )
```

14.6   Write two function subprograms, ROWSUM and COLSUM, to find the sums of the Ith row and Jth column respectively of an M×N matrix of maximum dimensions MAX.

14.7   Write a subroutine

```
     SUBROUTINE MAXELT( A, M, N, MAX, IMAX, JMAX, ELTMAX )
```

to find the largest element (ELTMAX) of an M×N matrix A of maximum dimensions MAX, and the row (IMAX) and column (JMAX) in which it occurs.

14.8   Write a subroutine to invert a square matrix. In addition to the obvious arguments, the subroutine should have an argument which is set to 0 on entry, and which should be changed to 1 on exit if the inverse cannot be found.

14.9   The following system, suggested by T. S. Wilson (cited by Fröberg, 1964), illustrates nicely the problem of ill-conditioning mentioned in Exercise 8.5:

$$10x+7y+ 8z+ 7w = 32$$
$$7x+5y+ 6z+ 5w = 23$$
$$8x+6y+10z+ 9w = 33$$
$$7x+5y+ 9z+10w = 31.$$

Use the Gauss reduction program in this chapter to show that the solution is $x = y = z = w = 1$. Then change the right-hand side constants to 32.01, 22.99, 32.99 and 31.01 (a change of about 1 in 3000) and find the new solution. Finally change the right-hand side constants to 32.1, 22.9, 32.9 and 31.1 and observe what effect this has on the 'solution'.

15

Introduction to Numerical Methods

One of the major scientific uses of modern digital computers is in finding numerical solutions to mathematical problems which have no analytical solutions, i.e. solutions which may be written down in terms of polynomials and the known mathematical functions such as logarithms, sines, exponentials, etc. In this chapter we look briefly at three areas where numerical methods have been highly developed: solving equations, evaluating integrals and derivatives, and solving differential equations.

15.1 Equations

In this section we consider how to solve equations in one unknown numerically. The general way of expressing the problem is to say that we want to solve the equation

$$f(x) = 0,$$

i.e. we want to find the value(s) of x that make the left-hand side vanish, where $f(x)$ is any given function of x. Such a value of x is called a **root** of the equation. There are mathematical solutions for a very small class of functions f. For example, if $f(x)$ is a polynomial of order two (i.e. a quadratic equation), there is a well-known formula for the solution. But there is no general method for finding an analytical solution for any given $f(x)$.

15.1.1 Newton's Method

This is perhaps the easiest numerical method for solving equations. The basic idea is as follows: given some initial guess at the root x, the method makes use of the first derivative $f'(x)$ to improve the guess by computing $x\dagger$, say, which in general is closer to the root than the first guess. The process is continued until a required accuracy is achieved. Fig. 15.1 illustrates Newton's method geometrically.

From the figure we see that

$$f'(x) = [f(x)-0]/(x-x\dagger).$$

Solving for $x\dagger$ gives

$$x\dagger = x - f(x)/f'(x)$$

Equation (1) is Newton's algorithm. It is implemented as follows:

1. Read in a starting x, and required accuracy (acc)
2. Compute $x\dagger$ with Newton's method and replace x by $x\dagger$
3. Print x and $f(x)$
4. While abs($f(x)$) $\geq acc$ repeat up to 20 times, say:
   4.1 Compute $x\dagger$ with Newton's method and replace x by $x\dagger$

4.2 Print x and $f(x)$

5 Stop.

It is necessary to limit step 4 since the process may not converge (see below).

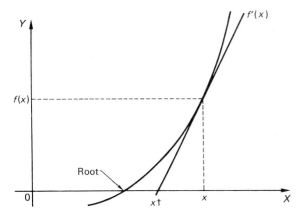

Fig. 15.1 Graphical derivation of Newton's method

Example

$$f(x) = x^3 + x - 3 = 0. \text{ Then } f'(x) = 3x^2 + 1.$$

It is usually possible to make a reasonable initial guess at x by inspection. Since there is clearly a root between $x = 1$ and $x = 2$, let us try $x = 2$ to start with. We will stop the process when $|f(x)| < 1E-6$, say (or after 20 iterations). The following program implements Newton's method, and prints out each new $x\dagger$ so that we can see the estimates converging to the root.

```
***** NEWTON'S METHOD TO SOLVE F(X) = 0 **************************

        F(X)  = X ** 3 + X - 3
        DF(X) = 3 * X ** 2 + 1

5       FORMAT( '          X', T20, 'F(X)' / )
15      FORMAT( F10.6, E15.4 )

        READ*, X, ACC
        PRINT 5
        X = X - F(X) / DF(X)
        PRINT 15, X, F(X)

10      IF( I .LT. 20 .AND. ABS( F(X) ) .GE. ACC )THEN
           X = X - F(X) / DF(X)
           PRINT 15, X, F(X)
           I = I + 1
           GOTO 10
        END IF

        STOP
        END
```

The output is a follows:

x	f(x)
1.461538	.1584+001
1.247788	.1906+000
1.214185	.4189−002
1.213412	.2235−005
1.213412	.5960−007

From the output we see that the process converges rapidly to the root. The method is so simple that it can even be implemented on a calculator without much effort. The program structure makes it clear that (1) Newton's algorithm is used at least once, and (2) there are two conditions which lead to the termination of the main loop.

Exercises

1   Try running the program with different starting values of x to see whether the algorithm always converges.
2   Try to find a non-zero root of

$$2x = \tan(x)$$

using Newton's method.

You might experience some trouble with the second one. For example, the following output results if we start the algorithm with $x = 2$ (a format editing code of G10.4 for X has been used instead of F10.6):

x	f(x)
3.639	.6735+001
5.905	−.1221+002
8.586	.1828+002
84.59	.1694+003
94.86	−.1890+003
279.1	.5588+003
467.5	−.9357+003
1597.	.3143+004
1599.	.3198+004
2446.	−.4894+004
4039.	−.8080+004

The estimates of the root are clearly diverging. In fact the method has jumped past roots near 4.604, 7.79, etc., as can be seen by sketching the graph carefully. This highlights the only serious problem that arises with Newton's method: the algorithm only converges to a root if the starting guess is 'close enough' to the root. And since 'close enough' depends on $f(x)$ and on the root, one can obviously get into difficulties here. The only remedy is some intelligent trial and error work on the initial guess.

Newton's method may also fail if $f(x)$ is very 'flat' near a root, since the algorithm requires division by $f'(x)$, which can get very small in this case. This can easily result in a floating point overflow. If the method fails to find a root, the Bisection method, as described in the next section, may be used.

Application

Newton's method may be built (hardwired) into calculators to evaluate reciprocals and nth roots, for example. To find the reciprocal of a number a amounts to solving the equation

$$f(x) = 1/x - a = 0 .$$

Applying equation (1) to this form of $f(x)$ gives, after a little algebra,

$$x\dagger = x(2 - ax) .$$

Note that this requires no divisions: it was used on old-fashioned computers with no division facility.

15.1.2   Newton's Method for Complex Roots

Newton's method can also find complex roots, as long,as the starting guess is complex. In this case the **COMPLEX** type specification must be used. The program above can then be amended as follows to find a complex root. Note that when variables of **COMPLEX** type are assigned and input/output the real part is given first.

```
***** NEWTON'S METHOD FOR COMPLEX ROOTS OF F(X) = 0 **************

        COMPLEX DF
        COMPLEX F
        COMPLEX X

        F(X)  = X ** 2 + X + 1
        DF(X) = 2 * X + 1

5       FORMAT( '         Re (x)       Im (x)' / )
15      FORMAT( 2F10.4 )

        ACC = 1E-6
        X = ( 1.0, 1.0 )
        PRINT 5
        X = X - F(X) / DF(X)
        PRINT 15, X
        I = 1

10      IF( I .LT. 20 .AND. ABS( F(X) ) .GE. ACC )THEN
          X = X - F(X) / DF(X)
          PRINT 15, X
          I = I + 1
          GOTO 10
        END IF

        STOP
        END
```

The output is:

Re (x)	Im (x)
.0769	.6154
-.5156	.6320
-.4932	.9090
-.4997	.8670
-.5000	.8660
-.5000	.8660

15.1.3   Example: Partial Pressures

This example illustrates how the numerical solution of polynomial equations arises in the manufacture of semiconductors (McCracken and Dorn, 1964).

When iodine vapour (I_2) and helium (He) are passed over germanium (Ge), some germanium combines with iodine to form GeI_2 and GeI_4. The resulting vapour is composed of I, I_2, GeI_2, GeI_4 and He. The problem is to find the partial pressures of these five gases under equilibrium conditions at 0°C where the total pressure is 76 cm of mercury. It can then be shown that

$$99.72z^4 + 2.870565E{-}7Z^2 + 6.674356E{-}16Z - 760 = 0 , \qquad (*)$$

where

$$p(GeI_4) = Z^4,$$

$$p(I_2) \frac{\sqrt{K_3}Z^2}{K^2},$$

$$p(I) = \left(\frac{K_1\sqrt{K_3}}{K_2}\right)^{1/2} Z,$$

$$p(GeI_2) = \sqrt{K_3}\ Z^2,$$

$$p(He) = X\left[\, 2Z^4 + \sqrt{K_3}\left(1 + \frac{1}{K_2}\right)Z^2 + 0.5\left(\frac{K_1\sqrt{K_3}}{K_2}\right)Z\right],$$

$K_1 = 1.3E{-}21$, $K_2 = 1.09E4$, $K_3 = 3.25E{-}17$, $X = 49.32$ and $p()$ means partial pressure.

The program below uses Newton's method to find the root of equation (*). The root will be between zero and 10 from physical considerations. The five respective partial pressures can then be found: 7.621, 1.428E−12, 4.3E−17, 1.573E−8 and 7.524E2. You may like to find the remaining three roots, two of which may be complex. Note the use of a **COMMON** block, and of a **BLOCK DATA** subprogram. Note also that **DOUBLE PRECISION** type is used because of the wide range of the coefficients of equation (*).

```
*****  NEWTON'S METHOD TO SOLVE F(Z) = 0  **************************
*****  F(Z) AND F'(Z) DEFINED AS FUNCTION SUBPROGRAMS  ************

        REAL K1
        REAL K2
        REAL K3
        DOUBLE PRECISION F
        DOUBLE PRECISION DF
        DOUBLE PRECISION Z

        DATA K1, K2, K3, X / 1.3E-21, 1.09E4, 3.25E-17, 49.32 /

5       FORMAT( '         Z', T20, 'F(Z)' / )
15      FORMAT( F10.6, E15.4 )

        READ*, Z, ACC
        PRINT 5
        Z = Z - F(Z) / DF(Z)
        PRINT 15, Z, F(Z)
        I = 1
```

```
10      IF( I .LT. 20 .AND. ABS( F(Z) ) .GE. ACC )THEN
          Z = Z - F(Z) / DF(Z)
          PRINT 15, Z, F(Z)
          I = I + 1
          GOTO 10
        END IF

        STOP
        END

        DOUBLE PRECISION FUNCTION F( X )

        DOUBLE PRECISION X
        COMMON / COEFFS / C0, C1, C2, C4

        F = C4 * X ** 4 + C2 * X ** 2 + C1 * Z + C0

        RETURN
        END


        DOUBLE PRECISION FUNCTION DF( X )

        DOUBLE PRECISION X
        COMMON / COEFFS / C0, C1, C2, C4

        DF = 4 * C4  * X ** 3 + 2 * C2 * X + C1

        RETURN
        END

        BLOCK DATA INIT

        COMMON / COEFFS / C0, C1, C2, C4

        DATA   C0, C1, C2, C4 / -760.0, 6.674356E-16, 2.870565E-7,
      $ 99.72 /

        END
```

15.1.4   The Bisection Method

Consider again the problem of solving the equation

$$f(x) = x^3 + x - 3 = 0 .$$

We attempt to find by inspection, or trial and error, two values of x, call them x_L and x_R, such that $f(x_L)$ and $f(x_R)$ have different signs, i.e. $f(x_L).f(x_R) < 0$. If we can find two such values, the implication is that the root lies somewhere in the interval between x_L and x_R, since $f(x)$ changes sign on this interval (see Fig. 15.2). In this example, $x_L = 1$ and $x_R = 2$ will do, since $f(1) = -1$ and $f(2) = 7$. In the Bisection method, we estimate the root by x_M, where x_M is the midpoint (hence the name 'bisection') of the interval $[x_L; x_R]$, i.e.

$$x_M = (x_L + x_R)/2 . \tag{2}$$

Then if $f(x_M)$ has the same sign as $f(x_L)$, as drawn in the figure, the root clearly lies between

x_M and x_R. We must then redefine the left-hand end of the interval as having the value of x_M, i.e. we let the new value of x_L be x_M. Otherwise, if $f(x_M)$ and $f(x_L)$ have different signs, we let the new value of x_R be x_M, since the root must lie between x_L and x_M in this case. Having redefined x_L or x_R as the case may be, we bisect again according to equation (2) and repeat the process until the distance between x_L and x_R is as small as we please.

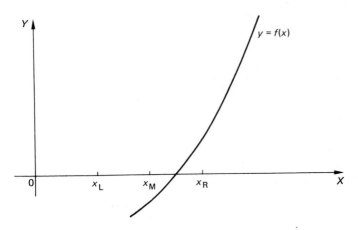

Fig. 15.2 The Bisection Method

The neat thing about this method is that we can calculate before starting how many bisections are needed to obtain a certain accuracy, given initial values of x_L and x_R. (With Newton's method, we can never be sure exactly how many iterations will be required.) Suppose we start with $x_L = a$, and $x_R = b$. After the first bisection the worst possible error, E_1, in x_M is

$$E_1 = |a-b|/2,$$

since we are estimating the root as being at the midpoint of the interval $[a; b]$. The worst that can happen is that the root is actually at x_L or x_R, in which case the error is E_1. After the second bisection, the error E_2 will obviously be half of E_1, i.e.

$$E_2 = |a-b|/4 = |a-b|/2^2.$$

Carrying on like this, after n bisections the worst possible error E_n is given by

$$E_n = |a-b|/2^n.$$

If we want to be sure that this is less than some specified error E, we must see to it that n satisfies the inequality

$$|a-b|/2^n < E,$$

i.e. $2^n > |a-b|/E,$

i.e. $n \log(2) > \log[|a-b|/E],$

i.e. $n > \log[(a-b)/E]/\log(2) .$ (3)

Since n is the number of bisections, it must be an integer. The smallest integer n that exceeds the right-hand side of inequality (3) will do as the maximum number of bisections required to guarantee the given accuracy E.

The following scheme may be used to program the Bisection method. It will work for any function $f(x)$ that changes sign (in either direction) between the two values x_L and x_R, which must be found beforehand by the user.

1   Read a,b and E
2   Initialize x_L and x_R
3   Compute maximum bisections n from inequality (3)
4   Repeat n times
     4.1   Compute x_M according to (2)
     4.2   If $f(x_L).f(x_M) > 0$ then
          4.2.1   Let $x_L = x_M$
         otherwise
          4.2.2   Let $x_R = x_M$
5   Print root x_M
6   Stop.

We have assumed that the method will not find the root exactly because of the minute chances of the .EQ. comparison being true with real variables. But if you are skeptical, you can replace step 4 in the plan with a conditional IF/GOTO structure!

An advantage of the Bisection method is that it is guaranteed to find you a root if you can find two starting values for x_L and x_R between which the function will change sign. You can also compute in advance the number of bisections needed to attain a given accuracy. Its disadvantage is that it is an inefficient method, in that successive bisections do not necessarily move closer to the root, as generally happens with Newton's method. In fact, it is interesting to compare the two methods on the same function to see how many more steps the Bisection method requires than Newton's method.

15.2 Integration

Although almost all respectable mathematical functions can be differentiated analytically, the same cannot unfortunately be said for integration. There is no general rule for integrating, as there is for differentiating. (This is an interesting fact of mathematical life which you may wish to ponder!) For example, the indefinite integral of a function as simple as

$$\exp(-x^2)$$

cannot be found mathematically. We therefore need a numerical method for evaluating (definite) integrals.

This is actually quite easy to do, and depends on the well-known fact that the definite integral of a function $f(x)$, say, between the limits $x = a$ and $x = b$, is equal to the area under $f(x)$ bounded by the x-axis and the two lines $x = a$ and $x = b$. So all numerical methods for integrating simply involve more or less ingenious ways of estimating the area under $f(x)$.

One rough and ready, yet perfectly valid way of doing this is by drawing the curve $f(x)$ on squared graph paper (the smaller the squares, the better) and counting the number of squares that fall under the curve. The only problem is what to do when the graph cuts across a square: do you count the square, or not, or how much of it do you count? The method that we will consider below, called the Trapezoidal Rule, or the Trapezium Rule, effectively approximates $f(x)$ by a straight line across each square that it crosses, for the compelling reason that every schoolchild knows how to calculate the area of the resulting shape: a series of trapeziums.

15.2.1 The Trapezoidal Rule

Before we derive the rule, a little notation will make the problem clearer. We want to integrate $f(x)$ with respect to x between the limits $x = a$ and $x = b$. We divide the area under $f(x)$ up into a lot of vertical panels of equal width. The width of a panel is universally called h (and referred to as panel width, or step length, or grid size, or what have you), and for some reason there are always n of them. One such panel is shown in Fig. 15.3. It should be fairly obvious then that, since a length $(b-a)$ of the x-axis has been cut up into n panels each of width h, h is given by

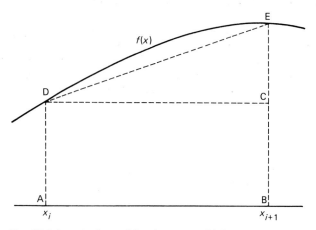

Fig. 15.3 A typical panel for the trapezoidal rule

$$h=(b-a)/n \ ,$$

or alternatively, n is given by

$$n=(b-a)/h \ . \tag{4}$$

The vertical edges of the panels will meet the x-axis at the points

$$x=a; x=a+h; x=a+2h; \ ... \ ; x=a+nh=b \ .$$

We denote these points by $X_0, X_1, X_2, \ ... \ , X_n$, so that

$$X_0=a$$
$$X_1=a+h$$
$$X_2=a+2h$$
$$....$$
$$X_i=a+ih \tag{5}$$
$$....$$
$$X_n=a+nh=b \ .$$

If we draw a straight line across the top of each panel, from the point $(X_0; f(X_0))$ to $(X_1; f(X_1))$, and then to the point $(X_2; f(X_2))$, etc, we will have a set of n trapeziums, and we can approximate the area under $f(x)$ by the area of these trapeziums. One such trapezium is shown in Fig. 15.3. The area of ABCDE is

$$h(AD+BE)/2 \ ,$$

i.e. $h[f(X_i)+f(X_i+h)]/2 \ .$

The area we are after is the sum of all such trapeziums,

i.e. $\int_a^b f(x)dx$ is approximately equal to S, where S is given by

$$S=0.5h[f(X_0)+f(X_1)]+0.5h[f(X_1)+f(X_2)]+...$$
$$+0.5h[f(X_n-h)+f(X_n)]$$
$$=0.5h[f(a)+f(b)+2\sum_{i=1}^{n-1} f(X_i)] \ . \tag{6}$$

$$f(x) = x^3$$

between the limits $x = 0$ and $x = 4$. (The point of taking a function that we can integrate exactly is that we can check the accuracy of the numerical method. The exact answer here is 64.)

The following subprogram TRAP computes the integral of any given function $f(x)$ between the given limits a and b, using the Trapezoidal Rule with a panel width of h (also given). It is assumed that h will be chosen in such a way that n as defined in equation (4) will be an integer. The function to be integrated, $f(x)$, may either be an external user-defined function, or an intrinsic function. TRAP is first shown integrating an external function:

```
      EXTERNAL F

15    FORMAT( F8.2, F12.4 )

      READ*, A, B, H
      PRINT 15, H, TRAP( F, A, B, H )

      STOP
      END

      REAL FUNCTION F( X )
***** USER-DEFINED INTEGRAND ***********************************

      F = X ** 3

      RETURN
      END

      REAL FUNCTION TRAP( FUN, A, B, H )
***** INTEGRATION WITH THE TRAPEZIUM RULE ************************
***** VARIABLES HAVE SAME MEANING AS IN TEXT ABOVE **************

      TRAP = 0
      N = NINT( (B - A) / H )

      DO 10 I = 1, N-1
* ***     USING THE NOTATION OF EQU.(5)
          TRAP = TRAP + FUN( A + I * H )
10    CONTINUE

* *** USING EQU.(6)
      TRAP = H / 2 * ( FUN( A ) + FUN( B ) + 2 * TRAP )

      RETURN
      END
```

Note the use of the intrinsic function **NINT**, which rounds the number of panels N to the nearest integer. Otherwise, rounding error and integer truncation could give the wrong value of N. Note also that since the argument F of TRAP is an external function, it must be declared as such in the calling program. However, this is not necessary inside TRAP, where its name is followed by a left bracket.

Table 15.1 shows the results obtained for some different values of h. It is clear that as h gets smaller, the estimated integral becomes more accurate.

Table 15.1 Effect of different steplengths

h	Integral (S)
1.00	68.0000
0.50	65.0000
0.10	64.0400
0.01	64.0004

This example assumes that $f(x)$ is a continuous function which may be calculated at any x. In practice the function could be discrete points supplied as a result of an experiment. For example, the speed of an object $v(t)$ might be measured every so many seconds, and one might want to estimate the distance travelled as the area under the speed–time graph. The external function F(X) must then be defined so that the data coincides with the values taken on by the argument of F inside TRAP.

TRAP may also be used as it stands to integrate an intrinsic function. Suppose we wanted to integrate COS(X) between the limits A and B. Only two lines need to be changed in the calling program, which is now:

```
        INTRINSIC COS

15      FORMAT( F8.2, F12.4 )

        READ*, A, B, H
        PRINT 15, H, TRAP( COS, A, B, H )

        STOP
        END
```

15.3   Numerical Differentiation

The Newton quotient for a general function $f(x)$ is given by

$$[f(x+h)-f(x)]/h , \qquad\qquad (*)$$

where h is 'small'. As h tends to zero, this quotient approaches the first derivative df/dx, also denoted $f'(x)$. The Newton quotient may therefore be used to estimate a derivative numerically. It is a useful exercise to do this with a few well-known functions to see how small you can make h before rounding errors cause problems (since expression (*) involves subtracting terms that eventually become equal when the limit of the computer's accuracy is reached). As an example, we use the Newton quotient to estimate $f'(x)$ for

$$f(x) = x^2$$

at $x = 2$, for various values of h (we know the exact answer is 4). The following program does this, and the results are shown in Table 15.2.

```
*****  NUMERICAL DERIVATIVES THE NEWTON WAY ***********************

        INTEGER   I
        REAL      DF
        REAL      H
        REAL      X

        F(X)  =  X ** 2
```

```
15        FORMAT( 2F14.8 )

          X = 2.
          H = 1.

          DO 10 I = 1, 9
              DF = ( F(X+H) - F(X) ) / H
              PRINT 15, H, DF
              H = H / 10.
10        CONTINUE

          STOP
          END
```

Table 15.2 Estimates of $f'(x)$ for $f(x) = x^2$

h	$f'(x)$
1.00000000	5.00000000
0.10000000	4.09999967
0.01000000	4.00999784
0.00100000	4.00096178
0.00010000	3.99947172
0.00001000	3.99351129
0.00000100	3.93390667
0.00000010	3.57627878
0.00000001	0.00000000

The results show that the best h for this particular problem is about $1E-4$. But for h much smaller than this the estimate becomes totally unreliable. Generally, the best h for a given problem can only be found by trial and error. Finding it constitutes one of the major problems of numerical analysis.

15.4   First Order Differential Equations

The most interesting situations in real life that we may want to model, or represent quantitatively, are usually those in which the variables change in time (e.g. biological, electrical, and mechanical systems). If the changes are continuous then the system can often be represented with equations involving the derivatives of the variables. Such equations are called **differential equations**. The main aim of a lot of modelling is to be able to write down a set of differential equations that describe the system being studied as accurately as possible. When one tries to 'solve' these equations one usually runs into difficulties, because only a very small class of differential equations can be solved analytically. This is where numerical methods come in. We will consider only the simplest method of numerical solution in this section: **Euler's Method**.

To illustrate the method, we will take an example from Newtonian mechanics of motion under gravity against air resistance. Suppose a parachutist of mass 100 kg steps out of a stationary hovering helicopter, but neglects to open his parachute for 24 seconds. We would like to find his velocity as a function of time during this period. Assuming that air resistance cannot be neglected (ask any parachutist!), the man falls subject to two vertical forces: gravity acting downwards, and air resistance acting upwards. The air resistance force is assumed to be proportional to the square of his velocity (this is fairly accurate). Applying Newton's second law to the parachutist, we have

$$ma = mg - pv^2 ,$$

where m is his mass, a his downward acceleration, g the acceleration due to gravity (9.8m/s^2), v his velocity, and p is a constant of proportionality. Dividing by m, we can rewrite this as

$$dv/dt = g - kv^2 , \tag{1}$$

where $k = p/m$. Equation (1) is the differential equation describing the motion of the parachutist under gravity. The constant k varies with shape and mass, and may be found experimentally from the **terminal velocity** of the falling object. This terminal velocity (v_T) is reached when the object stops accelerating, and may be found by equating the right-hand side of equation (1) to zero. Thus

$$v_T = \sqrt{(g/k)} .$$

For a man of 100 kg, k is found to be about 0.004. Before we proceed with the numerical solution of equation (1) we should note that this differential equation can be solved analytically, since it is of the type called variable separable. If you know about such things, you should be able to do the integraton and show that

$$v(t) = a[1 - \exp(-2akt)]/[1 + \exp(-2akt)] , \tag{2}$$

where a is a constant representing the terminal velocity, and we have used the fact that $v(0) = 0$ (the initial condition, deduced from the fact that the helicopter is stationary).

The basic problem to be overcome in trying to solve an equation like (1) numerically is the fact that a derivative (like dv/dt) cannot be represented exactly on a digital computer, since the limit (h tends to zero, where h is a small increment in t) cannot be taken exactly. We therefore need to approximate the derivative, and we use the Newton quotient to do this.

15.4.1   Euler's Method

We now consider how to solve

$$dv/dt = g - kv^2 \tag{1}$$

numerically for $0 < t \leqslant 24$ seconds (since the air resistance constant k will change when the parachute is opened at $t = 24$ seconds). Euler's method consists in replacing the derivative on the left-hand side of equation (1) by its Newton quotient. If we do this, we get

$$[v(t+h) - v(t)]/h = g - kv(t)^2 .$$

Making $v(t+h)$ the subject of the above equation results in

$$v(t+h) = v(t) + h[g - kv(t)^2]. \tag{4}$$

The point about equation (4) is that given v at some time t (like $t = 0$), we can compute v at time $t+h$. We can then replace $v(t)$ on the right-hand side of equation (4) by the $v(t+h)$ we have just found, and get $v(t+2h)$, and so on, until we have computed v over the whole time interval.

The only thing that isn't obvious about this exercise is what value to give h. Let us try $h = 2$ seconds. Then from equation (4), starting at $t = 0$, we get

$$
\begin{aligned}
v(2) &= v(0) + 2[9.8 - 0.004v(0)^2] \\
&= \quad 0 + 2[9.8 - \quad 0 \quad] \\
&= 19.6 \text{ m/s (the exact value is 18.64 m/s).}
\end{aligned}
$$

We have integrated equation (1) numerically from $t=0$ to $t=2$! Putting $v(2)$ into the right-hand side of equation (4) we can now find $v(4)$:

$$v(4) = v(2)+2[9.8-0.004\times19.6^2]$$
$$= 36.13 \text{ m/s (exact: 32.64).}$$

And again, $v(6)$ can now be computed:

$$v(6) = v(4)+2[9.8-0.004\times36.13^2]$$
$$= 45.29 \text{ m/s (exact: 41.08).}$$

We can go on like this as long as we like. In general, equation (4) gives us Euler's rule for computing the next $v\dagger$ once we have v:

$$v\dagger = v+h[g-kv^2]. \tag{5}$$

It is very easy to write a program to do this, and then we can also test the accuracy of the numerical method by trying different values of h. The following program uses Euler's method as implemented in equation (4) or (5) to compute v for the first 24 seconds of the parachutist's motion. Note that the DO-loop has been generalized to cover 24 seconds whatever the value of h.

```
*****  EULER'S METHOD FOR FREE FALL WITH AIR RESISTANCE ***********
*****  VARIABLES ARE ALL AS DEFINED IN TEXT ***********************

       REAL K

       G = 9.8
       READ*, K, H, T, V

       DO 10 I = 1, 24/H
          T = T + H
*  ***     FROM EQU.(5)
          V = V + H * ( G - K * V ** 2 )
          PRINT*, T, V
10     CONTINUE

       STOP
       END
```

Table 15.3 shows the results for $h=2$ and $h=0.5$, compared with the exact solution computed from equation (2). We see from the table that the numerical solution is quite a lot better for the smaller of the two h values, the worst error being about 3%. We also see that the parachutist's terminal velocity (49.5 m/s) is correctly computed with both values of h. The errors in fact get less and less as t approaches 24 seconds.

Table 15.3 Euler's method on equation (1)

Time (s)	Velocity (m/s)		
	$h=2$	$h=0.5$	Exact
2.0	19.60	18.94	18.64
4.0	36.13	33.45	32.64
6.0	45.29	42.00	41.08
8.0	48.48	46.22	45.50
10.0	49.28	48.11	47.65
12.0	49.45	48.92	48.65
14.0	49.49	49.26	49.11
16.0	49.50	49.40	49.32
18.0	49.50	49.46	49.42
20.0	49.50	49.48	49.46
22.0	49.50	49.49	49.48
24.0	49.50	49.49	49.49

Now let us see what happens when the man opens his parachute at $t=24$ seconds. The air resistance term k will be different now: for an open parachute $k=0.3$ is quite realistic. We can use the same program as before with a few minor changes, and obviously we need to supply new starting values for t and v: 24 and 49.49 respectively. Since $h=0.5$ worked well last time, we try the same value now. The results are rather surprising:

Time	Velocity
24.5	-313.0
25.0	$-.1500+005$
25.5	$-.3378+008$
26.0	$-.1712+015$
26.5	$-.4395+028$
....	ERROR

Not only does the man fly upwards: he also soon exceeds the speed of light! The results make nonsense physically: fortunately in this example our intuition tells us that something is wrong. The only remedy is to reduce h. Some experimenting will reveal that the results for $h=0.01$ are much better. Some of these are shown in Table 15.4. It is instructive to examine why the method breaks down for $h=0.5$ with the parachute open. Euler's method basically assumes that the derivative dv/dt ($=$ acceleration) is constant during the interval h. The use of the Newton quotient implies this. However, a glance at the correct results in Table 15.4 shows that this assumption doesn't hold over the period from $t=24$ to $t=24.5$ seconds. At the beginning of this interval there is an enormous deceleration of about 6 m/s^2 over a period of 0.01 seconds, whereas by the end of the first half-second, the new terminal velocity has been nearly reached. The only way to correct the problem is to go on reducing h until the results seem reasonable. The principle is that h must be small enough to make the derivative approximately constant over the interval h.

Table 15.4 Parachute open ($h = 0.01$)

Time (s)	Velocity (m/s)	
	Euler	Exact
24.01	42.24	43.18
24.02	36.99	38.32
24.03	32.98	34.46
24.04	29.81	31.32
24.05	27.25	28.72
24.06	25.12	26.53
24.07	23.32	24.67
24.08	21.79	23.06
24.09	20.46	21.66
24.10	19.30	20.43
24.20	12.69	13.32
24.30	9.85	10.24
24.40	8.34	8.60
24.50	7.45	7.62
24.60	6.88	7.01
24.70	6.51	6.60
24.80	6.27	6.33
24.90	6.10	6.15
25.00	5.98	6.02
25.50	5.76	5.77
26.00	5.72	5.73

Finally, we should note that Euler's method will be just as easy to compute if the air resistance term is not kv^2, but $kv^{1.8}$ (which is more accurate), although now an analytic solution cannot be found.

Euler's method in general
In general we want to solve a first order differential equation of the form

$$dy/dx = f(x, y), \quad y(0) \text{ given.}$$

Euler's method replaces dy/dx by its Newton quotient, so the differential equation becomes

$$[y(x+h) - y(x)]/h = f(x, y). \tag{6}$$

Denoting $y(x)$ by y, and $y(x+h)$ by $y\dagger$, we can use equation (6) to get $y\dagger$ in terms of y, starting with $y = y(0)$:

$$y\dagger = y + hf(x, y). \tag{7}$$

Equation (7) is repeated, replacing y by $y\dagger$ each time, until we have computed y over the required range of integration.

15.4.2   Bacteria Growth
Euler's method performs quite adequately in the parachutist problem, once we have got the right value of h. In case you think that the numerical solution of all differential equations is just as easy, we will now consider an example where Euler's method doesn't do too well.

Suppose a colony of 1000 bacteria are multiplying at a rate of 0.8 per hour per individual (i.e. an individual produces an average of 0.8 offspring every hour). How many bacteria are there after 10 hours? Assuming that the colony grows continuously and without restriction, we can model this growth with the differential equation.

$$dN/dt = 0.8N; \; N(0) = 1000; \tag{8}$$

where $N(t)$ is the population size at time t. This process is called **exponential growth**, and equation (8) may be solved exactly to give the well-known formula for exponential growth:

$$N(t) = 1000 \exp(0.8t) . \tag{9}$$

To solve equation (8) numerically, we apply Euler's algorithm to it by replacing dN/dt with its Newton quotient, to get

$$N(t+h) = N(t) + 0.8hN(t).$$

Using the notation of equation (5), this can be written more concisely as

$$N\dagger = N + 0.8hN , \tag{10}$$

where N takes the value of 1000 at time $t = 0$. Using equation (10) we compute N for $t = 0$ to 10, replacing N by $N\dagger$ after each calculation. Taking $h = 0.5$ gives the results depicted in Table 15.5, where the exact solution according to equation (9) is also given.

Table 15.5 Bacteria growth ($h = 0.5$)

Time	Population		
		Predictor–Corrector	
(hours)	Euler	(Section 15.4.3)	Exact
0.5	1400.	1480.	1492.
1.0	1960.	2190.	2226.
1.5	2744.	3242.	3320.
2.0	3842.	4798.	4953.
2.5	5378.	7101.	7389.
3.0	7530.	10509.	11023.
3.5	10541.	15554.	16445.
4.0	14758.	23019.	24533.
4.5	20661.	34069.	36598.
5.0	28925.	50422.	54598.
5.5	40495.	74624.	81451.
6.0	56694.	110443.	121510.
6.5	79371.	163456.	181272.
7.0	111119.	241915.	270426.
7.5	155567.	358034.	403428.
8.0	217794.	529890.	601845.
8.5	304911.	784236.	897847.
9.0	426876.	1160669.	1339429.
9.5	597626.	1717789.	1998194.
10.0	836676.	2542327.	2980955.

This time the numerical solution is not too good. In fact the error gets worse at each step, and after 10 hours of bacteria time it is about 72%. Of course, the numerical solution will improve a little if we try h smaller, but there would still always be some value of t, however big, where the error exceeds some acceptable limit.

We may ask why Euler's method works so well with the parachutist, but so badly with the bacteria. The answer, as we mentioned earlier, lies in the type of numerical approximation to the derivative that is used. By using the Newton quotient each time in Euler's method, we are assuming that the derivative changes very little over the small interval h, i.e. that the second derivative is very small. Now in the case of the parachutist, by differentiating equation (1) again with respect to time, we see that the second derivative is

$$-(2kv)dv/dt ,$$

which approaches zero as the object reaches its terminal velocity (since dv/dt approaches zero at terminal velocity). In the bacteria case, the second derivative of $N(t)$ is found by differentiating equation (8). We get

$$d^2N/dt^2 = 0.8dN/dt = 0.8^2N(t) .$$

This is far from zero at $t = 10$. In fact, it is approaching three million! Therefore the Newton quotient approximation gets worse at each step in this case.

There are better numerical methods for overcoming these sorts of problems. Two of them are discussed below. More sophisticated methods may be found in most textbooks on numerical analysis. However, Euler's method may always be used as a first approximation as long as you realize where and why errors may arise.

15.4.3   A Predictor-Corrector Method

One improvement on the solution of

$$dy/dx = f(x,y) , \qquad y(0) \text{ given} ,$$

is as follows. Euler says compute

$$y\dagger = y + hf(x,y) \tag{7}$$

repeatedly. But this way favours the old value of y in computing $f(x,y)$ on the right-hand side. Surely it would be better to say

$$y\dagger = y + h[f(x+h,y\dagger) + f(x,y)]/2 , \tag{11}$$

since this also involves the new value $y\dagger$ in computing f on the right-hand side? The problem is that $y\dagger$ is as yet unknown, so we cannot use it on the right-hand side of equation (11). But we could use Euler to estimate (predict) $y\dagger$ from equation (7) and then use equation (11) to correct the prediction by computing a better version of $y\dagger$, say y^*. So the full procedure is:

1)   Use Euler to predict

$$y\dagger = y + hf(x,y)$$

2)   Then correct $y\dagger$ as follows:

$$y^* = y + h[f(x+h,y\dagger) + f(x,y)]/2$$

3)   Replace y by y^* in step (1) and repeat.

This is called a **Predictor-Corrector** method. It can be applied to the bacteria growth problem as follows, and only requires one extra line in the computer program:

$$N\dagger = N + 0.8hN \text{ (predictor: as before)},$$

$$N^* = N + 0.8h(N\dagger + N)/2 \text{ (corrector)}.$$

The results using this method are also shown in Table 15.5, where the worst error has now been reduced to 15%. This is much better than the uncorrected Euler algorithm, although there is still much room for improvement.

15.5   Runge–Kutta Methods

There are a variety of formulae, under the general name of **Runge–Kutta**, of varying degrees of accuracy, which can be used to integrate almost any system of ordinary differential equations. The 'fourth-order' formula is given here, for reference. A derivation of this and the other Runge–Kutta formulae can be found in most books on numerical analysis (e.g. Conte and De Boor, 1972).

15.5.1   Runge–Kutta Fourth-Order Formula

The general differential equation is

$$dy/dy = f(x,y), \qquad y(0) \text{ given} \qquad\qquad (*)$$

The value of y at $x = h$ is then given by

$$y\dagger = y + (k_1 + 2k_2 + 2k_3 + k_4)/6$$

where

$$k_1 = hf(x,y)$$
$$k_2 = hf(x+0.5h, y+0.5k_1)$$
$$k_3 = hf(x+0.5h, y+0.5k_2)$$
$$k_4 = hf(x+h, y+k_3)$$

15.5.2   A Predator–Prey Model

The Runge–Kutta formulae may be adapted to integrate systems of differential equations. Here we use the fourth-order formulae to integrate the well-known predator–prey system,

$$dx/dt = f(x,y) = px - qxy$$
$$dy/dt = g(x,y) = rxy - sy$$

where $x(t)$ and $y(t)$ are the prey and predator populations respectively at time t, and p, q, r and s are biologically determined parameters. In this case, the vaules of x and y at some time t may be used to find $x\dagger$ and $y\dagger$ at time $t+h$ with the formulae

$$x\dagger = x + (k_1 + 2k_2 + 2k_3 + k_4)/6$$
$$y\dagger = y + (m_1 + 2m_2 + 2m_3 + m_4)/6$$

where

$$k_1 = hf(x, y)$$
$$m_1 = hg(x, y)$$
$$k_2 = hf(x+0.5k_1, y+0.5m_1)$$
$$m_2 = hg(x+0.5k_1, y+0.5m_1)$$
$$k_3 = hf(x+0.5k_2, y+0.5m_2)$$
$$m_3 = hg(x+0.5k_2, y+0.5m_2)$$
$$k_4 = hf(x+k_3, y+m_3)$$
$$m_4 = hg(x+k_3, y+m_3)$$

It should be noted that in this example x and y are the dependent variables and t (which does not appear explicitly in the equations) is the independent variable, whereas in the general formula (*) quoted in the previous section, y is the dependent variable, and x is the independent variable.

The next program implements this scheme for the predator prey model, taking $h = 1$ year, $x(0) = 105$, $y(0) = 8$, $p = 0.4$, $q = 0.04$, $r = 0.02$, and $s = 2$. The output shows the characteristic cyclic behaviour of the two populations (with a period in this case of 7 years: different parameters will change the period).

```
      COMMON / PARAMS / P, Q, R, S
      EXTERNAL F, G
      DATA P, Q, R, S / 0.4, 0.04, 0.02, 2.0 /

5     FORMAT( ' TIME          PREY      PRED' / )
15    FORMAT( F5.1, T10, 2F8.1 )

      READ*, X, Y, H
      PRINT 5

      DO 10 T = H, 20*H, H
        CALL RUNGE( F, G, X, Y, H )
        PRINT 15, T, X, Y
10    CONTINUE

      STOP
      END

      REAL FUNCTION F( X, Y )
      COMMON / PARAMS / P, Q, R, S

      F = P * X - Q * X * Y

      RETURN
      END

      REAL FUNCTION G( X, Y )
      COMMON / PARAMS / P, Q, R, S

      G = R * X * Y - S * Y

      RETURN
      END

      SUBROUTINE RUNGE( F, G, X, Y, H )
      REAL K1, K2, K3, K4
      REAL M1, M2, M3, M4

* *** FOURTH-ORDER RUNGE-KUTTA FOR TWO FIRST ORDER DEs
      K1 = H * F( X, Y )
      M1 = H * G( X, Y )
      K2 = H * F( X + K1 / 2, Y + M1 / 2 )
      M2 = H * G( X + K1 / 2, Y + M1 / 2 )
      K3 = H * F( X + K2 / 2, Y + M2 / 2 )
      M3 = H * G( X + K2 / 2, Y + M2 / 2 )
      K4 = H * F( X + K3, Y + M3 )
      M4 = H * G( X + K3, Y + M3 )

* *** NOW UPDATE X AND Y
      X = X + (K1 + 2 * K2 + 2 * K3 + K4) / 6.0
      Y = Y + (M1 + 2 * M2 + 2 * M3 + M4) / 6.0

      RETURN
      END
```

Output:

TIME	PREY	PRED
1.0	110.9	9.5
2.0	108.3	11.7
3.0	98.8	12.6
4.0	91.1	11.3
5.0	90.3	9.2
6.0	95.8	8.0
7.0	104.3	8.0
8.0	110.5	9.3
9.0	108.6	11.5
10.0	99.6	12.5
11.0	91.7	11.4
12.0	90.3	9.4
13.0	95.4	8.1
14.0	103.6	8.0
15.0	110.0	9.2
16.0	108.8	11.3
17.0	100.3	12.5
18.0	92.2	11.5
19.0	90.4	9.5
20.0	95.0	8.2

This program can be extended by including a reference file for the parameters and initial conditions, along the lines developed much more comprehensively by Furniss (1977) in the DRIVER interactive modelling package, as described briefly in Section 12.6.

The parameters (P, Q, R and S), initial values (X0 and Y0) and current values (X and Y) of the model are read into a reference file (called 'REF' in the example below) using list-directed input. This is done with a separate initializing program (which could be a subroutine of the program below).

The program asks the user for the reference file name, opens it, reads the data and rewinds it in readiness for updating it at the end of the program. The integration step-length (DT), number of integration steps (RUNTIM) and output intervals (INVL) are then keyed in, in response to a prompt. The user is then asked to specify whether the integration is to begin from the initial or current values in the reference file. The variables X and Y are initialized accordingly, and the model is run. Finally, the reference file is updated, using the latest current values of the variables. A sample run is given after the program below (the user's response is followed by the carriage return symbol ®).

```
        INTEGER RUNTIM
        CHARACTER*1 ANS
        CHARACTER*20 REFILE
        COMMON / PARAMS / P, Q, R, S
        EXTERNAL F, G

5       FORMAT( ' TIME            PREY      PRED' / )
15      FORMAT( F5.1, T10, 2F8.1 )
25      FORMAT( A )

* ***   FIRST READ THE REFERENCE FILE AND REWIND IT
        PRINT*, 'NAME OF REFERENCE FILE ?'
        READ 25, REFILE

        OPEN( UNIT = 1, FILE = REFILE )
        READ( 1, * ) T0, X0, Y0, T, X, Y
```

```
      READ( 1, * ) P, Q, R, S
      REWIND 1

* *** THEN KEY IN RUN SPECIFICATIONS AT KEYBOARD
      PRINT*, 'STEP-LENGTH, RUN TIME, OUTPUT INTERVALS ?'
      READ*, DT, RUNTIM, INVL
      PRINT*, 'START FROM SCRATCH (S), OR CONTINUE (C) ?'
      READ 25, ANS

      IF( ANS .EQ. 'S' )THEN
         T = T0
         X = X0
         Y = Y0
      END IF

      PRINT 5

* *** THEN OUTPUT THE STARTING VALUES
      PRINT 15, T, X, Y

* *** THEN RUN THE MODEL
      DO 10 IT = 1, RUNTIM
         T = T + DT
         CALL RUNGE( F, G, X, Y, DT )
         IF( MOD( IT, INVL ) .EQ. 0 )PRINT 15, T, X, Y
10    CONTINUE

* *** AND FINALLY UPDATE THE REFERENCE FILE
      WRITE( 1, * ) T0, X0, Y0, T, X, Y
      WRITE( 1, * ) P, Q, R, S
      CLOSE ( 1 )

      STOP
      END

      REAL FUNCTION F( X, Y )
      ....

      REAL FUNCTION G( X, Y )
      ....

      SUBROUTINE RUNGE( F, G, X, Y, H )
      ....

      END
```

Sample output:

```
NAME OF REFERENCE FILE ?
REF ®
STEP-LENGTH, RUN TIME, OUTPUT INTERVALS ?
0.1, 100, 10 ®
START FROM SCRATCH (S), OR CONTINUE (C) ?
C ®
TIME          PREY     PRED

20.0          95.0      8.2
```

21.0	103.0	8.0
22.0	109.6	9.1
23.0	109.1	11.2
24.0	100.9	12.4
25.0	92.5	11.6
26.0	90.3	9.6
27.0	94.7	8.2
28.0	102.7	8.0
29.0	109.4	9.1
30.0	109.3	11.1

The program can be made more interactive by allowing the user to change the parameters as well. The reference file can be generalized to include DT, RUNTIM and INVL. Finally, the program should make a copy of the reference file after reading it, but before updating it. This is a precaution against a system failure, which could result in the loss of the reference file if it occurs while the file is being updated. The copy should have a different name, and can be deleted with the appropriate job control statement once the update has been successfully completed.

15.6   Summary

* A numerical method is an approximate computer method for solving a mathematical problem which often has no analytical solution.

* A numerical method involves two distinct types of error: rounding error in the computer solution, and **truncation** error, where an infinite mathematical process like taking a limit is approximated by a finite process.

15.7   Exercises

15.1   Write down Newton's algorithm to find the cube root of 2. Taking 1.0 as the starting value, use a calculator to do the first few iterations, and observe how fast they converge.

15.2   Use Newton's method in a FORTRAN program to solve some of the following (you may have to experiment a bit with the starting value):

(a) $x^4 - x = 10$ (two real and two complex roots)

(b) $\exp(-x) - \sin(x) = 0$ (infinitely many roots)

(c) $x^3 - 8x^2 + 17x - 10 = 0$ (three real roots)

(d) $\log(x) = \cos(x)$

(e) $x^4 - 5x^3 - 12x^2 + 76x - 79 = 0$ (find the two roots near 2)

15.3   Use the Bisection method by hand to find the square root of 2, taking 1.0 and 2.0 as initial values for x_L and x_R. Continue bisecting until the maximum error is less than 0.05 (use inequality (3) of 15.1.4 to determine how many bisections are needed).

15.4   Write a subroutine ROOT(X, A, B, ACC) which uses the bisection method to find the root x of a given function $f(x)$. A and B are the starting limits for the bisection (supplied by the user through the calling program) and ACC is the maximum acceptable error. Write a separate function subprogram F(X) which defines $f(x)$, and which must be called by ROOT whenever function values are needed during the bisections. Write a main program which uses the subroutine to solve one of the equations in Exercise 15.2.

15.5 Use the trapezoidal rule by hand to evaluate
$\int_0^4 x^2 dx$, using a step-length of $h = 1.0$.

15.6 Consider the differential equation

$$dx/dt = 1-x, \quad x(0) = 0.$$

Use Euler's method by hand to estimate $x(1)$, using (a) two steps of length $h = 0.5$, and (b) four steps of length $h = 0.25$.

15.7 Use Euler's method by hand to evaluate the integral in Exercise 15.5 using the same step-length.

15.8 A human population N of 1000 at time $t = 0$ grows at a rate given by $dN/dt = aN$, where $a = 0.025$ per year per person. Use Euler's method to predict the population over the next 30 years:

    (i)   working in steps $h = 2$ years
    (ii) working in steps $h = 1$ year
    (iii) working in steps $h = 0.5$ years.

Compare your answers with the exact mathematical solution.

15.9 Radioactive substance A decays into substance B at a rate given by the equation

$$dx/dt = -rx$$

where x is the amount (in kg) of A present at time t, and r is a constant called the decay rate.

  (a) Solve for x as a function of time (analytically).
  (b) Show that the initial amount of A present is reduced by a half in time $T = 0.693/r$. (T is the half-life of A.)
  (c) If y is the amount of B present at time t, and if $y = 0$ at time $t = 0$, deduce an expression for y as a function of time.
  (d) Given $r = 0.0033$ per year and $x = 10$ kg at time $t = 0$, use Euler's method to find x as a function of time for a period of 450 years. Work in steps of $h = 15$ years and compare answers with the exact solution.

15.10 Some radioactive substances decay into other radioactive substances which in turn also decay. For example, Strontium 92 ($r_1 = 0.256$ per hr) decays into Yttrium 92 ($r_2 = 0.127$ per hr) which in turn decays into Zirconium. Write down a pair of simultaneous differential equations to describe what is happening.

    Starting with 5.E26 atoms of Strontium 92, use Euler's method to solve the equations up to $t = 8$ hours in steps of 1/3 hour.

15.11 Solve numerically $y' = x-y$ over the domain $[0; 1]$ using $h = 0.2$ and $y(0) = 1$.

15.12 The impala population $x(t)$ in the Kruger National Park may be modelled by the equation

$$dx/dt = [r-bx \sin (\omega t)]x \, ,$$

where r, b, and ω are constants. Write a program which reads values for r, b, and ω, and initial values for x and t, and which uses Euler's method to compute the impala population at monthly intervals over a period of two years.

15.13 Simpson's Rule is a method of numerical integration which is a good deal more accurate than the Trapezoidal Rule. The step-length h must be chosen so that there are an even number ($2n$) of panels. Using the notation of Section 15.2, the formula for Simpson's Rule is

$$(h/3)[f(a)+f(b)+2\sum_{i=1}^{n-1} f(X_{2i})+4\sum_{i=1}^{n-1} f(X_{2i-1})].$$

Write a subroutine to implement this formula. Try it out on the function $f(x)=x^3$ between any limits. You may find your answers surprising when you compare them with the exact mathematical solution.

15.14 The luminous efficiency (ratio of the energy in the visible spectrum to the total energy) of a black body radiator may be expressed as a percentage by the formula (McCracken and Dorn, 1964)

$$E=64.77T^{-4}\int_{4E-5}^{7E-5} x^{-5} (e^{1.432/Tx}-1)^{-1}dx$$

where T is the absolute temperature in degrees Kelvin, x is the wavelength in cm, and the range of integration is over the visible spectrum. Taking $T=3500K$, use Simpson's rule to compute E, firstly with 10 intervals, and then with 20 intervals, and compare the results.

Epilogue:
Programming Style

Throughout this book the emphasis has been on writing clear, coherent programs to solve interesting problems. A program which is written any old how, although it may do what is required, is going to be difficult to understand when you go through it again after a month or two, particularly if you want to make some changes to it. Serious programmers therefore pay a fair amount of attention to what is called **programming style**, in order to make their programs clearer and more readable both to themselves, and to other potential users. You may find this irritating, if you are starting to program for the first time, because you are naturally impatient to get on with the job. But a little extra attention to your program layout will pay enormous dividends in the long run, especially when it comes to debugging!

Some hints on how to improve your programming style are given below (the example in Section 7.6 gives a good idea of what is meant by programming style).

1) You should make liberal use of comment statements, both at the beginning of the program or subprograms, to describe briefly what the program does and any special methods that have been used (e.g. Euler's method for numerical integration), and also throughout the program to introduce various logical sections. Any restrictions on the size and type of data that may be used as input should be stated clearly (e.g. maximum size of a matrix).

2) *All* variables should be declared as **REAL**, **INTEGER**, etc., one by one, in alphabetical order.

3) You should describe briefly the function of *each* variable in comment statements at the beginning of the program.

4) Blank lines should be used to separate logical sections of the coding.

5) Coding inside **DO**-loops and block **IF** statements should be indented a few columns to make the logic more apparent.

6) Blanks should be used in statements in the following places:
   - on either side of arithmetic or logical operators;
   - on either side of the "=" symbol in assignment statements;
   - after all commas;
   - on either side of logical expressions in **IF**s, or of argument lists in functions and subroutines.

   However, blanks should be omitted in places in complex expressions, where this may make the structure clearer, e.g.

   ```
   IF( B*B .LT. 4.0*A*C )PRINT*, 'ROOTS ARE IMAGINARY'
   ```

7) It is *strongly* recommended that the **GOTO** statement should be used *only* in the **IF/GOTO** conditional repeat structure, as outlined in Section 7.17, and *nowhere else*!

8) A **DO**-loop should always end with a **CONTINUE** statement, with a label ending with 0. This way you can always insert additional lines into the loop without having to change the terminal statement label.

9)   Labels for **FORMAT** statements should end with 5. This way you can always introduce new **FORMAT** statements without fear of duplicating labels used to end **DO**-
loops elsewhere in the program.

10) **FORMAT** statements should be grouped together after the non-executable specification statements, but before the first executable statement. Alternatively, they may
be grouped together before the **END** statement.

11) Subprograms should be grouped in alphabetical order, with at least one blank line
preceding the subprogram name.

12) A subprogram should have only one **RETURN** statement.

13) The recommended order of statements in a program unit is given in Appendix C.

Appendix A
Summary of FORTRAN 77 Statements

All the statements of FORTRAN 77 are summarized below, with examples of their most usual forms. The use of some statements is not recommended, but they are given for completeness and historical interest, since you may one day be faced with a piece of antediluvian FORTRAN to decipher! All statement labels should appear in columns one to five, and all statements should start in column seven or beyond. Items in square brackets [parentheses] are optional.

ASSIGN
is used in conjunction with the assigned **GOTO** statement (see below). Its use is *not* recommended. It is also called a 'statement label assignment statement', and has the general form

```
      ASSIGN s TO n
```

where *s* is the label of a statement in the same program unit, and *n* refers to the assigned **GOTO**.
   ASSIGN may also be used to assign a **FORMAT** label number to an integer variable used as a label specifier in an input/output statement. E.g.

```
15    FORMAT( ' ', 3E16.4 )
      ....

      ASSIGN 15 TO K
      ....

      PRINT K, X, Y, Z
```

BACKSPACE
positions a sequential file at the beginning of the preceding record, e.g.

```
      BACKSPACE 2
      BACKSPACE ( 2 )
```

where the file in question is connected to unit 2. If the file is already in its initial position the statement has no effect. The general form is

```
      BACKSPACE ( [UNIT =] u [, IOSTAT = i] )
```

where the **IOSTAT** specifier is as defined in the **OPEN** statement.

BLOCK DATA

names a **BLOCK DATA** subprogram for the initialization of items in named **COMMON** blocks, e.g.

```
BLOCK DATA GOLLUM
```

CALL

invokes a subroutine, e.g.

```
CALL NAME( a1, a2, a3, .... )
```

where the arguments may be variables, array names, character substrings, procedure names, or constants. The number of arguments allowed depends on the compiler. If the subroutine has no arguments, the brackets are omitted, e.g.

```
CALL NAME
```

CHARACTER

specifies variables or arrays of type character. E.g.

```
CHARACTER*1 Y( 0:100 )
```

specifies the elements Y(0) to Y(100) of the array Y as character variables, each of length one. The general form is

```
CHARACTER*w VAR
```

where w is the length (in characters) of the variable.

CLOSE

disconnects a file from a unit (and vice versa), e.g.

```
CLOSE ( 7 )
```

The general form is

```
CLOSE ( [UNIT =] u [, IOSTAT = i] [, STATUS = ch] )
```

where the specifiers are defined as in the **OPEN** statement, and ch must have the character value 'KEEP' or 'DELETE'.

COMMON

allocates memory locations in a **COMMON** block of store which may be blank or named, E.g. the statement

```
COMMON / NAME / X, Y, Z
```

appearing in a number of program units will enable the variables listed to be referenced from any of the program units concerned. Different **COMMON** blocks may be named from the same program unit. Variables of type character may not be mixed with variables of any other type in a named **COMMON** block. A dummy argument may not appear in a **COMMON** statement in a subprogram. Blank **COMMON** is specified as follows:

```
COMMON A, B, C
```

COMPLEX

specifies variables or arrays of type complex, e.g.

```
COMPLEX X
```

The real and imaginary parts of X may be assigned as follows:

```
X = ( - 1.0, - 2.5 )
```

CONTINUE
is a dummy statement which does nothing, and is used, for example, to end a DO-loop.

DATA
assigns values to the listed variables during compile time. E.g.

```
DATA M, X / 2, 4.5 /
```

assigns the values 2 and 4.5 to M and X respectively. Other possibilities are:

```
REAL A(10), X(5)
DATA A / 10 * 1.0 /
DATA ( X(I), I = 2, 4 ) / 0.0, 1.0, 2.0 /
```

DIMENSION
declares an array, e.g.

```
DIMENSION X(10)
```

Its use is *not* recommended. It is better to specify the type as well, as in

```
REAL X(10)
```

DO
repeats a set of statements a specified number of times, e.g.

```
DO 100 I = 1, 100

     ....statements to be repeated

100    CONTINUE
```

if the DO-variable I is to be incremented in steps of 1, or

```
DO 90 K = M, N, J

     ....statements to be repeated

90    CONTINUE
```

if K is to be incremented in steps of J. The full definition is in Section 6.2.

DOUBLE PRECISION
specifies variables or arrays of type double precision real.

ELSE IF, ELSE, END IF
See **IF**

END
is the final statement in a (sub) program.

ENDFILE
writes an endfile record to the sequential file connected to the specified unit, e.g.

```
ENDFILE 3
ENDFILE ( 5 )
```

The general form is the same as for **BACKSPACE**.

ENTRY
allows a subprogram to be entered at different points. Its use is *not* recommended, since it defeats the purpose of writing subprograms as modular logical units. E.g.

```
SUBROUTINE SHOCK(  ...  )
PARAMETER ...
COMMON ...
DATA ...
...

ENTRY HORROR(  ...  )
...

ENTRY TERROR(  ...  )
...

RETURN
END
```

The **ENTRY** statements specify **ENTRY** names (HORROR and TERROR in this case). When the subprogram is referenced via an **ENTRY** name, e.g. with the statement

```
CALL HORROR(  ...  )
```

execution starts with the first executable statement following that **ENTRY** name. The non-executable code before the first **ENTRY** name applies to the whole subprogram, irrespective of the **ENTRY** point.

EQUIVALENCE
enables two or more items in the same program unit to share the same storage location. Its use is *not* recommended, except in extreme circumstances! E.g.

```
EQUIVALENCE ( A, B ), ( X, Y )
```

will enable A and B, on the one hand, and X and Y on the other, to be used interchangably in the same program unit. Bearing in mind that elements of an array occupy consecutive storage locations, the statements

```
REAL A(2), B(3), X(2,2)
EQUIVALENCE ( A(2), B(1), X(1,2) )
```

will implement the following (possibly surprising!) arrangement:

		A(1)	A(2) B(1)	B(2)	B(3)
X(1,1)	X(2,1)	X(1,2)	X(2,2)		

So A(1) and X(2,1) will share the same storage location, while B(2) and X(2,2) will share another! A dummy argument may not appear in a **EQUIVALENCE** statement in a subprogram.

EXTERNAL
specifies that a name, normally used for an intrinsic function, is to be used as an external procedure name, or that an external procedure is to be used as an actual argument in a subprogram reference. E.g.

```
EXTERNAL SQRT
```

FORMAT
See **PRINT**

FUNCTION
names a function subprogram, e.g.

```
FUNCTION NAME( a1, a2, a3, ... )
....

NAME = ....

RETURN
END
```

It is recommended that the function name be declared a specific type, e.g.

```
REAL FUNCTION NAME( a1, a2, ... )
```

in which case NAME must be similarly specified in the calling program. If the function has no arguments, empty brackets must still be used:

```
FUNCTION NAME( )
```

GOTO
transfers control unconditionally to the specified statement. E.g.

```
GOTO 70
```

transfers control unconditionally to the statement labelled 70. It is recommended that **GOTO** be used *only* in the conditional repeat structure as outlined in Section 7.17.

There are two other forms of **GOTO**: assigned **GOTO** and computed **GOTO**. Their use is *not* recommended, under *any* circumstances. The assigned **GOTO** is used in conjunction with the **ASSIGN** statement, and has the form

```
GOTO n ( s1, s2, ... )
```

E.g. the coding

```
ASSIGN 20 TO N
....

GOTO N ( 10, 20, 40 )
```

will transfer control to the statement labelled 20 after the execution of the **GOTO**. The computed **GOTO** has the form

```
GOTO ( s1, s2, ... ) n
```

where the s_i are statement labels, and n is an integer expression. If n has the value i, control is transferred to the statement with the *i*th label in the **GOTO**. E.g. the statement

```
GOTO ( 20, 50, 10, 30 ) N
```

transfers control to statement 20 if N has the value 1, to statement 50 if N has the value 2, etc.

IF

transfers control conditionally. There are three distinct **IF** statements.

1)   The logical **IF** is used when a single statement is to be executed under a certain condition, e.g.

```
IF( MK .GE. 50 )PRINT*, 'PASS'
```

where the **PRINT** statement is executed only if MK$\geqslant$50.

2)   The block **IF** statement is used when blocks of statements are to be executed under various conditions, e.g.

```
IF( MK .GE. 75 )THEN
   PRINT*, 'FIRST'
ELSE IF( MK .GE. 60 )THEN
   PRINT*, 'SECOND'
ELSE IF( MK .GE. 50 )THEN
   PRINT*, 'THIRD'
ELSE
   PRINT*, 'FAIL'
END IF
```

where each logical expression is only examined if the previous one is false. The **ELSE IF** and **ELSE** parts of the block **IF** statement are optional.

3)   The arithmetic **IF** is a 'dangerous statement, since its use tends to be coupled with the occurrence of numerous **GOTO** statements' (Balfour and Marwick, 1979, p.291). Its use is *definitely not* recommended! The general form is

```
IF( expression ) s1, s2, s3
```

where *s*1, *s*2 and *s*3 are the labels of executable statements. The expression is evaluated and control is transferred to statement *s*1, *s*2 or *s*3 according to whether the value of the expression is negative, zero or positive.

IMPLICIT

specifies a range of variables of a certain type. E.g.

```
IMPLICIT INTEGER ( A, X - Z )
```

specifies integer type for all variables starting with the letters A, X, Y and Z. Its use is *not* recommended, since it is better programming style to specify the type of each variable separately.

INQUIRE

investigates the properties of a file. There are two forms,

```
INQUIRE ( [UNIT =] u, specifier list )
INQUIRE ( FILE = ch, specifier list )
```

where *ch* is of type character. The specifiers are **IOSTAT**$=i$, **EXIST**$=log$, **OPENED** $=log$, **NUMBER**$=i$, **NAMED**$=log$, **NAME**$=ch$, **ACCESS**$=ch$, **SEQUENT-IAL**$=ch$, **DIRECT**$=ch$, **FORM**$=ch$, **FORMATTED**$=ch$, **UNFORMATTED**$=ch$,

RECL$=i$, **NEXTREC**$=i$, **BLANK**$=ch$, where i and *log* are integer and logical variables which are assigned appropriate values on execution of the statement. The specifiers have the same meanings as in the **OPEN** statement.

INTEGER
specifies variables or arrays of type integer, e.g.

```
INTEGER ZED
INTEGER X( 1000 )
```

INTRINSIC
specifies that an intrinsic function name is to be an actual argument of a subprogram. The name must be the specific name, e.g.

```
INTRINSIC ALOG
```

LOGICAL
specifies variables or arrays of type logical, e.g.

```
LOGICAL SWITCH
LOGICAL YESNO( 0:100 )
```

OPEN
connects a file to an input/output unit. The general form is

```
OPEN ( [UNIT =] u, specifier list )
```

where u is the input/output unit number. The remaining specifiers are optional, and may be in any order (this applies to all file handling statement, including **READ** and **WRITE**). The specifiers are as follows (i and ch stand for integer and character expressions respectively):

IOSTAT$=i$ (the I/O status specifier, defined below);
FILE$=ch$ (the file name);
STATUS$=ch$ ('OLD', 'NEW', 'SCRATCH', 'UNKNOWN');
ACCESS$=ch$ ('SEQUENTIAL', 'DIRECT');
FORM$=ch$ ('FORMATTED', 'UNFORMATTED');
RECL$=i$ (record length);
BLANK$=ch$ ('ZERO', 'NULL').

The I/O status specifier will set i to 0 if **OPEN** is executed without an error occurring, and to some positive value otherwise. If a file is a 'SCRATCH' file it must not be named, and will automatically be deleted at program termination. If the **BLANK** specifier has the value 'ZERO', all embedded and trailing blanks on input are treated as zeros. If it has the value 'NULL', all blanks are ignored, unless the input field is completely blank, in which case it is treated as zero.
E.g.

```
OPEN( 6, FILE = 'DATA', ACCESS = 'DIRECT', RECL = 56 )
```

PARAMETER
names a constant at compile time, e,g.

```
PARAMETER (G = 9.8 )
PARAMETER (PI = 4 * ATAN( 1 ) )
```

PAUSE
suspends execution of a program. Execution can only be resumed by the operator.

PRINT
prints the listed variables and literal messages according to a format which is either user-defined, or list-directed. An example of the former is

```
15      FORMAT( ' THE ANSWER IS', F5.2 )
        PRINT 15, X
```

or

```
15      FORMAT( A, F5.2 )
        PRINT 15, ' THE ANSWER IS', X
```

The items in the brackets of the **FORMAT** statement are called format specifications, or format editing codes. For example,

```
25      FORMAT( ' ', I4, F6.3, E12.4 )
        I = - 123
        X = 1.23448
        Y = - 0.00012349
        PRINT 25, I, X, Y
```

gives the output ('b' represents a blank)

```
-123b1.234bb-.1235-003
```

The initial blank is used for carriage control (see Section 9.2.3).
PRINT may be used with list-directed format as follows:

```
        PRINT*, 'THE ANSWER IS', X
        PRINT*, 'HOW''S THAT?'
```

Note that an apostrophe is printed by typing it twice in the message string.

PROGRAM
is an optional non-executable statement which may be used to name a main program, e.g.

```
        PROGRAM TEST
```

READ
inputs values for variables from an input device. The statement has three basic forms. The simplest is for list-directed input from the standard input device (usually the keyboard):

```
        READ*, A, B, C
```

The data must be separated by blanks or commas.
If the data is formatted according to a **FORMAT** statement with label n it may be read from the standard input unit as follows:

```
        READ n, A, B, C
```

Arrays may be read with implied **DO**-loops, e.g.

```
        INTEGER A( 20, 20 )
        REAL X(10)
        READ*, N, ( X(I), I = 1, N )
        READ 15, ( ( A( I,J ), J = 1, N ), I = 1, N )
```

The general form is

```
READ( [UNIT =] u, [FMT =] n, REC = 1, IOSTAT = i ) list
```

u is the input unit number (an asterisk for the standard input unit); *n* is the label of a **FORMAT** statement, in the case of formatted files (an asterisk for list-directed input); *l* is the record length, in the case of direct access files; *i* is the I/O status specifier which is set to 0 if neither an error nor an end-of-file condition occurs, to a positive value if an error occurs, and to a negative value if an end-of-file condition, but no error, occurs; *list* is the list of variables.

The unit specifier is the only obligatory one. The specifiers may be in any order, subject to the following exceptions: if the keyword [**UNIT** =] is omitted, *u* must be the first item; if the keyword [**FMT** =] is omitted, *n* must be the second item, and in this case the first item must be the unit number without the keyword. E.g.

```
READ( 5, * ) A, B, C
READ( *, * ) A, B, C
READ( 1, 15 ) A, B, C

READ( *, 15 ) A, B, C
READ( 2, REC = 75, IOSTAT = IS ) A, B, C
READ( 1 ) A, B, C
```

The first two statements above have the same effect as

```
READ*, A, B, C
```

assuming that the standard input number is 5.

REAL
specifies a variable or array of type real, e.g.

```
REAL K
REAL TIME( 0:200 )
```

RETURN
returns control from a subprogram to the calling program, and should be the penultimate statement in a subprogram.

RETURN has another form, called the 'alternate **RETURN**'. Its use is *not* recommended, since it allows returns to alternate points in the calling program. The following program segments illustrate its use:

```
. . . .

CALL DREAD( A, B, C, *10, *30 )
. . . .

END
SUBROUTINE DREAD( X, Y, Z, *, * )
. . . .

RETURN 1
. . . .

RETURN 2
. . . .

END
```

If the integer expression following the keyword **RETURN** is less than 1, or greater than the number of asterisks in the dummy argument list, a 'normal' return is executed. Otherwise, if it has the value i, control is returned to the statement in the calling program identified by the 'alternate return specifier' in the **CALL** statement corresponding to the ith asterisk in the dummy argument list. So **RETURN 1** effects a return to statement 10 in the calling program, while **RETURN 2** returns to statement 30.

Alternate **RETURN** can (but shouldn't!) be used in the same way with an **ENTRY** statement.

REWIND

repositions a sequential file at its initial point. The syntax is the same as for **BACK-SPACE**, e.g.

```
REWIND 3
REWIND( 2, IOSTAT = IOS )
```

SAVE

enables local variables in a subprogram to remain defined on exit and to be saved for the next reference, e.g.

```
SAVE A, B, C
```

All the items in a named **COMMON** block can be saved in this way, e.g.

```
SAVE / BLOB /
```

where BLOB is the name of the **COMMON** block.

STOP

terminates execution of a main program.

SUBROUTINE

names a subroutine subprogram, e.g.

```
SUBROUTINE NAME( a1, a2, a3, .... )
....

RETURN
END
```

No type or value is associated with the name, which is defined in the same way as a FORTRAN variable. If the subroutine has no arguments, the name is written without brackets, e.g.

```
SUBROUTINE NONE
```

WRITE

sends output records to an output unit. It has the general form

```
WRITE( list of specifiers ) list of variables
```

where the list of specifiers is the same as in the **READ** statement (which makes sense since **WRITE** is **READ** in reverse). The only difference is that an end-of-file condition is not meaningful with **WRITE**.

A useful feature of the input/output statements is embedded format, which can take the form

```
FT = '( T5, 3F8.2 )'
WRITE( *, FT ) A, B, C
```

where FT is a suitable character variable.

Appendix B
Intrinsic Functions

FORTRAN 77 has a large number of supplied, or 'intrinsic' functions, which are internally defined. Any program may use them, simply by reference to their names. Most intrinsic functions have two names: **generic** and **specific**. The generic name may be used without reference to the type of the function argument, and the value returned is of the same type as the argument. Specific names, however, require arguments of a specific type. For example, the argument for the function **ABS** may be real, integer, double precision or complex because **ABS** is the generic name of the function. However, its specific names are **ABS**, **IABS**, **DABS**, and **CABS**, for real, integer, double precision and complex arguments respectively. So while you can use **ABS** with any type of argument, you can only use **IABS** with an integer argument. The reason all the specific names are still around is to make FORTRAN 77 'upward compatible' with older versions of FORTRAN.

A complete list of intrinsic functions appears below, in alphabetical order of generic name. Functions without generic names appear at the end of the list. Where a function has two (or more) arguments, they are referred to as x_1, x_2, ... respectively in the description. The trigonometric functions all assume that the angles involved are in radian measure.

Generic Name	Specific Name	Arguments No.	Type	Function Value	Description
ABS	IABS	1	Integer	Integer	Absolute value
	ABS		Real	Real	
	DABS		Double	Double	
	CABS		Complex	Real	Length of vector in Argand diagram
ACOS	ACOS	1	Real	Real	Arc cosine
	DACOS		Double	Double	
AINT	AINT	1	Real	Real	Truncation of fractional part
	DINT		Double	Double	
ANINT	ANINT	1	Real	Real	Nearest whole number
	DNINT		Double	Double	
ASIN	ASIN	1	Real	Real	Arc sine
	DASIN		Double	Double	
ATAN	ATAN	1	Real	Real	Arc tangent
	DATAN		Double	Double	
ATAN2	ATAN2	2	Real	Real	Arc tangent (x_1/x_2)
	DATAN2		Double	Double	
CMPLX	CMPLX	1	Integer	Complex	Conversion to complex (imaginary part set to 0)
			Real		

Generic Name	Specific Name	Arguments No.	Type	Function Value	Description
COS	COS DCOS CCOS	1	Real Dcuble Complex	Real Double Complex	Cosine
COSH	COSH DCOSH	1	Real Double	Real Double	Hyperbolic cosine
DBLE	DBLE	1	Integer Real	Double	Conversion to double
DIM	IDIM DIM DDIM	2	Integer Real Double	Integer Real Double	Positive difference $(= x_1 - \min(x_1, x_2))$
EXP	EXP DEXP CEXP	1	Real Double Complex	Real Double Complex	Exponential
INT	INT IFIX IDINT	1	Real Real Double	Integer	Conversion to integer
LOG	ALOG DLOG CLOG	1	Real Double Complex	Real Double Complex	Natural logarithm (base e)
LOG10	ALOG10 DLOG10	1	Real Double	Real Double	Common logarithm (base 10)
MAX	MAX0 AMAX1 DMAX1	>1	Integer Real Double	Integer Real Double	Maximum value of $x_1, x_2, \ldots$
MIN	MIN0 AMIN1 DMIN1	>1	Integer Real Double	Integer Real Double	Minimum value of $x_1, x_2, \ldots$
MOD	MOD AMOD DMOD	2	Integer Real Double	Integer Real Double	Remainder when x_1 divided by x_2
NINT	NINT IDNINT	1	Real Double	Integer	Nearest integer
REAL	REAL FLOAT SNGL	1	Integer Integer Double	Real	Conversion to real
SIGN	ISIGN SIGN DSIGN	2	Integer Real Double	Integer Real Double	Transfer of sign (returns $ABS(x_1)$ if $x_2 \geq 0$; $- ABS(x_1)$ otherwise
SIN	SIN DSIN CSIN	1	Real Double Complex	Real Double Complex	Sine
SINH	SINH DSINH CSINH	1	Real Double Complex	Real Double Complex	Hyperbolic sine
SQRT	SQRT DSQRT CSQRT	1	Real Double Complex	Real Double Complex	Square root

Generic Name	Specific Name	Arguments No. Type	Function Value	Description
TAN	TAN	1 Real	Real	Tangent
	DTAN	Double	Double	
TANH	TANH	1 Real	Real	Hyperbolic tangent
	DTANH	Double	Double	
–	AIMAG	1 Complex	Real	Imaginary part
–	AMAX0	>1 Integer	Real	Maximum value of $x_1, x_2, \ldots$
–	MAX1	Real	Integer	
–	AMIN0	>1 Integer	Real	Minimum value of $x_1, x_2, \ldots$
–	MIN1	Real	Integer	
–	CHAR	1 Integer	Char	Conversion to char
–	CONJG	1 Complex	Complex	Complex conjugate
–	DPROD	1 Real	Double	Double precision product
–	ICHAR	1 Char	Integer	Conversion to integer (ASCII code)
–	INDEX	2 Char	Integer	Position of substring x_2 in string x_1
–	LEN	1 Char	Integer	Length of string
–	LGE	2 Char	Logical	$x_1 \geq x_2$ lexically
–	LGT	2 Char	Logical	$x_1 > x_2$ lexically
–	LLE	2 Char	Logical	$x_1 \leq x_2$ lexically
–	LLT	2 Char	Logical	$x_1 < x_2$ lexically

Note
'$x_1 < x_2$ lexically' means that the character string x_1 appears ahead of the string x_2 in the ASCII collating sequence (see Appendix D).

Appendix C
Order of Statements in a Program Unit

The *recommended* order of statements is as follows (general comment lines may go anywhere).

1 Initial statement: PROGRAM
                     or FUNCTION
                     or SUBROUTINE
                     or BLOCK DATA

2 Comment lines: general description of program;
                          description of all variables used.

3 Specification statements, in any order, except that the type specification of items in COMMON must precede the COMMON statement, and the type specification of items in a PARAMETER statement must precede the PARAMETER statement:

     INTEGER
     REAL
     DOUBLE PRECISION
     COMPLEX
     LOGICAL
     CHARACTER
     PARAMETER
     COMMON
     EXTERNAL
     INTRINSIC
     SAVE

4 DATA statements.
5 Statement functions.
6 FORMAT statements.
7 Executable statements.
8 END statement.

The following table from the FORTRAN 77 Standard shows the *required* order of statements (horizontal lines indicate groups of statements which cannot be mixed, while vertical lines indicate groups of statement which may be mixed).

	PROGRAM, FUNCTION, SUBROUTINE or BLOCK DATA statement		
Comment lines	FORMAT and ENTRY statements	PARAMETER statements†	IMPLICIT statements
			Other specification statements†
		DATA statements	Statement functions
			Executable statements
END statement			

†Type specification of items in a **PARAMETER** statement must precede the **PARAMETER** statement. This also applies to items in **COMMON**.

Appendix D
ASCII Character Codes

ASCII codes, which define the ASCII lexical collating sequence, use seven bits per character, so there are 128 possible codes, from 0 to 127. Codes 0 to 31 and code 127 are for special non-printing 'control' characters. Codes 32 to 126 are for characters that can be printed, and are as follows:

32	(blank)	64	@	96	
33	!	65	A	97	a
34	"	66	B	98	b
35	#	67	C	99	c
36	$	68	D	100	d
37	%	69	E	101	e
38	&	70	F	102	f
39	'	71	G	103	g
40	(	72	H	104	h
41	)	73	I	105	i
42	*	74	J	106	j
43	+	75	K	107	k
44	,	76	L	108	l
45	–	77	M	109	m
46	.	78	N	110	n
47	/	79	O	111	o
48	0	80	P	112	p
49	1	81	Q	113	q
50	2	82	R	114	r
51	3	83	S	115	s
52	4	84	T	116	t
53	5	85	U	117	u
54	6	86	V	118	v
55	7	87	W	119	w
56	8	88	X	120	x
57	9	89	Y	121	y
58	:	90	Z	122	z
59	;	91	[	123	{
60	<	92	\	124	¦
61	=	93	]	125	}
62	>	94	^	126	~
63	?	95	_		

Some of the special control codes are as follows:

  7 Beep
  9 Tab
10 Line feed
11 Home
12 Form feed
13 Carriage return
27 Escape

Appendix E
Solutions to Selected Problems

1.1

```
READ*, A, B
SUM = A + B
DIFF = A - B
PROD = A * B
QUOT = A / B

PRINT*, ' THE SUM IS:           ', SUM
PRINT*, ' THE DIFFERENCE IS: ', DIFF
PRINT*, ' THE PRODUCT IS:      ', PROD
PRINT*, ' THE QUOTIENT IS:     ', QUOT

STOP
END
```

1.2

```
READ*, C, V
E = C * V * V / 2
PRINT*, ' ENERGY OF CONDENSOR: ', E

STOP
END
```

3.1 (a) Comma invalid
     (e) Asterisk invalid
     (g) Plus is valid though unnecessary
     (h) Comma invalid

3.2 (a) Real
     (b) Invalid: the decimal point is not an alphanumeric character
     (c) Invalid: the first character must be a letter
     (d) Invalid: quotes are not alphanumeric
     (e) Real
     (f) Integer
     (g) Invalid: more than six characters
     (h) Invalid: plus is not alphanumeric

3.3   (a)   `P + W / U`
(b)   `P + W / (U + V)`
(c)   `(P + W / (U + V)) / (P + W / (U - V))`
(d)   `X ** 2`
(e)   `X ** 2.5`
(f)   `X ** 0.5`
(g)   `X ** (Y + Z)`
(h)   `( X ** Y ) ** Z`
(i)   `X ** Y ** Z`
(j)   `X - X ** 3 / ( 3 * 2 ) + X ** 5 / ( 5 * 4 * 3 * 2 )`
(k)   `( - B + ( B ** 2 - 4.0 * A * C ) ** 0.5 ) / ( 2.0 * A )`

3.4   (a)   `I = I + 1`
(b)   `I = I ** 3 + J`
(c)   `X = ( A + B ) / ( C * D )`

3.7   `I = 2 ** 34 - 1 + 2 ** 34`

3.8

```
REAL TEMPC
REAL TEMPF

READ*, TEMPC
TEMPF = 9 * TEMPC / 5 + 32
PRINT*, 'TEMPERATURE IN DEGREES FAHRENHEIT IS:', TEMPF

STOP
END
```

3.10   A = 5.0; B = 6.0; C = 7.0; D = 2.0; E = 10.0

3.11

```
T = A
A = B
B = T
```

3.12

```
A = A - B
B = B + A
A = B - A
```

3.13   A = 4; X = 1+1/2+1/3+1/4.
The same effect can be achieved much more elegantly using the **DO** statement described in Chapter 6:

```
      X = 0
      DO 10 K = 1, 4
         X = X + 1.0 / K
10    CONTINUE
```

3.14

```
      AI = E / (R ** 2 + (2 * PI * F * HL - 1 /
     $ (2 * PI * F * C)) ** 2) ** 0.5
```

4.1   You should get a picture of tangents to a curve.

4.2   (a) 4

(b) 2

(c) The algorithm (attributed to Euclid!) finds the HCF (highest common factor) of two numbers by using the fact that the HCF divides exactly into the difference between the two numbers, and that if the numbers are equal, the HCF is equal to them.

5.1

```
INTEGER APPLES
INTEGER BOX
INTEGER FULL
INTEGER LEFT

READ*, BOX, APPLES
FULL = APPLES / BOX
LEFT = MOD( APPLES, BOX )
PRINT*, FULL, LEFT

STOP
END
```

5.2   (a) `C = SQRT( A ** 2 + B ** 2 )`

(b) `THETA = THETA * 3.141593 / 180`
`C = SQRT( A ** 2 + B ** 2 - 2 * A * B * COS( THETA ) )`

5.3   (a) `LOG( X + X ** 2 + A ** 2 )`

(b) `LOG10( Y )`

(c) `( EXP( 3 * T ) + T ** 2 * SIN( 4 * T ) )`
`* COS( 3 * T ) ** 2`

(d) `4 * ATAN( 1 )`

(e) `1 / COS( X ) ** 2 + 1 / TAN( X )`

(f) `ACOS( ABS( A / X ) )`

5.4

```
REAL M1
REAL M2

READ*, M1, M2, E, A
CONV = 3.141593 / 180
A = CONV * A
UP = M2 * (1 + E) * TAN( A )
DOWN = (M1 - E * M2) + (M1 + M2) * TAN( A ) ** 2
B = ATAN( UP / DOWN ) / CONV
PRINT*, ' ANGLE OF DEFLECTION IS ', B, ' DEGREES'

STOP
END
```

6.1
```
      INTEGER I
      INTGER SUM

      SUM = 0

      DO 10 I = 1, 100
         SUM = SUM + I
10    CONTINUE

      PRINT*, SUM

      STOP
      END
```

6.2
```
      SUM = 0

      DO 10 I = 1, 100
         SUM = SUM + 1.0 / I
10    CONTINUE

      PRINT*, SUM

      STOP
      END
```

6.3
```
      INTEGER FACT
      INTEGER K
      INTEGER N

      READ*, N
      FACT = 1

      DO 20 K = 1, N
         FACT = K * FACT
         PRINT*, K, FACT
20    CONTINUE

      STOP
      END
```

6.4 (a)
```
      READ*, N
      PI = 1

      DO 30 K = 1, N
         PI = PI + ( - 1 ) ** K / ( 2.0 * K + 1 )
30    CONTINUE

      PI = 4 * PI
      PRINT*, ' PI =', PI, 'AFTER', N, ' TERMS'

      STOP
      END
```

6.4   (b)

```
      READ*, N
      PI = 0

      DO 30 K = 1, N
        PI = PI + 1.0 / ( 4 * K - 3 ) / (4 * K - 1 )
30    CONTINUE

      PI = 8 * PI
      PRINT*, ' PI =', PI, 'AFTER', N, ' TERMS'

      STOP
      END
```

6.5

```
      REAL A
      REAL E
      REAL L
      REAL P
      REAL U
      INTEGER N

      A = 1
      N = 6

      DO 10 I = 1, 10
        N = 2 * N
        A = SQRT( 2 - SQRT( 4 - A ** 2 ) )
        L = N * A / 2
        U = L / SQRT( 1 - A ** 2 / 4 )
        P = (U + L) / 2
        E = (U - L) / 2
        PRINT*, N, P, E
10    CONTINUE

      STOP
      END
```

6.6

```
      PI = 3.14159
      READ*, H

      DO 10 X = -1, 1+H, H
        F = X * SIN( PI * (1 + 20 * X ) / 2 )
        PRINT*, X, F
10    CONTINUE

      STOP
      END
```

6.7

```
X = 1

DO 10 I = 1, 10
   E = 1 / ( (1 - X) ** (1 / X) )
   PRINT*, X, E
   X = X / 10
10    CONTINUE

STOP
END
```

6.8

```
X = 0
DO 20 I = 1, 4
   X = X + 1.0 / I
20    CONTINUE

STOP
END
```

6.9

```
PI = 3.141593
BIGT = 1
READ*, N
DO 10 T = 0, 1, 0.1
   FS = 0
   DO 20 K = 0, N-1
      J = 2 * K + 1
      FS = FS + SIN( J * PI * T / BIGT ) / J
20    CONTINUE
   PRINT*, T, FS * 4 / PI
10    CONTINUE

STOP
END
```

7.1   (a)
```
IF( E .GT. F )THEN
     G = E
   ELSE
     G = F
   END IF
```

(b) `IF( D .GT. 0 ) X = - B`

(c) `IF( MOD( K, 2 ) .EQ. 0 ) X = - X`

7.2   1   Repeat 10 times
        1.1   Read number
        1.2   If number > 0 then
            1.2.1   Increase positive counter
            but if number = 0 then
            1.2.2   Increase zero counter
            otherwise
            1.2.3   Increase negative counter

2   Print counters.

```
* *** COUNTING POSITIVES, ZEROS AND NEGATIVES ********************
*                                                                 *
***** DESCRIPTION OF VARIABLES **********************************
*                                                                 *
*     I       : COUNTER        / NNEG   : NEGATIVES               *
*     NPOS    : POSITIVES      / NZERO  : ZEROS                   *
*     NUMBER  : THE NUMBER                                        *
*****************************************************************

      INTEGER   I
      INTEGER   NUMBER
      INTEGER   NNEG
      INTEGER   NPOS
      INTEGER   NZERO

      NPOS = 0
      NZERO = 0
      NNEG = 0

      DO 100 I = 1, 10
         READ*, NUMBER
         IF( NUMBER .GT. 0 )THEN
            NPOS = NPOS + 1
         ELSE IF( NUMBER. EQ. 0 )THEN
            NZERO = NZERO + 1
         ELSE
            NNEG = NNEG + 1
         END IF
  100 CONTINUE

      PRINT*, NPOS, ' ARE POSITIVE'
      PRINT*, NZERO, ' ARE ZERO'
      PRINT*, NNEG, ' ARE NEGATIVE'

      STOP
      END
```

7.4   1   Read first number
         2   Store it in BIG
         3   Set POS and I to 1
         4   Repeat 99 times
            4.1   Read next number
            4.2   Increase I by 1
            4.3   If number > BIG then
                4.3.1   Store it in BIG
                4.3.2   Set POS to I
         5   Print BIG and POS.

```
* *** POSITION AND VALUE OF LARGEST NUMBER IN A LIST *************

        INTEGER I
        INTEGER POS

        REAL     BIG
        REAL      X

        READ*, X
        BIG = X
        POS = 1

        DO 10 I = 2, 100
          IF( X .GT. BIG )THEN
            BIG = X
            POS = I
          END IF
10      CONTINUE

        PRINT*, BIG, ' AT POSITION', POS

        STOP
        END
```

7.5 1 Declare all variables integer
2 Set c to the amount of change in cents
3 Number of \$5 notes is $c/500$ (N.B. integer division)
4 Replace c by mod $(c,500)$ (the remainder)
5 Print \$5
6 \$1 $= c/100$
7 $c = \text{mod}(c,100)$
8 Print \$1
9 Etc., etc., etc.

7.6

```
        REAL    A
        REAL    B
        REAL    C
        REAL    D
        REAL    E
        REAL    F
        REAL    X
        REAL    Y

        READ*, A, B, C
        READ*, D, E, F

        IF( ABS( A * E - D * B ) .LT. 1E-5 )THEN
          IF( ABS( E * C - B * F ) .LT. 1E-5 )THEN
```

```
      PRINT*, 'LINES COINCIDE'
   ELSE
      PRINT*, 'LINES PARALLEL'
   END IF
ELSE
   X = ( E * C - B * F ) / ( A * E - D * B )
   Y = ( A * F - D * C ) / ( A * E - D * B )
   PRINT*, 'X = ', X
   PRINT*, 'Y = ', Y
END IF

STOP
END
```

7.7

```
*     COZ    : SUM OF TAYLOR SERIES / IT      : COUNTER            *
*     TERM   : GENERAL TERM          / X       : ANGLE (RADIANS)   *
******************************************************************

      INTEGER  IT

      REAL     COZ
      REAL     TERM
      REAL     X

      READ*, X
      TERM = 1
      COZ = 0
      IT = 0

10    IF( ABS( TERM ) .GT. 1E-5 )THEN
         COZ = COZ + TERM
         IT = IT + 1
         TERM = - TERM * X  ** 2 / (2 * IT) / (2 * IT - 1)
         GOTO 10
      END IF

      PRINT*, 'BY TAYLOR:', COZ
      PRINT*, 'BY INTRINSIC FUNCTION:', COS( X )
      PRINT*, 'TERMS IN SERIES:', IT

      STOP
      END
```

7.8

```
      INTEGER M
      INTEGER N

      READ*, M, N

10    IF( M .NE. N )THEN

20       IF( M .GT. N )THEN
            M = M - N
            GOTO 20
         END IF

30       IF( N .GT. M )THEN
            N = N - M
            GOTO 30
         END IF

         GOTO 10
      END IF

      PRINT*, M

      STOP
      END
```

7.11

```
      G = 9.8
      PI = 4 * ATAN( 1 )
      ANG = 50
      ANG = ANG * PI / 180
      X = 0
      Y = 0
      T = 0
      U = 60
      DT = 0.5
      PRINT*, '    TIME            HORIZONTAL        VERTICAL'
      PRINT*, ' '

10    IF( Y .GE. 0 )THEN
         PRINT*, T, X, Y
         T = T + DT
         X = U * COS( ANG ) * T
         Y = U * SIN( ANG ) * T - 0.5 * G * T ** 2
         GOTO 10
      END IF

      STOP
      END
```

7.12   Move the **PRINT** statement to immediately after the **IF**.

8.1 (a) Execution: 3/4 is evaluated as 0, and **LOG(0)** is undefined.
(b) Compilation: TO is BASIC, not FORTRAN!
(c) Compilation: > should be **.GT.**.
(d) Compilation: a right bracket is missing before the /.
(e) Compilation: either omit **THEN** or J = 10.
(f) Execution: division by 0, because 4/5 is evaluated as 0.
(g) No error, but the statement is redundant.
(h) Execution: argument of **SQRT** is negative because **COS(2)** is negative.
(i) Compilation: juxtaposed operators. −I should be in brackets.
(j) No error, but this will repeat endlessly, since the **GOTO** should come before **END IF**.

9.1 (a) M=117N= −27   X= −12.4
            .1235+004

(b) The effect is to set N = 14; X = 729.12; Y = 3.61 and J = 35.

9.2 (a) −738   (b) 738
(c)   38.14   (d) −100.6
(e)   .9877+004   (f)   −.44−004

9.3

```
      OPEN( UNIT = 1, FILE = 'VOLTS' )
      READ( 1, *, IOSTAT = IOS )

10    IF( IOS .EQ. 0 )THEN
        READ( 1, *, IOSTAT = IOS )
        GOTO 10
      END IF

      BACKSPACE 1
      READ*, T, V
      WRITE( 1, * )T, V
      ENDFILE 1

      STOP
      END
```

10.1 (a)

```
      DO 70 I = 0, 99
        N(I) = I
70    CONTINUE
```

10.1 (b)

```
      DO 80 I = 1, 50
        N(I) = 2 * I
80    CONTINUE
```

10.2

```
* *** BINARY TO DECIMAL FIRST ***********************************

      INTEGER BIN(5)
      INTEGER DEC
      INTEGER I
```

```
25        FORMAT( 5I1 )
35        FORMAT( 'OBINARY:', 5I1, 5X, 'DECIMAL:', I3 )
45        FORMAT( 'ODECIMAL:', I13 / ' BINARY: ', 5I1 )

          READ 25, ( BIN( I ), I = 1, 5 )

          DO 90 I = 1, 5
            DEC = DEC + BIN( I ) * 2 ** ( 5-I )
90        CONTINUE

          PRINT 35, ( BIN ( I ), I = 1, 5 ), DEC

* ***  NOW FOR THE DECIMAL TO BINARY CONVERSION

          DO 70 I = 1, 5
            BIN( I ) = 0
70        CONTINUE

          READ*, NUM
          DEC = NUM

          DO 10 I = 5, 1, -1
            BIN( I ) = MOD( NUM, 2 )
            NUM = NUM / 2
     10   CONTINUE

          PRINT 45, DEC, ( BIN( I ), I = 1, 5 )
          STOP
          END
```

10.3

```
          INTEGER F( 100 )

          F(1) = 1
          F(2) = 1

          DO 10 N = 3, 100
            F( N ) = F( N-1 ) + F( N-2 )
10        CONTINUE
```

10.4 1   Initialize: $n = 3; p(1) = 2; j = 1$ (counts the primes)
     2   While $n < 1000$ repeat
       2.1 $i = 1$
       2.2 $rem = \text{mod } (n, p(i))$
       2.3   While $rem \neq 0$ and $p(i) < \sqrt{n}$ repeat
          2.3.1 $i = i+1$
          2.3.2 $rem = \text{mod } (n, p(i))$
       2.4   If $rem \neq 0$ then
          2.4.1 $j = j+1$ (another prime has been found!)
          2.4.2 $p(j) = n$
       2.5 $n = n+2$ (only test odd numbers for primality)
     3   Print all the $p(j)$s.

10.6

```
      REAL X(100)
      REAL Y(100)
      DATA S1, S2, S3, S4, S5 / 5 * 0.0 /

5     FORMAT( A, F7.3 )

      OPEN( 1, ACCESS = 'DIRECT', RECL = 20, FILE = 'EXPT' )
      READ( 1, REC = 1 )N

      DO 10 I = 1, N
        READ( 1, REC = I+1 )X(I), Y(I)
        S1 = S1 + X(I) * Y(I)
        S2 = S2 + X(I)
        S3 = S3 + Y(I)
        S4 = S4 + X(I) ** 2
        S5 = S5 + Y(I) ** 2
10    CONTINUE

      B = (S1 - S2 * S3 / N) / (S4 -S2 ** 2 / N)
      A = (S3 - B * S2) / N
      R = (N * S1 - S2 * S3) / SQRT( N * S4 - S2 ** 2 ) /
     $ SQRT( N * S5 - S3 ** 2 )
      PRINT 5, ' A:', A, ' B:', B, ' R:', R

      STOP
      END
```

11.1

```
      INTEGER     POS
      CHARACTER*1 STP
      CHARACTER*1 TEXT( 80 )

5     FORMAT( 80A1 )
15    FORMAT( ' ', 80A1 )

      STP = '.'
      READ 5, TEXT

* *** FIRST FIND THE FULL STOP ...
      J = 1
      POS = J

10    IF( TEXT( J ) .NE. STP )THEN
        POS = J
        J = J + 1
        GOTO 10
      END IF

* *** NOW PRINT THE TEXT BACKWARDS ...
      PRINT 15, ( TEXT( J ), J = POS, 1, -1 )

      STOP
      END
```

11.2

```
* *** ZELLER'S CONGRUENCE
* *** APPEARS NOT TO WORK FOR DATES >= 1ST JAN 9000.

        INTEGER     C
        INTEGER     DAY
        INTEGER     F
        INTEGER     IY
        INTEGER     K
        INTEGER     M
        INTEGER     MONTH
        INTEGER     Y
        INTEGER     YEAR
        CHARACTER*9 NAMDAY( 0:6 )

5       FORMAT( T6, I2, I3, I5, ' : ', A )

        NAMDAY(0) = 'SUNDAY    '
        NAMDAY(1) = 'MONDAY    '
        NAMDAY(2) = 'TUESDAY   '
        NAMDAY(3) = 'WEDNESDAY'
        NAMDAY(4) = 'THURSDAY '
        NAMDAY(5) = 'FRIDAY    '
        NAMDAY(6) = 'SATURDAY '

* *** READ THE DATE IN ENGLISH
        READ*, DAY, MONTH, YEAR

* *** CONVERT THE DATE INTO REQUIRED FORM
        IY = YEAR
        M = MONTH - 2
        IF( M .LE. 0 ) M = M + 12
        IF( M .GE. 11 ) IY = IY - 1
        K = DAY
        C = IY / 100
        Y = MOD( IY, 100 )
        F = INT(2.6 * M - 0.2) + K + Y + INT(Y / 4) + INT(C / 4)
     $  - 2 * C
        F = MOD( F, 7)

* *** PRINT OUT DATE AND DAY OF THE WEEK
        PRINT 5, DAY, MONTH, YEAR, NAMDAY(F)

        STOP
        END
```

11.3

```
        INTEGER     TIE
        CHARACTER*20 NAME
        CHARACTER*20 TOPSTU( 100 )

5       FORMAT( A20, I4 )
15      FORMAT( A, I4, A / )
25      FORMAT( ' ', A )
```

```
        MAX = - 2 ** 34

        DO 10 I = 1, 100
          READ 5, NAME, MARK

* ***   FIND OUT IF THIS MARK IS BEST SO FAR ...
        IF( MARK .GT. MAX )THEN

* ***        ... IN WHICH CASE RECORD IT, WITH NAME ...
           MAX = MARK
           TIE = 1
           TOPSTU( TIE ) = NAME

* ***     OR IF IT TIES WITH THE CURRENT BEST ...
        ELSE IF( MARK .EQ. MAX )THEN

* ***        ... IN WHICH CASE ADD NAME TO THE LIST
           TIE = TIE + 1
           TOPSTU( TIE ) = NAME
        END IF
10      CONTINUE

* ***  NOW DAZZLE THE MASSES BY PRINTING THE LIST!
        PRINT 15, ' THE BEST MARK OF ', MAX, ' WAS OBTAINED BY:-'
        PRINT 25, ( TOPSTU( I ), I = 1, TIE )

        STOP
        END
```

11.4

```
        CHARACTER*80 NEW
        CHARACTER*80 OLD
        CHARACTER*1 BLNK

5       FORMAT( 80A )
15      FORMAT( ' ', A80 )

        BLNK = ' '
        READ 5, OLD
        LENG = INDEX( OLD, '/' )
        NOBL = 0
        NEWI = 0

        DO 10 I = 1, LENG
          IF( OLD( I:I ) .NE. BLNK )THEN
            NEWI = NEWI + 1
            NOBL = NOBL + 1
            NEW( NEWI:NEWI ) = OLD( I:I )
            IF( MOD( NOBL, 5 ) .EQ. 0 )THEN
              NEWI = NEWI + 1
              NEW( NEWI:NEWI ) = BLNK
              NOBL = 0
            END IF
          END IF
10      CONTINUE
```

```
      PRINT 15, NEW

   STOP
   END
```

12.1

```
   REAL X
   REAL H

   F( X ) = X ** 3

   X = 1
   H = 1

   DO 10 I = 1, 30
      DERIV = ( F( X+H ) - F( X ) ) / H
      PRINT*, H, DERIV
      H = H / 2
10    CONTINUE

   STOP
   END
```

12.2

```
   REAL FUNCTION E( X )

   E = 1
   ERR = 1E-6
   K = 1
   TERM = 1

10    IF( ABS( TERM ) .GE. ERR )THEN
         TERM = TERM * X / K
         E = E + TERM
         K = K + 1
         GOTO 10
      END IF

   RETURN
   END
```

12.3

```
   REAL FUNCTION FACT( N )

   FACT = 1
   DO 10 I = 1, N
      FACT = FACT * I
10    CONTINUE

   RETURN
   END
```

12.4

```
      INTEGER FUNCTION BIN( N, R )
      INTEGER R

      BIN = 1
      DO 90 I = 1, R
        BIN = BIN * (N + 1 - I) / I
90    CONTINUE

      RETURN
      END
```

13.2

```
      INTEGER  BING( 99 )
      INTEGER  I
      INTEGER  LIST( 99 )
      INTEGER  NUM
      INTEGER  SEED

   15 FORMAT( 9I3 )

      DO 90 I = 1, 99
        LIST( I ) = 0
   90 CONTINUE

      READ*, SEED

      DO 80 I = 1,99
        NUM = 99 * URAND( SEED ) + 1

   10   IF( LIST( NUM ) .EQ. -1 )THEN
          NUM = 99 * URAND( SEED ) + 1
          GOTO 10
        END IF

        BING( I ) = NUM
        LIST( NUM ) = -1
   80 CONTINUE

      PRINT 15, BING

      STOP
      END
```

13.3

```
* *** WE MAY JUST AS WELL GENERATE RANDOM CO-ORDINATES IN THE
* *** 1ST QUADRANT, AND COUNT THE PROPORTION THAT FALL INSIDE
* *** THE UNIT QUARTER-CIRCLE THAT FITS INTO THIS QUADRANT.

* *** By the way, this is a desperately inefficient method.

      INTEGER   I
      INTEGER   IX
      INTEGER   NUM

      REAL      PI
      REAL      X
      REAL      Y

15    FORMAT( '0', A, F8.4 )

      READ*, IX
      PI = 0
      NUM = 50000

      DO 90 I = 1, NUM
        X = URAND( IX )
        Y = URAND( IX )
        IF( X*X + Y*Y .LT. 1.0 ) PI = PI + 1
90    CONTINUE

      PI = 4 * PI / NUM
      PRINT 15, 'PI IS ROUGHLY = ', PI

      STOP
      END
```

13.5 Theoretically, the probability of a DFII crash is 1/4, while that of a DFIV crash is 5/16: more can go wrong with it, since it has more engines!

13.6 On average, A wins 12 of the possible 32 plays of the game, while B wins 20, as can be seen by drawing the 'game tree'. However, if B plays intelligently, it can be shown from the tree that he can always force a win. The following program is not intelligent!

13.6

```
*         ATURN: TRUE FOR A'S TURN, FALSE FOR B'S               *
*                  RECORDED AFTER EACH TURN                     *
***************************************************************

      INTEGER AWIN
      INTEGER GOAL
      INTEGER OLD
      INTEGER R
      INTEGER TOT
      LOGICAL ATURN

5     FORMAT( A, F8.2 )
```

```
        READ*, IS
        AWIN = 0
        GOAL = 8
        N = 1000

        DO 10 I = 1, N
          R = INT( 3 * URAND( IS ) + 1 )
          OLD = R
          ATURN = .TRUE.
          TOT = R

20      IF( TOT. LT. GOAL )THEN
          R = INT( 3 * URAND( IS ) + 1 )

30        IF( R. EQ. OLD )THEN
            R = INT( 3 * URAND( IS ) + 1 )
            GOTO 30
          END IF

          TOT = TOT + R
          ATURN = .NOT. ATURN
          OLD = R
          GOTO 20
        END IF

        IF( TOT. EQ. GOAL )THEN
          IF( ATURN )AWIN = AWIN + 1
        ELSE
          IF( .NOT. ATURN )AWIN = AWIN + 1
        END IF

10      CONTINUE

        PA = FLOAT( AWIN ) / N
        PB = 1 - PA
        PRINT 5, ' PROB A WINS:', PA, ' PROB B WINS:', PB

        STOP
        END
```

14.1

```
        SUBROUTINE TRANS( A, MAX, N )
        REAL A( MAX, MAX )

        DO 10 K = 1, N

          DO 20 J = K, N
            T = A( K, J )
            A( K, J ) = A( J, K )
            A(J, K ) = T
20        CONTINUE
```

```
10      CONTINUE

        RETURN
        END
```

14.5

```
        SUBROUTINE ROWSWP( A, N, MAX, I, J )
        REAL A( MAX, MAX )

        DO 10 K = 1, N
          TEMP = A(I, K)
          A(I, K ) = A(J, K)
          A(J, K ) = TEMP
10      CONTINUE

        RETURN
        END
```

14.6

```
        REAL FUNCTION ROWSUM( A, N, MAX, I )
        REAL A( MAX, MAX )

        ROWSUM = 0

        DO 10 J = 1, N
          ROWSUM = ROWSUM + A(I, J)
10      CONTINUE

        RETURN
        END

        REAL FUNCTION COLSUM( A, M, MAX, J )
        REAL A( MAX, MAX )

        COLSUM = 0

        DO 10 I = 1, M
          COLSUM = COLSUM + A(I, J)
10      CONTINUE

        RETURN
        END
```

14.7

```
        SUBROUTINE MAXELT( A, M, N, MAX, IMAX, JMAX, ELTMAX )
        REAL A( MAX, MAX )

        ELTMAX = A(1, 1)
        IMAX = 1
        JMAX = 1
```

```
DO 10 I = 1, M

   DO 20 J  = 1, N
      IF( A(I, J) .GT. ELTMAX )THEN
         ELTMAX = A(I, J)
         IMAX = I
         JMAX = J
      END IF
20    CONTINUE

10 CONTINUE

   RETURN
   END
```

15.1 $x_0 = 1$; $x_1 = 1.333$; $x_2 = 1.2639$; $x_3 = 1.2599$; $x_4 = 1.2599$ . . .

15.2 (a) The real roots are 1.856 and -1.697. The complex roots, which always occur in complex conjugate pairs, are $-0.079 \pm 1.78i$.
(b) 0.589, 3.096, 6.285 . . . (roots get closer to multiples of π).
(c) 1; 2; 5
(d) 1.303
(e) The real roots are 1.768 and 2.241. I couldn't find any more. Can you?

15.3 Successive bisections give 1.5, 1.25, 1.375, 1.4375 and 1.40625. The exact answer is 1.414214, so the last bisection is within the required error.

15.5 22 (the exact answer is 21.3333).

15.6 $x(1) = $ (a) 0.75, (b) 0.6836 (0.6321 exactly).

15.7 i.e. solve $dy/dx = x^2$ numerically. Answer is 14. (This is effectively the rectangular rule for integration.)

15.8 The exact answer is 2117 (i.e. $1000 \exp(rt)$).

15.12

```
READ*, R, B, W, X
H = 1

DO 10 T = 1, 24
   X = X + H * (R - B * X * SIN( W * T )) * X
   PRINT*, T, X
10 CONTINUE

STOP
END
```

15.14 With 10 intervals, the efficiency is 14.512723%. With 20 intervals, it is 14.512664%. These results justify the use of 10 intervals in any further computations involving this problem. This is the standard way of testing the accuracy of a numerical integration: halve the step-length and see how much the solution changes.

Bibliography

Balfour A. and Marwick D.H., *Programming in Standard FORTRAN 77*, Heinemann, London, 1979.
Bennet W.R., *Scientific and Engineering Problem-Solving with the Computer*, Prentice-Hall, Englewood Cliffs, New Jersey, 1976.
Bitter G.G., *Microcomputer Applications for Calculus*, PWS Publishers, Boston, 1983.
Breuer S. and Zwas G., *Mathematical-Educational Aspects of the Computation of π*, International Journal of Mathematical Education in Science and Technology, **15** (1984) pp. 231–44.
Conte S.D. and De Boor C., *Elementary Numerical Analysis: An Algorithmic Approach* (2nd edition), McGraw Hill, New York, 1972.
Ellis T.M.R., *A Structured Approach to FORTRAN 77 Programming*, Addison-Wesley, London, 1982.
Fröberg C.-E., *Introduction to Numerical Analysis*, Addison-Wesley, Reading, Massachusetts, 1965.
Furniss P.R., *Description and Manual for the Use of DRIVER – An Interactive Modelling Aid*, South African National Scientific Programmes 17, Pretoria, 1977.
Kass G.V., Pre-University School, University of the Witwatersrand, Johannesburg, 1977 (unpublished).
Kemeny J.G. and Kurtz T.E., *BASIC Programming*, Wiley, New York, 1967.
Knuth D.E., *The Art of Computer Programming. Volume. 2: Seminumerical Algorithms*, Addison-Wesley, Reading, Massachusetts, 1968.
McCracken D.D., *A Guide to FORTRAN IV Programming*, Wiley, New York, 1965.
McCracken D.D. and Dorn W.S., *Numerical Methods and FORTRAN Programming*, Wiley, New York, 1964.
Spain J.D., *BASIC Microcomputer Models in Biology*, Addison-Wesley, Reading, Massachusetts, 1982.

Index